Introduction to Electronic Amplifiers

Rodney B. Faber
Oklahoma State University
The Technical Institute

Charles E. Merrill Publishing Company
A Bell & Howell Company   Columbus, Ohio

Merrill's International Series in Electrical and Electronics Technology

SAMUEL L. OPPENHEIMER
Consulting Editor

BOYLESTAD	*Introductory Circuit Analysis*
FABER	*Introduction to Electronic Amplifiers*
HARTKEMEIER	*Fortran Programming of Electronic Computers*
HERRICK	*Introduction to Electronic Communications*
HERRICK	*Mathematics for Electronics*
LENERT	*Semiconductor Physics, Devices, and Circuits*
OPPENHEIMER	*Semiconductor Logic and Switching Circuits*
PRISE	*Electronic Circuit Packaging*
TOCCI	*Fundamentals of Electronic Devices*
TURNER	*Digital Computer Analysis*

International Standard Book Number: 0–675–09215–9

Library of Congress Catalog Card Number: 79–149244

1 2 3 4 5 6 7 8 — 76 75 74 73 72 71

PRINTED IN THE UNITED STATES OF AMERICA

To Gladys and Judy

PREFACE

This text is intended for use in electronics technology programs in technical institutes and colleges. It deals primarily with transistor circuitry, but a small amount of tube amplifier material is included for those who wish it. A knowledge of dc and ac circuit analysis including elementary vector algebra (complex notation) for RLC circuit calculations is necessary background for students using the book. Calculus is not required.

The book is designed to meet the needs of students beginning their amplifier work, and is not intended to be encyclopedic in its coverage. It emphasizes fundamentals, in order to provide good preparation both for work in industry and for further study in any of the several areas of specialization.

Inevitably there will be differences among users of a text such as this. To accommodate such differences, the material has been arranged so that certain portions of many of the chapters can be left out if desired. For example, some teachers might wish to omit some topics such as the detailed analysis and design of bias circuits covered in Sections 3.9 through 3.11, and rely instead on the simplified design method presented in Section 3.7. The hybrid-π presentation of Section 4.10, the material on transducer gain and maximum available gain in Section 6.7, the distortion analysis of Section 7.13, and other sections in several of the chapters may also be omitted in order to suit individual programs. These deletions will not affect the continuity of the book.

The technician is concerned with practical matters — the problems encountered in industrial practice, and the techniques and attitudes that are necessary for the solution of such problems. Because of this, consideration is given to topics such as measurements, troubleshooting, the practical design of certain circuits, etc. In addition, an attempt has been made to provide a rational basis for the use of approximations, which are so important to technical work. Finally, examples involving realistic component values are used to illustrate each topic, and manufacturers' data sheets are used and are included in Appendix B.

A significant feature of this text is the avoidance of an early recitaton of all the variations of amplifier circuits. Instead, a unified development in terms of the most commonly-used circuit type is presented. Concentrating initially on one circuit type permits the student to become accustomed to amplifier techniques before having to face the confusion of alternative amplifier forms.

The topic sequence illustrates this presentation feature. The first chapter introduces semiconductor principles and the characteristics of the semiconductor diode and the junction transistor. Chapters 2 through 8 then deal with the common-emitter amplifier, from first principles through biasing, equivalent circuits, frequency response, power amplifiers, and feedback. Chapter 9 then examines the common-base and emitter-follower amplifiers; Chapter 10 treats the field-effect transistor, and Chapter 11 takes up tube amplifiers. Appendix A contains a brief treatment of power supplies for those who wish to include an introduction to this subject in their amplifier course.

A textbook is not created in a vacuum. Many of the ideas that have found their way into this book have resulted from my teaching experiences. I want to express my appreciation to colleagues and students who have contributed to these experiences. Special thanks is due Wendy Flanagan of the Merrill Editorial Staff, for her advice and enthusiasm in transposing manuscript to printed page.

RODNEY B. FABER

TABLE OF CONTENTS

CHAPTER 1

Principles of Semiconductor Devices

1.1 Introduction

Almost all electronic equipment must include the means for amplifying electrical signals. Radio receivers must amplify very weak radio waves — sometimes only a few millionths of a volt at the antenna — until they are strong enough to make a loudspeaker fill a room with sound. Transducers used in medical and scientific investigations generate signals in the microvolt (μv) and millivolt (mv) range. These signals must be amplified by factors of thousands and millions before they will be strong enough to operate indicating instruments or recorders. Thus electronic amplifiers are a constant and important ingredient of electronic systems.

The early history of electronics was dominated by the vacuum tube as the principal amplifying device, but since the invention of the transistor in 1948, the tube has been gradually supplanted by various types of transistors until now the majority of electronic functions are performed by the transistor.

The characteristics of the transistor — and its more recent development, the integrated circuit — which have made possible many of the major developments of electronics in recent years, may be listed briefly as follows:

Very little heat
Extremely small size
Physical ruggedness
High reliability
Long operating life

1.2 Semiconductors

The phenomena associated with current flow in semiconductor materials form the basis for transistor action. Semiconductors are materials which are

1

intermediate between conductors and insulators with respect to their ability to conduct current. One of their most important characteristics is that a *doping* process, the addition of very small quantities of certain substances, alters their conductivity drastically.

Two types of doped material are possible, known as *n*-type and *p*-type. The properties of these two are such that when they are joined closely together, the combination will permit electron flow from the *n*-type to the *p*-type, but not from the *p* to the *n*. In other words, when used in an electric circuit, if the applied voltage is of such a polarity as to force electron flow through the junction in the favorable direction mentioned above, current will flow readily; if, however, the applied voltage is in the opposite direction, very little current will flow.

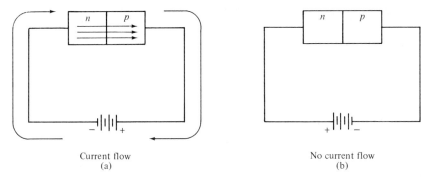

Current flow   No current flow
(a)   (b)

FIGURE 1–1
Piece of semiconductor material containing a pn *junction in an electric circuit*

Figure 1–1 illustrates this action. A piece of semiconductor material consisting of adjacent *n* and *p*-regions forms an electric circuit with a battery and a resistor. As indicated by the arrows in part (a), electrons flow from the *n*-type material across the junction into the *p*-type material, then through the resistor into the positive terminal of the battery. The negative terminal of the battery is of course supplying electrons to the *n*-material to replace those that go across the junction. Part (b) shows the same circuit except with the battery polarity reversed. In this case, since free electrons cannot flow across the junction from the *p*-region to the *n*-region, there is no current.

Crystal Structure in Transistors

The semiconductors in transistors are used in their crystalline form; this means that their atoms are joined together in a regular pattern, which is repeated over and over. This repeated pattern is called a crystal lattice and is the result of the valence bond sharing of electrons between neighboring atoms. For example, two commonly used semiconductors are germanium and silicon. Both of these are valence 4 materials; that is, they have four valence electrons. The crystalline structure that occurs in this case is the consequence of the sharing of each of an atom's four valence electrons with each of four neighboring atoms. Figure 1–2 illustrates the relations by means of a two-dimensional diagram. In this diagram the small circles represent the entire atom except for the

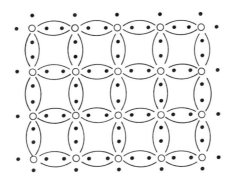

FIGURE 1–2
Crystal lattice structure of germanium or sillcon

valence electrons. The only electrons shown separately are the valence electrons, indicated by the small dots. The double lines joining the atoms represent the valence bond forces between adjacent atoms.

Electrons and Holes

Free electrons may be produced by the breaking loose of electrons from covalent bonds. This can come about as the result of collisions by other electrons, heat, strong electric fields, and the like. Such influences are sources of energy which contribute to raising the energy level of the valence bond electron to the point where it can escape from its position. When an electron has thus been freed from its covalent bond, the vacancy it leaves behind is called a *hole*.

Due to its thermal energy, the free electron will move about in the material. Whenever it comes too close to another electron, the force of repulsion between the two will cause it to "rebound," so that such encounters have the characteristic of collisions. The path of a free electron will thus be erratic, or random, in its nature as it moves from one "collision" to another. As long as it does not come too close to the nucleus of some atom that has lost an electron, it will stay free.

Electrons such as this can take part in current flow if an electric field is applied to the material, as will happen, for example, if electrodes are attached to opposite sides of the material and a battery is connected to the electrodes. The electron movement that then occurs is essentially a drift of the electrons between the atoms in a direction determined by the electric field. There are of course collisions along the way, so that the drift still has an erratic character. In addition, some electrons come too close to the nuclei of atoms that have lost electrons. These electrons recombine with such atoms and are lost from the current. All the time, of course, more free electrons are breaking out of other covalent bonds — assuming that the external energy causing disruption of covalent bonds is still being applied.

The electron movement described is not the only way in which current flows in a semiconductor. Wherever an atom has lost an electron, nearby bound electrons, lacking sufficient energy to become free electrons, may nevertheless receive enough energy from some external source to jump into the empty position. Not as much energy is required to make this move as to break completely clear. Another nearby electron may then move into the vacancy created by the previous move. Since each electron, in filling a hole, creates a new hole at the position it left, the hole in effect moves. The direction of motion of the hole is opposite to the direction of movement of the electrons.

If an electric field is applied, this action will take place in an average direction determined by the electric field. Note, however, the distinct difference between this form of current flow and the other. The first case is a general movement of free electrons between the atoms, while the second case does not involve free electrons, but is instead a series of motions in sequence, by different electrons, each consisting of a move from one covalent bond position to another.

The two types of movement have distinctly different characteristics, and these differences affect the performance of electronic devices (such as transistors) which are made from semiconductor materials. So it is necessary to distinguish between the two. The drift of free electrons is known as *electron current* or *electron flow*, while the current consisting of electrons jumping from one covalent bond position to another is called *hole current* or *hole flow*.

The Effect of Temperature on the Semiconductor

In pure semiconductor materials the creation of a free electron is always accompanied by the creation of a hole. The "free" electrons and "free" holes created in this way are known as *electron-hole pairs*. At normal room temperatures there are always a certain number of these created by thermal energy. Conduction in the pure semiconductor depends on these electron-hole pairs. As the temperature rises, more electrons leave their covalent bond positions due to the increase in thermal energy. This creation of more electron-hole pairs means that more charges are available for current flow, or in other words that the conductivity has increased.

The Effects of Impurities

The pure semiconductor in which we are interested, such as germanium or silicon, has four valence electrons. This permits sharing valence electrons with four neighbors. If only a small quantity of another material — one whose atoms have either three or five electrons in the outer orbits — is added while the crystal is forming, or in some other appropriate way, certain very significant differences occur in the crystal structure.

Adding a valence 3 impurity, for example, means that every impurity atom, having only three valence electrons, leaves one covalent bond position vacant in its association with its neighboring semiconductor atoms. In other words, the impurity atom can supply only three of the four valence electrons needed to pair with its four neighboring atoms, and the fourth bond position is left vacant. *Thus, the addition of a quantity of atoms of this type creates a quantity of holes available for possible conduction.* Figure 1–3 illustrates this. These

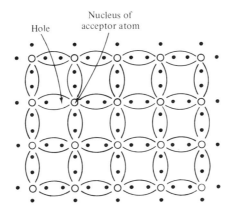

FIGURE 1–3
Portion of the lattice structure of a semiconductor which has had acceptor *impurities added*

impurities are often called *acceptor* impurities since the holes thus created can "accept" electrons.

The addition of a valence 5 material to the pure semiconductor, on the other hand, creates a source of free electrons since only four of its five valence electrons can go into covalent bonds. The fifth electron of each impurity atom is available for current flow, since it is not bound by covalent bond forces. These impurities are often designated *donor* impurities since they in effect "donate" electrons. Figure 1–4 depicts the crystal structure, showing the fifth valence electron.

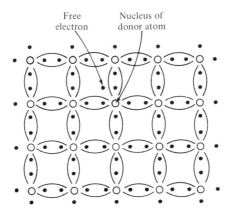

FIGURE 1–4
Portion of the crystal structure of a semiconductor which has had donor *impurities added*

p-Type Semiconductors

The semiconductor to which valence 3 impurities have been added is known as a *p*-type material because the effect of the impurity is to create holes, or positive charges available for conduction.

It should be carefully noted that although the material is so named because of its free positive charges, it is still electrically neutral. The impurity atoms used have one less *valence* electron than the semiconductor valence 4 atom, but these impurity atoms are normal, electrically neutral atoms. The presence of so-called free positive charges does not indicate that the material has a net positive charge any more than the presence of free electrons in a piece of copper would mean the copper is negatively charged.

n-Type Semiconductors

The addition of impurities having five valence electrons creates what is called an *n*-type material. The reasoning is similar: the impurity creates free electrons, or negative charges, consequently the name *n*-type. This material too is electrically neutral. The free electrons are balanced by the usual positive charges associated with the atoms.

Majority Carriers and Minority Carriers

In the pure semiconductor at room temperature there are an equal number of free electrons and holes. Due to thermal energy some electrons have been liberated from valence bonds, and every such electron has left behind it a hole.

A typical *n*-type material has its share of such electron-hole pairs but in addition has a much larger quantity of free electrons due to the effect of the impurity. These impurity-caused electrons are not associated with holes. *Consequently a normal n-type material has a large number of free electrons and a small number of holes.* The electrons in this case are considered majority carriers — since the major portion of any current flow is by electron flow — and the holes are called minority carriers.

In a p-type material, on the other hand, the holes predominate due to the effect of the impurity. The holes are, therefore, called the majority carriers, while the relatively small number of electrons, created by normal thermal energy, are the minority carriers.

1.3   pn Junctions

If a piece of semiconductor material is manufactured so that it has an *n* region in contact with a *p* region, free electrons from the *n* region initially will flow into the *p* region. This flow occurs due to the thermal energy of the electrons, which causes a random movement in all directions. When there are a quantity of particles localized in one region, as there are in the *n* region, such random movement — called *diffusion current* — causes a net flow out of this region.

The loss of electrons from the *n* region, and the gain of electrons by the *p* region, cause a difference of potential across the junction of the two regions. The polarity of this potential is such as to oppose further flow of charges so that a condition of equilibrium exists. Figure 1–5 is a graph showing the po-

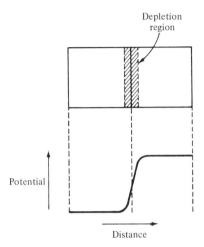

FIGURE 1–5
Barrier potential across a pn *junction*

tential. The *n* material has lost electrons — which are negative charges — while the *p* material has acquired electrons. The *n* material is, therefore, positive relative to the *p* material. Since this potential tends to prevent the movement of electrons from the *n* region into the *p* region, it is often called a *barrier potential*.

Figure 1–5 also shows a region extending to either side of the junction, marked *depletion region*. The electrons and holes taking part in the initial movement across the junction depleted this region of its free charges. The potential built up by this charge distribution then keeps the region in this condition. The depletion region figures in several phenomena that will be encountered briefly in later pages.

Forward-Biasing of the pn Junction

If a battery is connected to a *pn* junction by means of electrodes as shown in Figure 1–6, with the negative terminal of the battery connected to the *n* side, the effect of the battery will be to make the depletion region narrower, and lower the potential of the *n* side relative to the *p* side. The difference of potential between the two sides will be decreased below the equilibrium point, and current can once again flow across the junction. This polarity of applied voltage is called *forward-bias*, and the resulting current flow is referred to as *forward current*.

Should the applied potential be quite small (less than a few tenths of a volt), the barrier potential will be reduced only slightly below the equilibrium point,

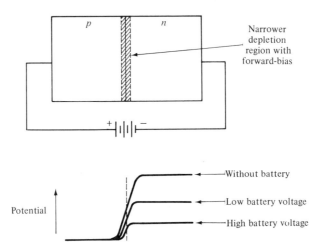

FIGURE 1–6

Effect of forward-bias on the barrier potential and the depletion region

and only a small number of charges in the material — those that happen to be in the uppermost energy levels — will possess enough energy to cross the junction. So the current will be quite small.

Increasing the applied voltage above a certain level, however, will lower the barrier enough that a much greater number of electrons will be found to have the energy required. The voltage required for this in the case of germanium must usually exceed two or three tenths of a volt. In silicon it must be

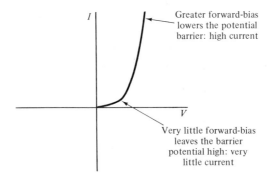

FIGURE 1–7

Current flow for various values of applied forward-bias potential

greater than approximately five or six tenths of a volt. The graph of Figure 1–7 illustrates the effect. The increase in the rate of rise of the current as the applied voltage is increased is typical of *pn* junctions.

Reverse-Biasing of the pn Junction

The polarity of applied voltage just considered causes current flow across the *pn* junction, and therefore current flows in the entire circuit. What happens if the applied voltage is reversed? To consider this, we need to go back briefly for one additional fact.

In the earlier discussion we omitted consideration of the effects of the minority carriers. While the majority carriers from each side (holes from the *p* material, electrons from the *n* material) are diffusing across the junction and building up a charge which becomes the barrier potential, the minority carriers are also available for conduction. The potential barrier is not a barrier at all for these charges, but instead attracts them. Thus minority carriers from the *p* region (electrons) are attracted by the positive charge being built up in the *n* region, and vice versa, and there is a minority current flow. The direction of this current is, of course, opposite to that of the majority carriers. Since the effect of these carriers, upon arrival, is to *decrease* the barrier potential, they cause more majority carrier flow, so that there is a continual small current in both directions.

Now, if the battery of Figure 1–6 is reversed, to provide what is known as reverse-bias, it widens the depletion region, and increases the barrier potential above the equilibrium value, as Figure 1–8 illustrates. This increase in the

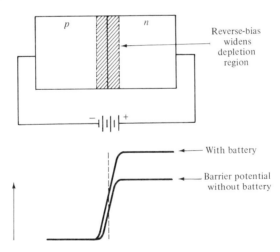

FIGURE 1–8

Effect of reverse-bias on the barrier potential and the depletion region

barrier potential due to reverse-bias stops the small forward current which has been flowing. While the forward current is thus cut off by the battery, the reverse current — composed of the minority carriers — continues to flow. Since the minority carrier quantities are very restricted, the amplitude of the reverse current is restricted. It rises to a maximum at a low value of reverse voltage, and further increase of the voltage produces little increase in reverse current.

When this effect is added to the information originally shown in Figure 1–7, the result is the normal *volt-ampere characteristic* of the *pn* junction, as shown in Figure 1–9. Note the leveling off of the reverse current.

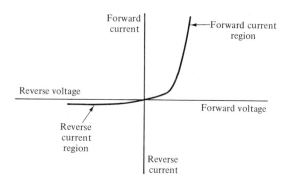

FIGURE 1–9
Volt-ampere characteristic of the pn *junction*

The reverse current is usually very small compared with the forward current. For example, the forward current for a particular silicon *pn* junction might range up to 100 milliamperes (ma) while the reverse current might be only a fraction of a microampere (μa) — a ratio of many thousands between forward and reverse currents. Similar ratios would be typical of junctions involving forward currents of many amperes.

1.4 Manufacture of Semiconductor Devices

The usual semiconductor devices require the material to be in the form of a single crystal. One method of obtaining the single crystal form is a crystal "growing" process. This consists of starting with a small piece of the semiconductor in the crystal form, and a crucible of the non-crystalline material heated to the molten state. The small piece — called a *seed crystal* — is inserted in the molten material and withdrawn very slowly. The molten material clings to the solid material, cooling and solidifying into a single crystal as it is withdrawn. This method permits growing large single crystals of the semiconductor, and is referred to as *crystal pulling*.

The Grown Junction

One method of forming *pn* junctions is to add the appropriate impurity material while the crystal is being grown. The process can start with a melt of a material, for example, then while the crystal pulling is proceeding, the addition of a *p* impurity to the melt converts the forming crystal from *n*-type to *p*-type. Figure 1–10 illustrates the general form of the crystal grown in this way, and the dotted lines show how it may be sawed into small pieces, each of which will contain a junction.

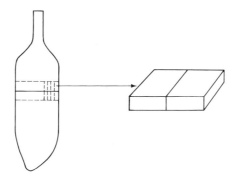

FIGURE 1-10
Semiconductor crystal with grown junction

The Alloy Junction

Another form of fabrication is the alloy technique. In this method a small dot of, for example, *p*-type impurity is placed on a piece of *n*-type semiconductor material, and the combination is heated. The impurity element melts and forms a liquid alloy combination with the semiconductor material. Upon cooling, the liquid alloy region recrystallizes. This region then constitutes the *p* material, and the junction between this and the *n* region forms the desired

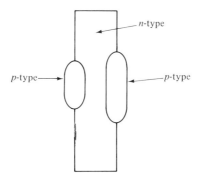

FIGURE 1-11
General form of the alloy junction

pn junction. Figure 1–11 shows the general appearance of the alloy junction construction, the example illustrated being a device which utilizes two *pn* junctions.

The Diffused Junction

If a piece of *p*-type semiconductor material is heated in an atmosphere containing an *n*-type impurity in vapor form, the vapor impurity will penetrate or diffuse into the solid. The depth of penetration will depend upon the time and the temperature of the exposure. The penetrated region will be an *n*-region;

the junction between it and the rest of the piece is then the desired *pn*-junction. The penetration of the surface is very uniform, so that very straight junctions may be formed by starting with very flat surfaces.

For example, by highly polishing the surface, and carefully controlling the conditions during the diffusion, two *pn*-junctions can be formed with less than 100 millionths of an inch separation. For certain types of semiconductor devices such close spacing is an important advantage.

The Planar Passivated Construction

A semiconductor device made by the diffusion process so that the edges of the junctions are formed beneath a protective layer of insulation (such as silicon dioxide) on one side of the material is called a *planar* device. The insulation protects the junctions from impurities in the atmosphere, preventing any change from the original optimum conditions. Thus the junctions are stabilized or *passivated,* and this form of construction is often known as *planar passivated.* Figure 1–12 illustrates the basic diffused planar construction.

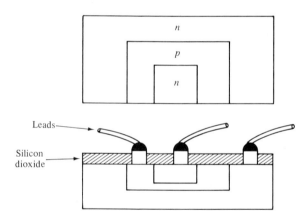

FIGURE 1–12
Planar passivated junction construction

Epitaxial Construction

Layers of *n* or *p*-material may be grown on a crystal by depositing out of a vapor. Such layers have different characteristics from those obtained by diffusion into the crystal. This process is called *epitaxial growth.*

1.5 The Semiconductor Diode

The volt-ampere graph of the *pn* junction, shown in Figure 1–9, reveals as its distinguishing feature an essentially unidirectional characteristic. The current that will flow in response to an applied potential can be thousands of times greater when the applied voltage is in one direction than in the other.

The difference is so great that for many purposes the small reverse current can be considered negligible.

This feature makes the *pn* junction a very important device even in the very simple form discussed so far, without considering the part it plays as the heart of the transistor. A great many problems in electrical and electronic circuits may be solved by use of this one-way current characteristic. When used for such purposes, the *pn* junction is called a *diode* or, more specifically, a *semiconductor diode*. The two parts of the diode are called the *cathode* (the *n* region) and the *anode* (the *p* region).

The Schematic Symbol of the Semiconductor Diode

In electronic circuit drawings the semiconductor diode is represented by a standard symbol whose use is best explained by means of Figure 1–13. Part (a) in this figure contains a simple circuit in which the diode is shown in physical

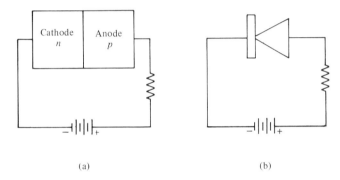

(a)   (b)

FIGURE 1–13
Use of the circuit symbol for the semiconductor diode

form as a *pn* junction in a piece of semiconductor material. In part (b) of this figure the diode represented by the standard symbol is shown in the same circuit for comparison. In the use of this symbol the arrow points in the direction that the majority carrier *holes* flow when the diode is forward-biased. Thus the majority carrier *electrons* flow *against* the arrow. In this example the diode is forward-biased.

As a memory aid concerning the biasing of *pn*-junctions, notice that forward-bias requires the *N* (for negative) terminal of the voltage supply to be connected to the *n* material, with the *P* (positive) terminal connected to the *p* material. Reverse-bias requires just the opposite — the *P*-terminal connected to the *n* material, and the *N*-terminal to the *p* material.

Static Characteristics of the Diode

The volt-ampere characteristic of the *pn*-junction was illustrated in Figure 1–9. The characteristics of all semiconductor diodes have somewhat the same general appearance. At low values of forward-bias the diode current is quite low, and it increases very slowly at first as the forward-bias is increased. But at about 0.2 to 0.25 volt (v) in the germanium diode, and about 0.6 to 0.7 v in the silicon diode, the current increases more rapidly, and above these voltages the curve is very steep. This is summarized in Figure 1–14. This figure also

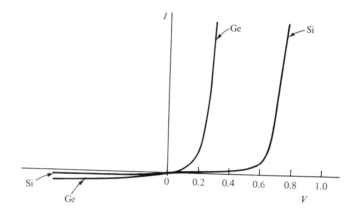

FIGURE 1–14
Typical germanium and silicon diode characteristics

shows that the silicon unit has much lower reverse current — or "leakage current" as it is often called — than the germanium. This also is typical.

For many purposes, the static curve of the diode can be approximated by straight lines as shown in Figure 1–15. The approximation of (a) simply ex-

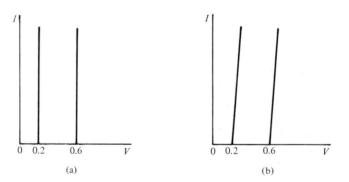

FIGURE 1–15
Straight-line approximations of diode curves

presses the fact that these diodes are characterized by a fairly fixed direct current (dc) voltage drop, and beyond this the voltage changes only slightly with changes of current. In (b) a rough approximation of the average slope of the upper leg is added. For many purposes this information is all that is needed, with respect to circuit voltages and currents. Where more detail is necessary, manufacturers sometimes publish the characteristic curves. When published curves are not readily available, such data may be obtained by measurement on representative units.

Manufacturers' Specifications

Although the volt-ampere curves of semiconductor diodes are very similar in appearance, other aspects of their characteristics differ tremendously. Some are built to carry very heavy currents while others can safely pass only small currents. The maximum value of voltage which can be safely applied in the reverse direction differs greatly depending upon the construction. The maximum power which the unit can dissipate without exceeding its maximum allowable temperature varies from milliwatts to many watts.

Information of this type is usually listed by the manufacturer in catalogs or data books. A sample of such specifications is given in Table 1–1.

TABLE 1–1

Typical Diode Specifications

Type	Max. Req'd Fwd. Voltage at Indicated Fwd. Current		Max. Reverse Current when Tested at Indicated Reverse Vltg.		Max. Allowable Reverse Voltage	Max. Allowable Power Dissipation	Max. Allowable dc Fwd. Current
	(v)	(ma)	(μa)	(v)	(v)	(mw)	(ma)
SILICON DIODES:							
1N625	1	4	1	20	30	200	20
1N914	1	10	0.025	20	100	250	110
1N3604	1	50	0.05	50	75	250	115
1N4451	1	300	0.05	30	40	500	250
GERMANIUM:							
1N34	1	5	50	10	60		50
1N63	1	4	50	50	100		40
1N309	1	100	100	20	30		100

*Adapted from General Electric Catalog 640.12

Nonlinearity in the Diode

A linear relationship is one which can be expressed by a straight-line equation — that is, one in which all variables are to the first power. Thus the relation between current and voltage in an ordinary resistor is $I = V/R$, whose graph is shown in Figure 1–16(a).

But the relation between current and voltage in a diode circuit is not linear, as shown by the diode curve of part (b). However, the portion of the characteristic between A and B is only slightly curved. Thus for many purposes, a portion such as AB may be considered linear. In addition, the portion between

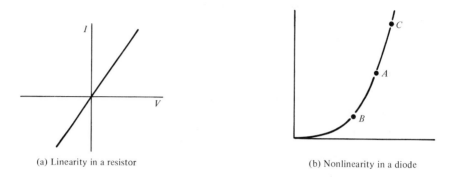

(a) Linearity in a resistor   (b) Nonlinearity in a diode

FIGURE 1–16
Linearity and nonlinearity

A and *C* is even less curved. In some cases the portion *AC* might be considered linear enough while the portion *BC* was not linear enough. This would depend entirely upon the requirements of the circuit in which the diode was to be used. In some applications, diodes are operated in such a way that a small fluctuating voltage, or *signal*, is impressed on the diode in series with a larger dc voltage. A simplified representation of such a circuit is given in Figure 1–17, in which the small signal is indicated by the generator symbol.

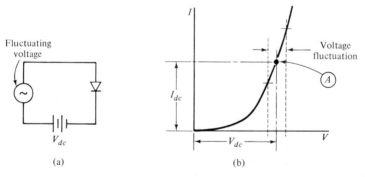

(a)   (b)

FIGURE 1–17
Small-signal and larger dc voltage

In cases of this sort, the location of the *operating point A*, and the amplitude of the fluctuation about this point, determine whether a linear or nonlinear region is being used. Thus such factors determine whether the resulting current fluctuation is an undistorted reproduction of the applied voltage fluctuation.

Diode Resistance

The ratio of the dc voltage in Figure 1–17 to the resulting dc current gives a resistance sometimes called the dc resistance of the diode.

$$R_D = \frac{V_{dc}}{I_{dc}} \tag{1-1}$$

Its value varies with the voltage, due to the diode nonlinearity. Figure 1–18(a) illustrates this.

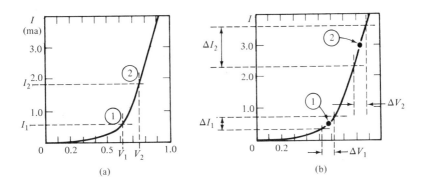

FIGURE 1–18
Diode dc resistance and small-signal resistance

At point 1, $R_{D1} = V_1/I_1$; at point 2, $R_{D2} = V_2/I_2$. Note that although V increased only moderately from point 1 to point 2, the current I more than tripled. Obviously R_{D2} is not the same value as R_{D1}.

If small voltage changes such as in Figure 1–17(b) are considered, another resistance may be defined. This is the ratio of the change in voltage to the change in current, or

$$r_d = \frac{\Delta V}{\Delta I} \tag{1-2}$$

The resistance defined by Equation (1–2) is known as the small-signal resistance. It is also often referred to as the dynamic resistance, or the incremental resistance.

Figure 1–18(b) shows that this resistance too is quite variable and dependent upon the location of the operating point. For example, at point 1 an increment of voltage equal to 0.10 v produces an increment of 0.4 ma in the current. Thus

$$r_{d1} = \frac{\Delta V_1}{\Delta I_1} = \frac{0.1}{0.0004} = 250 \text{ ohms}$$

At point 2, the slope of the curve is much steeper. That is, the same increment of voltage causes a much greater change in the current. Thus we can expect that the incremental resistance will be much smaller. Taking the values from the graph, we obtain

$$r_{d2} = \frac{\Delta V_2}{\Delta I_2} = \frac{0.1}{0.0013} \cong 77 \text{ ohms}$$

1.6 Load Line Analysis of Diodes

In designing circuits using electronic devices it is often necessary to predict the operating point; that is, the dc voltage drop across the device and the current through it. The circuits are not usually as simple as that used in the examples above; normally there is a resistance in series with the device. When this is the case, the operating point cannot be obtained by simply using Ohm's Law because of the nonlinear nature of electronic devices. Instead, a graphical method of analysis is necessary, utilizing what is known as a load line.

Although graphical analysis is not as commonly applied to diode circuits as it is to transistor and vacuum tube amplifier circuits, the simplicity of the diode circuit makes it especially convenient for introducing the technique. Later work will expand the method in the analysis of amplifier circuits.

When used for diode circuits, the graph of the diode characteristics and the graph of the resistance in series with the diode are combined in such a way that their point of intersection on the graph marks the operating point. Consider Figure 1–19. The Kirchhoff voltage equation for this circuit is

$$V_1 = IR + V_2 \qquad\qquad \textbf{(1–3)}$$

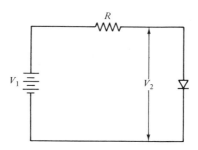

FIGURE 1–19
Simple diode circuit

In this equation, V_2 may be considered a variable since it may be any value over the range of the diode's curve, depending upon the circuit in series with it. For a given circuit, the values of V_1 and R will be fixed, or V_1 and R may be considered constants.

Now we may draw a graph of current I versus voltage V_2 for a range of voltages, and we will have a graph showing all the possible values of I for this circuit with any diode. This might be called the graph of the circuit which is connected to the diode. As an example, consider the circuit of Figure 1–20. We could solve the circuit Equation (1–3) for I, obtaining

$$I = \frac{V_1 - V_2}{R} \qquad\qquad \textbf{(1–4)}$$

and by letting V_2 range from 0 to 10 v, find out what values of I the circuit could give. But since the graph of voltage and current relations in a resistor is a straight line, it is only necessary to plot two points and draw the line through

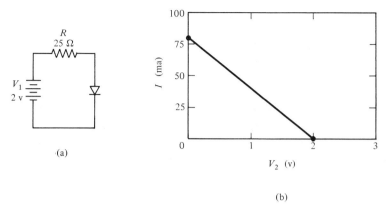

FIGURE 1–20
Current versus voltage for resistance in series with diode

them. Convenient points are where the line would cross the two axes, or where
the two conditions, (1) $I = 0$, and (2) $V_2 = 0$, prevail.

When $I = 0$, from Equation (1–3) we have

$$V_1 = IR + V_2$$
$$2 = (0)(25) + V_2$$
$$V_2 = 2 \text{ v}$$

While when $V_2 = 0$, we have from Equation (1–4)

$$I = \frac{V_1 - V_2}{R}$$
$$I = \frac{2 - 0}{25}$$
$$I = 0.08 \text{ amp or } 80 \text{ ma}$$

Thus we have found the V, I values at *two points:*

$$(1) \quad I = 0, V_2 = 2$$
$$(2) \quad V_2 = 0, I = 80 \text{ ma}$$

It should be noted that when $I = 0$, then $IR = 0$ so that $V_2 = V_1$; and
when $V_2 = 0$, $I = V_1/R$. Thus in general the two points are

$$(1) \quad I = 0, V_2 = V_1$$

or *on the voltage axis at the value of V_1;* and

$$(2) \quad V_2 = 0, I = \frac{V_1}{R}$$

or *on the current axis at the value V_1/R.*

These two points are plotted on the graph in Figure 1–20, and a straight
line has been drawn between them. This line represents the only values of V_2

and I that can exist in this circuit, regardless of what diode is placed in the circuit. The only question is *where on this line will the operating point be for the particular diode used?*

This can be answered very simply. Placing the diode characteristic curve on the same graph results in an intersection of the two graphs. Since one graph represents the only values that can exist for the circuit connected to the diode, and the other graph (the diode curve) represents the only values that can exist for the diode, the point which is on *both* graphs — the point of intersection — must represent the only values that can exist for both resistor and diode together in the circuit. This is shown in Figure 1–21, in which the straight line of the above example is drawn on the curve for the diode used.

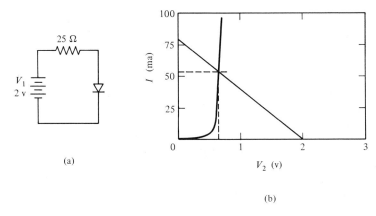

(a)

(b)

FIGURE 1–21
Load line drawn on diode characteristics

The resistance in series with the diode is called the *load*, or *load resistance*, for the circuit, and therefore the line we have just constructed is called a *load line*. The point at which it crosses the diode curve is the *operating point*. Projecting downward to the voltage axis gives the value of the voltage across the diode; projecting horizontally to the current axis gives the diode current. In this case they are:

$$I = 54 \text{ ma}$$
$$V_2 = 0.65 \text{ v}$$

Example 1–1

The diode that was used in connection with Figure 1–21 is now to be placed in a different circuit, and the results will be compared. In the new circuit the voltage V_1 will be the same as before, but the series resistance will be increased to 100 ohms. The two points for drawing the load line then are:

$$(1) \quad I = 0, V_2 = V_1 = 2 \text{ v}$$
$$(2) \quad V_2 = 0, I = \frac{V_1}{R_L} = \frac{2}{100} = 20 \text{ ma}$$

The diode curve used in the previous example is reproduced in Figure 1–22.

These two points and the load line are shown on this graph. The load line for
the original circuit is shown also for comparison. The new operating point is at:

$$I = 14 \text{ ma}$$
$$V_2 = 0.58 \text{ v}$$

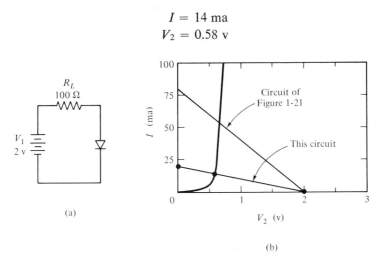

(a)

(b)

FIGURE 1–22
Circuit and load line

Example 1–2

A small signal is impressed on a diode circuit as shown in Figure 1–23. The
signal is a voltage fluctuation of 0.4 v. Since it acts in series with the dc voltage
V_1, the total voltage fluctuates from 1.8 to 2.2 v. When the signal is not present,

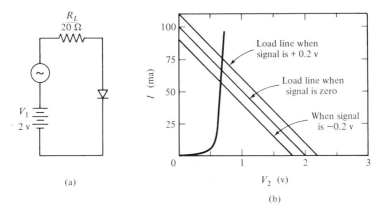

(a)

(b)

FIGURE 1–23
Load line construction when input voltage fluctuates

or is momentarily at zero, the total voltage is V_1. The load line for this zero
signal condition is shown in the figure.

When the signal voltage adds to or subtracts from V_1, the total voltage applied to the circuit is changed, and the position of the load line changes. Thus when the total voltage rises to 2.2 v, the two load line points become

$$(1) \quad I = 0, V_2 = 2.2$$

$$(2) \quad V_2 = 0, I = \frac{2.2}{20} = 110 \text{ ma}$$

The load lines for both extreme signal conditions — which change the total voltage to 1.8 at one extreme and 2.2 at the other — are drawn on Figure 1–23. From these load lines can be determined the effect of the signal on the diode voltage and on the circuit current. Note that due to the steepness of the diode characteristic, the diode voltage changes very little (roughly 0.04v) even though the impressed signal changes a total of 0.4 v, and even though the diode current changes by a large amount.

1.7 The Transistor

If two *pn* junctions are combined as shown in Figure 1–24, with the region between the two junctions made very narrow, the structure is called a transistor. The three sections of the transistor are the emitter, base, and collector

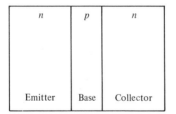
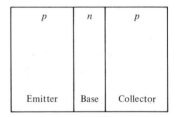

(a) *npn* transistor   (b) *pnp* transistor

FIGURE 1–24
Basic form of the transistor

as indicated on the diagram. The transistor in part (a) of the figure is called an *npn*-type; that in part (b) is a *pnp*-type.

Let us examine voltage and current relations in a transistor. For convenience we will at first deal only with the *npn*-type. In Figure 1–25(a) an *npn*-transistor without externally applied potentials is shown, along with a graph of the barrier potentials resulting from the diffusion of charges across each junction as explained in Section 1.3.

In part (b) external bias voltages are connected so as to forward-bias the emitter-base junction and reverse-bias the collector-base junction. Recall from Section 1.5 that forward-biasing requires connecting the supply N-terminal to the *n* material, and supply P-terminal to the *p* material. The effect on the barrier potentials is shown in the graph: the forward-bias lowers the barrier at

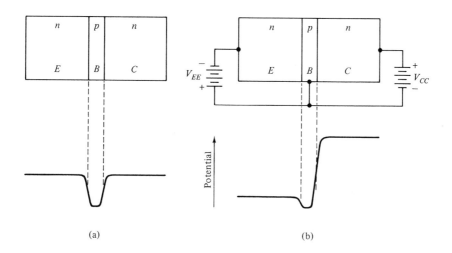

(a)   (b)

FIGURE 1-25
Potentials in the unbiased and biased transistor

the emitter-base junction; the reverse-bias raises the barrier at the other junction. Normally, if the junctions were isolated, the effect would be to cause ample current flow of majority carriers across the forward-biased junction and a slight leakage current across the reverse-biased one. But the fact that the two *pn* junctions share the same *p* region changes things dramatically, and we find instead *that the reverse-biased junction has a large current flow across it also.*

The explanation for this is in the fact that the base region is very thin and very wide, so that most of the electrons that arrive in the base from the emitter due to the forward-bias encounter the base-collector junction and the large base-collector potential hill before they manage to traverse the long path sideways to the lead that would take them out of the base. Although the polarity of the base-collector potential is such as to prevent flow of base and collector majority carriers (which would be electrons moving to the left and holes moving to the right), it is *attractive* for the carriers from the emitter. Thus nearly all of the current from the emitter normally goes to the collector, with only a small portion flowing out of the base lead. The collector portion flows out of the collector into the P-terminal of V_{CC}, out the N-terminal, and from there directly to the P-terminal of V_{EE}. The much smaller base current portion flows out of the base by way of the base lead, joins the collector current, and returns with it to the *P*-terminal of V_{EE}. These currents are illustrated in Figure 1-26. If we designate the current in the emitter lead as I_E, the current in the collector lead as I_C, and the current in the base lead as I_B, we have the relationship

$$I_E = I_C + I_B \qquad (1\text{-}5)$$

In addition to the current coming from the emitter, there is a small reverse current across the reverse-biased collector-base junction. This is the reverse

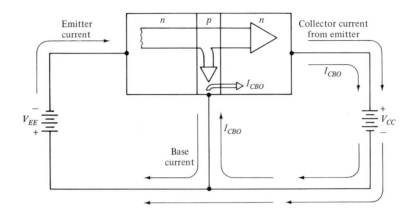

FIGURE 1–26
Currents in the transistor

current discussed in Section 1.3. It consists of holes flowing from collector to base, and electrons flowing from base to collector, and is supplied by electrons flowing into the base from the N-terminal of V_{CC}, and flowing out of the collector into the P-terminal of V_{CC}. This current is called the *collector cutoff current* and is designated I_{CBO}. It is also often referred to as the collector leakage current.

Thus the current in the collector lead is composed of that which came from the emitter, plus the cutoff current I_{CBO}. The portion of the collector current which came from the emitter may be designated as αI_E, so that

$$I_C = \alpha I_E + I_{CBO} \tag{1–6}$$

The symbol h_{FB} is very commonly used for α in transistor work. Using this symbol, Equation (1–6) would be

$$I_C = h_{FB}I_E + I_{CBO} \tag{1–6a}$$

The value of α (or h_{FB}) is always less than one in normal operation of a transistor, and usually is greater than 0.9.

When the emitter current is zero, the collector current consists only of the small cutoff current I_{CBO}, and the collector is said to be *cut off*. As the emitter current is increased from zero, the collector current increases by αI_E. For example, in the case of a transistor with $\alpha = 0.98$, an emitter current increase from zero to 1 ma causes the collector current to increase from I_{CBO} to $I_{CBO} + 0.98$ ma; an emitter current of 2 ma causes a collector current of $I_{CBO} + (2)(0.98)$ ma or $I_{CBO} + 1.96$ ma, and so on. Thus fluctuations of emitter current cause similar fluctuations of collector current.

Amplifying Action of the Transistor

The fact that fluctuations of emitter current cause similar fluctuations of collector current is not in itself remarkable. But since the emitter-base junction is forward-biased, only very small voltage changes are required to cause fairly large current changes. (Recall that in one of the diode examples above, an actual voltage change of only about 0.04 v across the diode caused a current change of about 20 ma). That is, the forward-biased junction has quite a low dynamic resistance.

The reverse-biased junction, however, has a very high resistance. For example, the diode specifications listed in Section 1.5 showed instances of reverse currents of $1\mu a$ and less for 20 v impressed — or resistances in the order of megohms. Thus the collector-to-base voltage has little effect on the collector current, as long as it is great enough to maintain the barrier potential illustrated in Figure 1–25. This means that a large resistance can be inserted in series with the collector as shown in Figure 1–27, without greatly disturbing

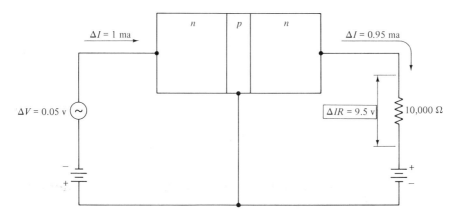

FIGURE 1–27
Example of transistor action

the collector current relation to the emitter current, as given by Equation (1–6). When this is done, collector current fluctuations caused by quite small emitter-base voltage fluctuations result in voltage changes across the resistor that are quite large — often hundreds of times larger than the emitter-base voltage change. As an example, consider the typical case shown in Figure 1–27.

Here the emitter-base junction is forward-biased by the voltage V, so that small voltage changes may cause considerable change of current. In this example an increment of 0.05 v causes a current change of 1 ma. If this transistor has $\alpha = 0.95$, then the emitter current change of 1 ma causes a collector current change of 0.95 ma. The result is a change in the IR drop produced in the 10,000 ohms resistance by the collector current flow. This change will be

$$(\Delta I)(R) = (0.95 \times 10^{-3})(10 \times 10^3)$$
$$\Delta IR = 9.5 \text{ v}$$

This voltage increment is $9.5/0.05 = 190$ times as great as the voltage change which initiated the action.

In essence, the transistor permits transferring a given current change from a low resistance circuit to a high resistance circuit. Thus the name *transistor*, referring to the *transfer of resistance*. Because of this property, the transistor can be used to *amplify* signal voltage fluctuations: a small ΔV input can result in a large ΔV output. These effects will be examined in more detail later.

The Schematic Symbol of the Transistor

In circuit drawings the transistor is represented by the symbol shown in Figure 1–28.

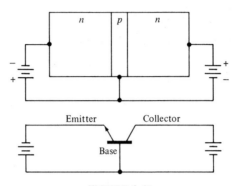

FIGURE 1–28
Transistor schematic symbol

1.8 Static Characteristics of the Transistor in the Common-Base (CB) Configuration

In Sections 1.5 and 1.6, the volt-ampere curves of diodes were used to analyze various characteristics and operating conditions. Graphs of the volt-ampere relations for transistors are similarly useful. The static characteristics of transistors, however, are more complex than those of diodes. It is necessary to consider both the input characteristics, or volt-ampere relations of the emitter-base junction, and the output characteristics, or volt-ampere relations of the collector-base junction. In addition, each of these graphs will consist of a family of curves rather than a single curve.

The CB Connection

The method of connecting the transistor which we have used for our discussion so far, and which is shown in Figure 1–28, is called the *CB* or grounded-base connection. In this arrangement the base is common to both the input circuit (the emitter-base loop) and the output circuit (the collector-base loop).

The input or emitter characteristics typically have the appearance shown in Figure 1–29. Note the similarity to the diode curves of the previous sections. Note also that a family of curves is shown, because the collector-base voltage has some effect on the emitter current flow. However, at values of collector voltage appreciably above zero the effect is slight, and it is quite common to consider I_E as a function only of V_{EB} for routine practical work. Thus, often in practical work only one curve is shown for the input characteristic.

The output, or collector, characteristics have the appearance illustrated in Figure 1–30. Again a family of curves is necessary. The output characteristics show collector current versus collector voltage for a number of different values

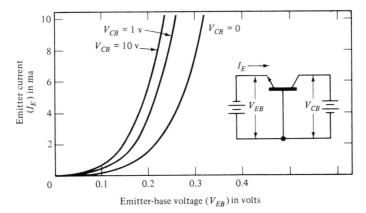

FIGURE 1–29

Typical input characteristics of the transistor in the common-base connection

of emitter current. It might seem that it would be more convenient to use a graph of collector current versus emitter current, but we shall find later that the type of curves shown in Figure 1–30 permit load-line analysis that is very important.

Note that the graph shows a small value of collector current even when the emitter current is zero. In the *CB* circuit this collector leakage current is identified by the notation I_{CBO}. This is the collector cutoff current discussed earlier.

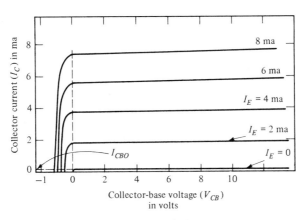

FIGURE 1–30

Typical common-base output characteristics

1.9 The Transistor in the Common-Emitter (CE) Configuration

The transistor can also be connected as shown in Figure 1–31. In this arrangement the *emitter* is common to both the input (the circuit connected to the base and the emitter) and the output (the circuit connected to the collector and emitter).

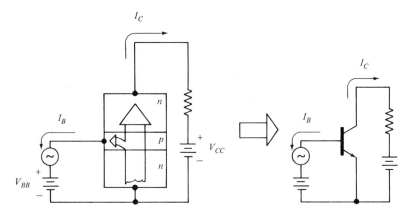

FIGURE 1–31
Common-emitter transistor connection

When connected in this manner, with the voltage polarities shown, the base-emitter junction is forward-biased, and the collector-base junction is reverse-biased because V_{CC} is greater than V_{BB} and thus holds the collector more positive than the base. Thus the relative junction potentials are the same as in the *CB* arrangement.

Since only a small portion of the emitter current goes to the base lead, and most of it goes to the collector, the input current is much smaller than the output (collector) current. Thus when a signal voltage fluctuation is applied to the input as indicated by the generator symbol in the figure, the input current fluctuation will be much smaller than the output current fluctuation. The *CE* circuit therefore provides signal current amplification as well as the voltage amplification that the *CB* gives.

The *CE* input characteristics are similar to the common-base, except that they display base current (I_B) versus base-emitter voltage (V_{BE}). Typical output or collector characteristics for the *CE* connection are illustrated in Figure 1–32.

Note that this family of curves presents collector current versus collector-emitter voltage for a number of values of base current I_B. Note also that the value of base current for each curve is quite small compared to the corresponding value of collector current.

Finally, it should be observed that a small collector current flows even when the base current is zero. This is the collector cutoff current, or the collector current that flows when the base is open-circuited, and is identified by the notation I_{CEO}. The *CE* collector cutoff current is much larger than the *CB* cutoff current.

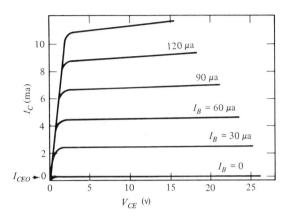

FIGURE 1–32
Typical common-emitter output characteristics

Current Relations in the Common-Emitter Connection

The characteristic curves of Figure 1–32 show that when the base current is zero, only the small collector cutoff current I_{CEO} flows. When the base current is increased from zero, the collector current increases in proportion, but by a much larger amount. This is a consequence of a forward-biasing of the base-emitter junction, causing emitter current to flow. Of this emitter current, a small portion goes to the base lead, and a much larger portion goes to the collector.

If we designate the collector current that flows due to the forward-bias as βI_B, we have

$$I_C = \beta I_B + I_{CEO} \tag{1–7}$$

A symbol often used instead of β is h_{FE}. When this is used, the equation becomes

$$I_C = h_{FE} I_B + I_{CEO} \tag{1–7a}$$

A relationship exists between β or h_{FE} of the *CE* and α or h_{FB} of the *CB*. For example, if α is 0.99, then 1 percent of I_E goes to the base, and 99 percent goes to the collector. Thus the collector's share is 99 times the base's share, so that apparently $\beta = 99$.

This can be expressed in a more general way by writing Equation (1–6)

$$I_C = \alpha I_E + I_{CBO} \tag{1–6}$$

and substituting for I_E, from Equation (1–5),

$$I_E = I_C + I_B \tag{1–5}$$

This results in

$$I_C = \alpha(I_C + I_B) + I_{CBO}$$
$$I_C - \alpha I_C = \alpha I_B + I_{CBO}$$
$$I_C(1 - \alpha) = \alpha I_B + I_{CBO}$$

$$I_C = \frac{\alpha}{1 - \alpha} I_B + \frac{1}{1 - \alpha} I_{CBO} \tag{1–8}$$

This equation expresses the collector current as composed of two parts — one a multiple of I_B and the other a multiple of the *CB* leakage current I_{CBO}. But this is the form in which Equation (1–7) expresses the current:

$$I_C = \beta I_B + I_{CEO} \tag{1–7}$$

It is evident from this that the multiplier $\alpha/(1 - \alpha)$ of Equation (1–8) is the same as β in Equation (1–7), and $I_{CBO}(1/(1-\alpha))$ in Equation (1–8) is the term I_{CEO} of Equation (1–7).

In addition, the term $1/(1 - \alpha)$ which occurs above can be shown to be equal to $\beta + 1$ (or $h_{FE} + 1$).

To summarize the above findings:

$$\beta = \frac{\alpha}{1 - \alpha} \tag{1–9}$$

$$\beta + 1 = \frac{1}{1 - \alpha} \tag{1–10}$$

$$I_{CEO} = \frac{1}{1 - \alpha} I_{CBO} \tag{1–11}$$

$$I_{CEO} = (\beta + 1) I_{CBO} \tag{1–11a}$$

We now see that Equation (1–7) can be written as

$$I_C = \beta I_B + (\beta + 1) I_{CBO} \tag{1–12}$$

$$I_C = h_{FE} I_B + (h_{FE} + 1) I_{CBO} \tag{1–12a}$$

1.10 pnp-Transistors

The transistor structure discussed so far has been the *npn*-type, but *pnp*-units are also frequently used. In the *pnp*-transistor, the currents and voltages are all opposite to those of the *npn*-transistor, but the principle of operation is otherwise essentially the same. Figure 1–33 shows both types in the common-

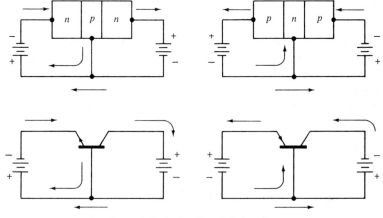

Arrows indicate direction of electron flow

FIGURE 1-33
npn *and* pnp-*transistors in the common-base circuit*

base connection. The normal operating voltages for each are shown for comparison. The emitter-base junction is forward-biased, and the collector-base junction is reverse-biased in each case. Note that the memory aid for biasing holds true for both: Negative to *n* and Positive to *p* for forward-bias; Negative to *p* and Positive to *n* for reverse-bias.

The schematic symbol for the *pnp*-unit has the emitter arrow pointing into the transistor, while the *npn* emitter arrow points out. The direction of the arrow is the direction that conventional current takes in the emitter under forward-bias conditions, or *opposite the electron flow direction.*

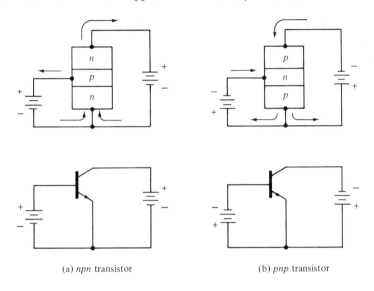

(a) *npn* transistor   (b) *pnp* transistor

FIGURE 1–34
npn *and* pnp *transistors in the common-emitter circuit*

Figure 1–34 gives the common-emitter configuration for both types. Again, the base-emitter junction is forward-biased and the collector-base junction is reverse-biased.

1.11 Introduction to Load Line Analysis of Transistors

Load line analysis, introduced in Section 1.6 in connection with diode circuits, is a powerful tool for the analysis of operating conditions in transistor circuits. Construction of the load line for transistors is the same as for diodes. Consider Figure 1–35, showing a common-emitter amplifier circuit in part (a), and the collector characteristics of the transistor in (b).

The two points used in drawing the load line are:

(1)   On the voltage axis at $V = V_{CC}$
(2)   On the current axis at $I = V_{CC}/RL$

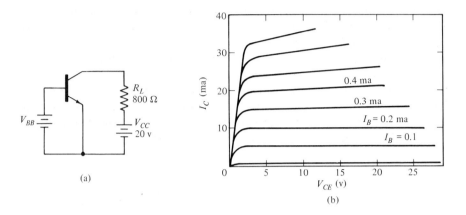

(a)

(b)

FIGURE 1-35
Circuit and collector curves for load line analysis

For the circuit shown this gives

    (1)   On the voltage axis at 20 v

    (2)   On the current axis at $I = \dfrac{20}{800} = 25$ ma

Figure 1–36 shows these points plotted, and the load line drawn.

    In Section 1.6 we showed that the intersection of the load line with the volt-ampere curve of the diode gave the only possible operating point for a particular diode operating in a particular circuit. The same thing holds true here — except that in the case of the transistor more than just one curve is involved. An infinite number of curves intersect with the load line in Figure 1–36. Thus more information is needed: the value of base current. This will determine which transistor curve represents the operating condition.

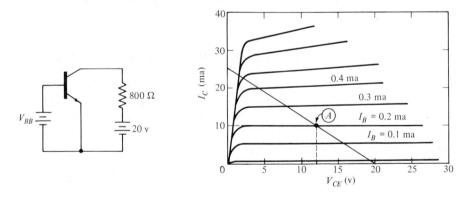

FIGURE 1-36
Load line drawn on the transistor collector curves

Assume that in the circuit of Figures 1–35 and 1–36 the voltage applied to the base-emitter junction causes 0.2 ma of base current to flow. For this particular condition, then, only points along the $I_B = 0.2$ ma curve of the transistor can exist for the transistor. Thus only the intersection of the load line with the 0.2 ma I_B curve can satisfy both the transistor's operating condition and the attached circuit. The operating point must therefore be at point A in Figure 1–36. The value of collector voltage V_{CE} for this operating point is indicated by the dashed line in the figure projecting down to the voltage axis. The collector current is shown by the line projecting horizontally to the current axis.

Amplifying Action in the Transistor as Shown by Load Line Analysis

It is evident that in the common-emitter transistor circuit, the base current controls the collector voltage and collector current, within the operating limits of the transistor and the associated circuit. It is this that marks the transistor as a uniquely valuable device. The example used above will serve to demonstrate this. The circuit and collector curves of Figure 1–36 are repeated in Figure 1–37 along with the base-emitter curve for the transistor.

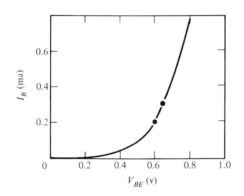

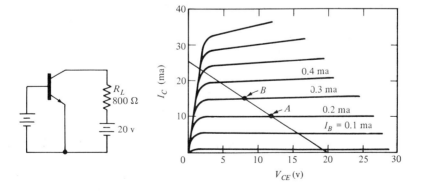

FIGURE 1-37
Circuit and curves for demonstrating amplifying action of transistor

The operating point in the example above resulted from a base current of 0.2 ma; the base-emitter curve in Figure 1–37 shows that this base current is produced by a base-emitter voltage of 0.6 v. Now let us change the applied base-emitter voltage from 0.6 to 0.65 v. The curve shows that this causes the base current to change from 0.2 ma to 0.3 ma. On the collector curves the load line reveals that this change in the base current causes the operating point to move from *A*, at which the collector voltage was 12 v, to *B*, at which the collector voltage has decreased to 8 v.

Thus a change of 0.05 v (from 0.6 to 0.65) in the base-emitter voltage has produced a change of 4 v (from 12 to 8) in the collector voltage. The ratio of the collector voltage change to the base voltage change is 4/0.05 = 80. In other words, a voltage change at the base has resulted in a voltage change 80 times as great at the collector.

1.12 Small-Signal α and β

In Sections 1.7 and 1.8 the control of the collector current by the emitter current or base current was expressed by α (or h_{FB}) for the common-base circuit, and β (or h_{FE}) for the common-emitter. Thus for the common-base,

$$I_C = \alpha I_E + I_{CBO} \tag{1–6}$$

or
$$I_C = h_{FB}I_E + I_{CBO} \tag{1–6a}$$

while for the common emitter,

$$I_C = \beta I_B + I_{CEO} \tag{1–7}$$
$$I_C = h_{FE}I_B + I_{CEO} \tag{1–7a}$$

As a consequence of the basic nonlinearity of electronic devices, relationships such as those represented by α and β are not constant over the entire operating range depicted by curves like Figure 1–37. The nonlinearity is usually greater for large changes. Since amplifier operation often involves small changes of voltage and current — that is, small signals — it is customary to use "small-signal" values of α and β. These are related to small increments, and not to the total or dc value.

Thus,

$$\Delta I_C = \alpha'(\Delta I_E) = h_{fb}\Delta I_E$$
$$\Delta I_C = \beta'(\Delta I_B) = h_{fe}\Delta I_B$$

in which the prime marks and the lower case subscripts *fb* and *fe* differentiate the small-signal values from the large-signal or dc values. Note carefully that these two relationships show only ΔI_C, ΔI_B, etc. They do not involve the total I_C, I_B, or I_E, and they do not include the cutoff currents. These are *incremental* relations only.

More exact definition of these two *current gain* factors is as follows.

$$h_{fb} = \frac{\Delta I_C}{\Delta I_E}\bigg|V_{CB} \text{ constant} \tag{1–13}$$

$$h_{fe} = \frac{\Delta I_C}{\Delta I_B}\bigg|V_{CE} \text{ constant} \tag{1–14}$$

A test circuit capable of making the measurements expressed in the above definitions is shown in Figure 1–38 for the case of the common-emitter current gain factor h_{fe}. The figure shows also the graphical method which could be

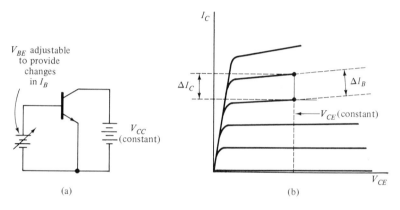

FIGURE 1–38
Operating conditions for definition of h_{fe}

applied to a set of collector curves in order to calculate the value of h_{fe} from published manufacturer's data.

Both parts of this figure stress the constant V_{CE}. Note in the test circuit, for example, that with a constant supply voltage connected *directly* to the collector, any change in I_C caused by changes in I_B will have no effect on V_{CE}. This would not be true if there were any resistance (such as R_L in Figure 1–37) in series with the applied voltage, since then $\Delta I_C R_L$ would cause a change in voltage. This was evident in the example illustrated in Figure 1–37.

It is for this reason that h_{fb} and h_{fe} are known as *short-circuit* current gain factors. In order to properly measure h_{fe} or h_{fb}, all resistance in series with the collector must be shorted out, or else the collector supply voltage must be re-adjusted to its original value after I_B and I_C have changed.

The reason for the constant voltage requirement is that h_{fb} and h_{fe} are used as universal figures of merit, for the purpose of comparing different transistors *under the same conditions*.

In order to fully benefit from his knowledge of the value of h_{fb} (or h_{fe}) of a transistor, the user should understand that this figure does not represent conditions that would exist in all circuits, but only in a test circuit meeting the constant V_{CE} requirement. Later in the book we shall discuss methods of applying the universal figure of merit to individual circuit conditions.

Beyond this, the experienced user also understands that the current ratio in an actual amplifier circuit containing load resistance is always *less* than the value of h_{fb} or h_{fe}. Figure 1–39 shows why this is so, in terms of *CE* curves. The vertical line represents zero load resistance, or constant V_{CE}, while the sloping load line represents the operation of a typical amplifier. *It is apparent*

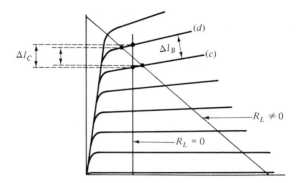

FIGURE 1–39
Actual current gain, $\Delta I_c/\Delta I_B$, is smaller than h_{fe} when R_L is not zero

that when the signal moves along the sloping load line (representing an amplifier) from base current curve (c) to base current curve (d), the resulting ΔI_C is less than in the case of the vertical load line (representing the constant $V_C C$ condition).

1.13 Operating Limitations of Transistors

Operating conditions exceeding certain limits either cause permanent damage to transistors, or temporarily alter their operating characteristics. The limits which must be observed are listed by the manufacturer in published specifications for each type of transistor. The following is a brief treatment of each of the commonly encountered limits.

Maximum Voltage Rating

In most applications the collector-base junction is subjected to the highest voltages, so that it is customary to specify either the maximum allowable collector-base voltage or the maximum allowable collector-emitter voltage, or both. In detailed specifications the breakdown voltage is usually given for all three possible combinations: collector-emitter, collector-base, and emitter-base. The voltage breakdown which can occur is of two general types: *avalanche breakdown* and *reach-through* (also called punch-through).

Avalanche Breakdown

This form of voltage breakdown arises when free electrons and holes in the semiconductor are accelerated enough by the applied potential so that collisions with bound electrons produce more free electrons, which cause even more collisions and thus a cumulative increase resulting in large currents. This process is similar to that occurring in ionization of a gas.

A closely allied form of breakdown, called *Zener breakdown*, is initiated by the direct rupture of covalent bonds due to high voltage rather than by the acceleration of free electrons. Zener breakdown and avalanche breakdown are difficult to distinguish from each other, and the two names are often used interchangeably.

Reach-Through

In this form of breakdown, the width of the collector-base junction depletion region due to reverse-bias becomes great enough so that it extends completely across the base region to the emitter. In Section 1.3 the barrier potential gradient was shown to begin at the edge of the depletion region (see Figure 1-5). Since this potential is of the correct polarity to attract the majority carriers of the emitter region, the extending of the depletion region to the emitter material results in the emitter current going directly to the collector without requiring forward-biasing of the base-emitter junction. The control normally exercised by the base-emitter junction voltage is destroyed, and there is in effect a short-circuit from emitter to collector, as a result of the collector potential *reaching through* the base region to the emitter.

The construction of the transistor determines which type of breakdown occurs at the lower voltage and is therefore the limiting factor in a particular transistor. The manufacturer usually lists the breakdown voltage rating under a heading such as "Maximum Ratings" or "Absolute Maximum Ratings." This rating should not be exceeded under the worst conditions to be encountered by the transistor in the circuit, taking into account the variations in operating conditions that occur.

Symbols used for breakdown voltage rating are:

BV_{CBO} Breakdown voltage from collector to base with the emitter open-circuited

BV_{CEO} Breakdown voltage from collector to emitter with the base open-circuited

BV_{EBO} Breakdown voltage from emitter to base with the collector open

The collector-to-emitter breakdown voltage is affected by the condition of the emitter-base circuit. Consequently, additional ratings are often given, for either a specified resistance connected from base to emitter (BV_{CER}) or for base shorted to emitter (BV_{CES}). Other symbols sometimes encountered are $V_{(BR)CEO}$, V_{CEO}, etc. In general, since breakdown results in a drastic increase in current, the collector characteristics in the vicinity of collector-base or collector-emitter breakdown have the appearance illustrated in Figure 1-40.

Maximum Power Dissipation

The temperature rise of a transistor above the temperature of its surroundings (that is, above the *ambient* temperature) is determined by the power dissipated in the transistor and its ability to rid itself of heat. If the ambient temperature and/or the power dissipation is too great, the temperature will exceed the safe limit.

The power dissipation in a transistor is principally the power dissipated in its junctions. Under dc conditions junction power is found from the product of the junction voltage and the junction current. In normal operation the two

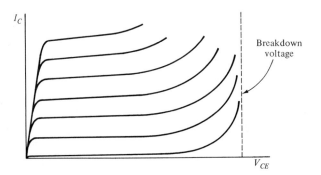

FIGURE 1–40
Breakdown characteristics of the transistor

junctions carry approximately the same current, but the collector-base junction has much higher voltage across it. Consequently, collector dissipation is often the major concern. For example, in a germanium transistor with 0.4 v base-emitter bias and 20 v on the collector, the collector dissipation will constitute about 98 percent of the total dissipation.

The maximum allowable collector dissipation or the maximum allowable total dissipation are listed by the manufacturer with either the ambient temperature specified or the temperature of the outside case of the transistor specified. If the ambient or case temperature exceeds the specified value, the transistor must be *derated*. That is, its maximum allowable power dissipation must be lowered. The symbol frequently used for collector dissipation is P_C.

1.14 Junction Capacitances

Associated with *pn*-junctions are capacitances which can be very important in the operation of semiconductor diodes and transistors. Two types of capacitance occur, one associated primarily with reverse-biased junctions and the other with forward-biased junctions. Both capacitances change value considerably with changes in the junction operating conditions. This is often a disadvantage, although in certain applications the ability to control the capacitance value of a junction becomes extremely useful.

Transition Capacitance

An ordinary conductor or semiconductor having an even distribution of positive and negative charge carriers has a net charge of zero. At a *pn*-junction, however, this charge neutrality is upset by the diffusion of charges across the junction. The depletion region in effect is "storing" a net charge representing the difference in charge which has occurred between the two sides as a result of the movement. Since capacitance is defined as the ratio of stored charge to the difference of potential, a junction is therefore accompanied by a capacitance. The width of the depletion region, and therefore the total amount of charge which has been moved, varies with the junction voltage. Consequently, the capacitance varies with the voltage.

This capacitance is known as the depletion-region capacitance or the transition region capacitance. Other names are space-charge capacitance and barrier capacitance. Although both junctions in a transistor have this capacitive effect, it is predominant at the reverse-biased collector-base junction. Symbols which have been used for the collector transition capacitance are C_{TC} and C_c.

Diffusion Capacitance

In addition to the charge difference between the two sides of a depletion region in the case of a reverse-biased junction, a difference in charge also is associated with the current flow across a forward-biased junction, since the arrival of charges on the other side creates excess charge there. Since the current flow across a forward-biased junction is called *diffusion current*, the capacitance resulting from this current flow is called *diffusion capacitance*. Both junctions exhibit this effect, but it is predominant in the forward-biased base-emitter junction. The symbol for diffusion capacitance is usually C_D. Since it is the predominant base-emitter capacitance, it is sometimes referred to as C_e, C_{be}, or $C_{b'e}$. The value of the diffusion capacitance is dependent upon the current.

1.15   Zener Diodes

Voltage breakdown in diodes results in the characteristic shown in Figure 1–41. Diodes may be designed with sufficient dissipation rating so they may be operated in the breakdown region without damage. Such diodes are known as Zener diodes, avalanche diodes, or breakdown diodes. The important feature

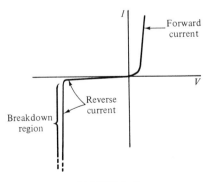

FIGURE 1–41
Voltage breakdowns in diodes

of the Zener diode is that the voltage in the breakdown region is almost constant over a wide range of current, and is quite stable. In addition, the value of voltage at which breakdown occurs can be controlled in manufacture. Units are available with breakdown voltage ratings, or *Zener voltages*, from a few volts to a few hundred volts.

These features permit breakdown diodes to be used as a means of regulating supply voltages so they are very constant. A simplified example of this is illustrated in Figure 1–42. The load line construction shows that a large change in

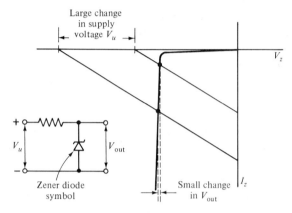

FIGURE 1–42
Application of Zener diode

the unregulated supply V_U causes only a small change in the regulated output voltage V_{out}.

The incremental, or dynamic, resistance of the Zener in its breakdown region is a measure of its quality. The ideal Zener would have a perfectly vertical characteristic here, or for a given ΔI, ΔV would be zero. This would give perfect regulation in the example above.

Thus in the practical Zener diode, the dynamic resistance in the breakdown region,

$$r = \frac{\Delta V}{\Delta I}$$

should be small. The manufacturer usually specifies the value of this dynamic resistance at some particular value of reverse current.

CHAPTER 2

Introduction to Amplifiers

2.1 Introduction

This chapter is a very important part of the book. The ideas and methods described here form the foundation of amplifier analysis. Although they are given first in a simple form, they lead to more advanced techniques which will be encountered frequently. So it is important to study these ideas carefully.

2.2 The Elemental Amplifier Circuit

Figure 2–1(a) illustrates a simple *CE* transistor circuit, and shows along with it the *CE* graphical input and output characteristics of the transistor used in the circuit. The load line for this circuit is drawn on the output curves, using the methods developed in Chapter 1.

A brief review of load line construction might be helpful at this time.

1. Point (1) is on the voltage axis at $V_{CE} = V_{CC}$; that is, at the value of the supply voltage, which is 20 v in this circuit.

2. Point (2) is on the current axis at $I_C = V_{CC}/R_C$. Therefore $I_C = 20/5000 = 4$ ma for this point.

3. The straight line connecting these two points is the load line. It is the graph of the equation $V_{CE} = V_{CC} - I_C R_C$, and any point at which this straight line intersects the transistor curves (including any possible transistor curves in between the ones shown!) is a possible "operating point" for this amplifier circuit. That is, in *this* circuit the transistor's collector current and collector-to-emitter voltage can only be of such values that the voltage drop $I_C R_c$ and the voltage V_{CE} add up to V_{CC}. For example, points A and B are possible operating points, but point C is not. Although C is certainly possible for this transistor *in some circuits*, it is not possible in *this* circuit.

41

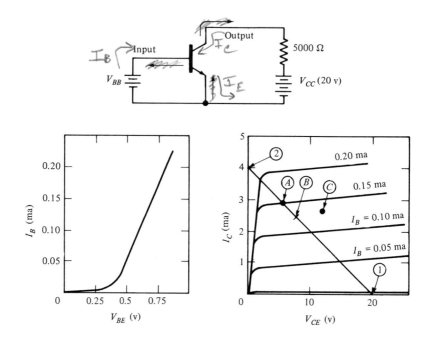

FIGURE 2–1 (a)
*Simple transistor amplifier circuit with graphical input and output
characteristics for the transistor used (Arrows indicate direction of
electron flow in each part of circuit)*

4. Given the collector characteristics for a particular transistor, and a
particular load resistor with its load line, the actual position of the
operating point along the load line is then determined by the value of
base current. In Figure 2–1, point (A) illustrates what happens when the
transistor's base current is 0.15 ma in this circuit: the intersection of
the load line with the 0.15 ma base current curves shows that the transistor's collector current must be approximately 2.9 ma, and its collector-
to-emitter voltage, or V_{CE}, must be approximately 5.5 v — as read off the
scales by projecting horizontally to the left, and vertically downward, from
the point of intersection.

Now assume that initially the value of V_{BB}, shown connected between the
base and the emitter, is such as to cause 0.10 ma of base current to flow. Then
the operating point is at point 3, giving $I_C = 2.0$ ma. (Figure 2–1(a) is repeated below without points A, B, and C, as Figure 2–1(b) for convenient
reference in the following discussion.) Next assume that V_{BB} is changed from
the above value to a value such as to cause a base current of 0.15 ma. Such a
change of base current will of course cause a change in collector current —

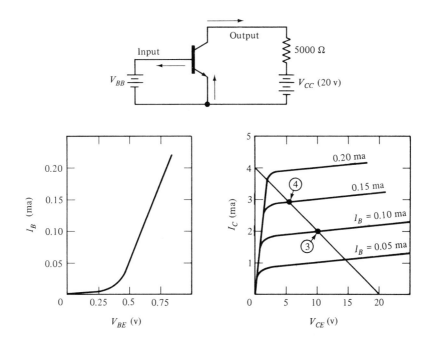

FIGURE 2-1(b)
*Simple transistor amplifier circuit with graphical input and output
characteristics for the transistor used (Arrows indicate the direction
of electron flow in each part of circuit)*

since the operating point will have moved to point 4. The collector current at
this point is approximately 2.9 ma.

Thus, a change in I_B of 0.05 ma (from 0.10 ma to 0.15 ma) has produced a
change in I_C of about 0.90 ma. This can be summarized as follows:

$$\Delta I_B = 0.15 - 0.10 = 0.05 \text{ ma}$$
$$\Delta I_C = 2.9 - 2.0 = 0.90 \text{ ma}$$

We can express the ratio of the collector current change to the base current
change as

$$A_i = \frac{\Delta I_C}{\Delta I_B} = \frac{0.90}{0.05} = 18$$

In other words, a small change in the input current, I_B, has caused a larger
change in the output current, I_C, in this circuit. This is referred to as *current
amplification, or current gain.*

It is also possible to have voltage amplification. Consider the curve of I_B
versus V_{BE} for the same transistor shown in Figure 2–1. Note that this particular transistor requires 0.6 v of forward-bias to produce a base current of

0.10 ma, and that V_{BE} must change from 0.6 v to 0.7 v to cause I_B to change from 0.10 to 0.15 ma so as to produce the change in operating point discussed above. The change in collector voltage caused by this operating point change can be read from the load line: V_{CE} goes from 10.0 v to about 5.5 v. Thus this analysis has provided the following information:

$$\Delta V_{BE} = 0.7 - 0.6 = 0.1$$
$$\Delta V_{CE} = 10.0 - 5.5 = 4.5$$

The *voltage amplification* then is

$$A_v = \frac{\Delta V_{CE}}{\Delta V_{BE}} = \frac{4.5}{0.1} = 45$$

2.3   Measurement in the Amplifier Circuit

The input and output current changes and the input and output voltage changes can be measured in a circuit of this sort, by inserting the appropriate meters. Figure 2–2 shows the arrangement. Since the currents are quite small

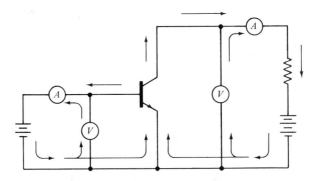

FIGURE 2–2
Necessary meters for measuring A_i and A_v in a simple amplifier circuit

in this circuit, the voltmeters should have very high resistance so that voltmeter current passing through the ammeter will not contribute appreciable error. (Note the arrows indicating directions of electron flow.) The base-emitter voltmeter might have to be an electronic voltmeter.

2.4   Polarity in the CE Circuit

The reader might have observed in the above analysis that the directions of change of the input voltage, ΔV_{BE}, and the output voltage, ΔV_{CE}, were opposite: an *increase* of the input voltage, or a positive change, caused a *decrease* in the output voltage, or a negative change. Thus it might have been more correct to express the output change as

$$\Delta V_{CE} = -4.5 \text{ v}$$

and the voltage gain as

$$A_v = \frac{-4.5}{0.1} = -45$$

Some amplifier circuits are characterized by this change of direction; others show the same direction of change for both input and output. It is quite common (but not necessarily universal) to express the amplification as a negative quantity, as above, when the amplifier is the polarity inverting type.

2.5 Introduction to Some Amplifier Terminology

In the discussions so far, the emphasis has been on showing in a simple way how an electronic amplifier can produce an "output" that is greater than the "input." The input and output used in the examples were either voltage changes or current changes. This is because the transmission or manipulation of information is the basis of most uses of electronic amplifiers, and such information is often represented by the relative amplitudes of electrical quantities, or else by *changes* from one amplitude to another.

For example, sound is the result of rapid changing of air pressure against our ear drums due to something vibrating in the air. A device capable of producing voltage or current variation proportional to the air pressure variation, or in other words, a microphone, may be used to help transmit the information contained in the sound, by telephone or by radio, to much greater distances than the sound would travel through the air as pressure waves. The electrical output of a microphone, however, is quite small and usually has to be amplified for successful transmission and reception.

The simple amplifier shown in Figure 2–1 had only a source of dc voltage connected between base and emitter, and for our purposes, changes in this voltage were used as a means of simulating an input signal. In testing an amplifier of this sort, such changes could be produced by adjusting a control on the power supply providing the voltage, so that its output was set first at 0.7 v; then reset to 0.8 v, and so on. However, in the use of amplifiers the signal that is to be amplified is applied to the input from some device such as the microphone mentioned above or from some other amplifier circuit. Such a source of signal is usually represented in amplifier circuit drawings by a *generator symbol*, as shown in Figure 2–3.

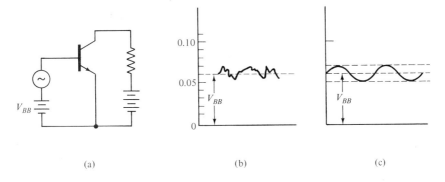

(a)   (b)   (c)

FIGURE 2–3
AC generator in series with input

The methods by which such signal sources are connected to practical amplifier circuits will be studied in detail in the rest of this book. At the present time it will simply be assumed that the signal is produced by a signal generator connected directly in series with the transistor input and the base-emitter supply voltage, as shown in Figure 2–3(a), so that the signal voltage is superimposed on the dc supply voltage.

Although *actual signals may be of any form*, it is convenient, and quite common, to test amplifiers with sine wave signals. Part (b) in Figure 2–3 shows a nonsinusoidal signal such as might be produced by a microphone, superimposed on V_{BB}. Part (c) of the figure shows a sine wave signal, as often used for testing.

In the simple amplifier circuit discussed above, the required initial base current of 0.10 ma, from which the current changed by 0.05 ma, was presumed to be the result of a battery or other source of dc connected from base to emitter. In Figure 2–3 this dc supply was in series with the alternating current (ac) generator, and the graph of base-emitter voltage showed that the ac voltage fluctuated about the dc voltage. That is, it caused the total base-emitter voltage to fluctuate a small amount above and below the *average* value (0.6 v) which was set by the dc supply. This voltage variation will of course cause a current variation above and below an average value. The dc values of voltage and current are called the *bias*. They are also known as the *quiescent* values. They determine the *operating point* or *quiescent point* about which the signal fluctuates.

Corresponding to the dc base current are the values of dc collector current and dc collector voltage determined by the intersection of the load line with the particular base current curve on the collector characteristics. These values of I_C and V_{CE} are also referred to as quiescent values. In the absence of an input signal, I_C and V_{CE} remain at these values (unless disturbed by certain effects which will be considered in subsequent chapters). But when there is an input signal, the I_B fluctuations cause I_C and V_{CE} fluctuations above and below these quiescent values. The ΔV and ΔI effects we examined earlier were examples of this.

The quiescent values and the signal-caused fluctuations are often distinguished from each other by referring to them as dc components and ac or signal components, respectively. The value of the dc components, or the quiescent currents and voltages, may be determined by considering the circuit with the ac input signal "turned off" — or with the signal generator left out of the circuit.

2.6 Biasing the Elemental Amplifier Circuit

The simple base biasing arrangement used in the earlier example has several disadvantages. One of these is the fact that every different amplifier circuit would require a different value of base supply voltage. It is more convenient to be able to use one value of supply voltage for a number of circuits. This may be done by using the arrangement of Figure 2–4. This permits different circuits to use the same value of supply voltage and still obtain different values of quiescent base current according to the needs of the individual circuits simply by using different values of resistance for R_b. The arrows indicate electron flow direction for the dc component.

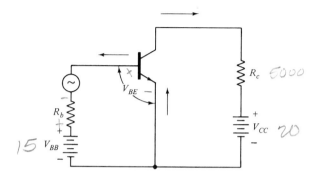

FIGURE 2–4
Basic amplifier circuit showing use of biasing resistor

The voltage equation for the base-emitter circuit is

$$V_{BB} = I_B R_b + V_{BE} \qquad \text{(2–1)}$$

This equation can be solved for the necessary value of R_b needed to achieve a given desired value of I_B:

$$R_b = \frac{V_{BB} - V_{BE}}{I_B} \qquad \text{(2–2)}$$

As an example of the application of this method, recall the previous circuit in which the desired quiescent base current was 0.10 ma. Assume that it was desirable to use a supply voltage of 15 v for the base circuit.

Then
$$R_b = \frac{V_{BB} - V_{BE}}{I_B}$$

$$R_b = \frac{15 - 0.6}{(0.10)(10^{-3})} = \frac{14.4}{10}(10^5)$$

$$R_b \cong 144 \text{ kilohms}$$

In other words, a base biasing resistor of 144 kilohms would provide the necessary base current of 0.10 ma with a bias supply of 15 v.

If the input curves (or other equivalent information) are not available for the transistor being used, the base-emitter voltage drop may be estimated. For small signal transistors it will often be in the range of 0.6 to 0.7 v for silicon and 0.2 to 0.3 v for germanium transistors. Using these estimates will give quite good accuracy for such circuits when the supply voltage is not extremely low. For example, an error of 0.1 or 0.2 v in the estimate of V_{BE} will cause an error of only about 1 or 2 percent with a supply voltage of 10 v.

In fact, for much routine work — such as temporary experimental circuits, "one-of-a-kind" test set-ups, quick design estimating, and the like — V_{BE} may often be left out of the calculation entirely, without excessive error. In other words, in the equation

$$R_b = \frac{V_{BB} - V_{BE}}{I_B}$$

the V_{BE} term may be omitted if $V_{BE} \ll V_{BB}$. This gives

$$R_b \cong \frac{V_{BB}}{I_B}$$

As an example, in the illustration above, where $V_{BB} = 15$, neglecting the V_{BE} of 0.6 would give

$$R_b = \frac{15}{(0.10)(10^{-3})} = 150 \text{ kilohms}$$

The correct value was 144 kilohms. Using the approximation of 150 kilohms would cause an error of less than 5 percent, which would be acceptable for many purposes.

In the *CE* circuit which we have been considering, and which is, incidentally, the most commonly used transistor amplifier circuit, the polarity of bias voltage required for the base is the same as that required for the collector. Consequently, the circuit of Figure 2–4 may be simplified by eliminating V_{BB}, and simply connecting R_b to V_{CC}, as in Figure 2–5(a). Note the arrows indi-

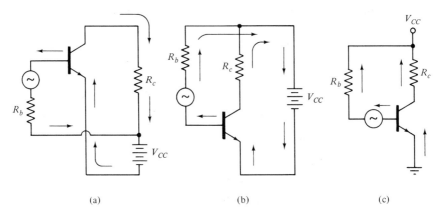

(a)   (b)   (c)

FIGURE 2–5
Basic CE amplifier using single-supply biasing

cating the direction of electron flow for the dc component in each part of the circuit and compare with Figure 2–4.

Figure 2–5 also shows two other forms in which this circuit is often drawn; all three are exactly identical in actual connections, as the reader may check for himself. The form shown at the extreme right simply omits the battery symbol; it is always understood to be connected from the terminal marked V_{CC} to the "ground" terminal ($\doteqdot$) or to some other appropriately designated terminal, even though it may not actually be shown.

2.7 Signal Connections to the Amplifier Circuit

If a transistor is to be used to amplify the output from a microphone or some other source of signal, it might be connected as shown in Figure 2–6(a). Its output is connected from base to emitter, directly in parallel with V_{BB} and

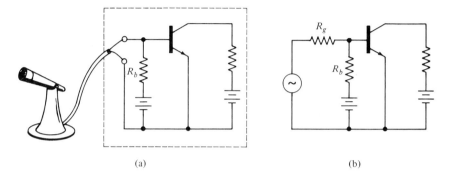

(a)   (b)

FIGURE 2–6
Connection of signal source to amplifier

R_b. Part (b) of this figure shows the microphone represented by its Thevenin equivalent circuit: a voltage generator V_g representing the open-circuit output signal voltage of the microphone, and a resistance R_g representing its equivalent source resistance. The connection shown results in the fluctuating signal from the microphone being superimposed on the dc base-to-emitter bias.

However, the microphone resistance might very well be such that when shunted across the circuit in this way, it drastically alters the bias, upsetting the desired operating conditions. For example, the transistor of Figure 2–1 had a dc input resistance of

$$R = \frac{V}{I} = \frac{0.6}{(0.10)(10^{-3})} \cong 6000 \text{ ohms}$$

and the biasing resistor was 143 kilohms. If a microphone having a resistance of 500 ohms were connected as shown here, the largest part of the bias current from V_{BB} would go through the microphone instead of through the base-emitter junction. The base current would be less than one-tenth the desired value.

To prevent difficulties of this sort, a capacitor may be placed in series with the input signal lead, as shown in Figure 2–7. This capacitor may be chosen with large enough value of capacitance so that its reactance is very small at the frequency of signal being used. Thus, it will not block ac signal, yet it does block dc — thereby preventing the low resistance source from acting as a short circuit or heavy shunt for the transistor's dc bias. Note the arrows indicating the direction of electron flow for the dc component in each part of the circuit.

This type of circuit might not be suitable for an amplifier handling very low frequency signals, or very slowly changing dc, since the amount of capacitance required to produce low reactance at such frequencies might be impractical. For the time being, the amplifiers under consideration will be types intended for signal frequencies in the audio range — from about 20 or 30 Hertz

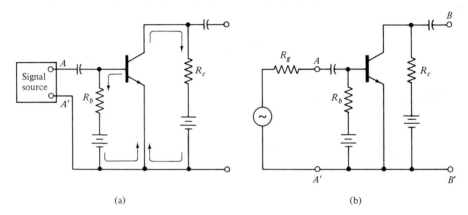

FIGURE 2–7
Blocking capacitors

(Hz) to somewhere between 10,000 and 20,000 Hz. Some audio amplifiers, in fact, are designed to handle signals no lower than 100 or 200 Hz.

Figure 2–7 also shows a capacitor connected at the juncture of R_c and the transistor's collector. This serves the same purpose — it prevents other connected circuits from disturbing the collector dc conditions. The output of the amplifier is considered to be terminals B-B'. The capacitor blocks the dc, but when properly chosen in value so as to have low reactance at the signal frequency, does not impede the signal component.

At this point it might be well to look at the same kind of circuit using a single supply. In Figure 2–8, part (a) illustrates the form of drawing that has been used most in this text up to now, while part (b) shows the other frequently encountered form, mentioned earlier.

2.8 Signal Relations in the CE Amplifier Circuit

Consider the *CE* amplifier circuit shown in Figure 2–9. This circuit is the same as in the earlier example, except for the signal connections and the use of single-supply biasing. The performance of this amplifier will now be analyzed, by means of the load line, with a small ac signal applied to the input from the signal source V_g.

The input signal voltage at terminals A-A' will be a sine wave of 0.1 v peak amplitude, while the dc component at B-B' as a result of the bias circuit will be 0.6 v. Thus, the total input conditions at A-A' and B-B' will be as shown in (a) and (b) of Figure 2–10.

The graph in (b) shows that the effect of the signal is to cause the base-emitter voltage to swing from its quiescent value of 0.6 v upward to 0.7 and downward to 0.5 v in each cycle. The input characteristics of Figure 2–9 show

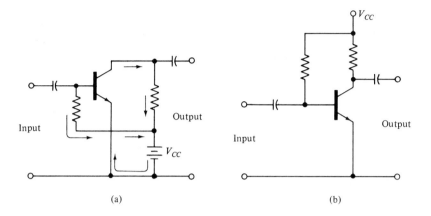

FIGURE 2–8
Common-emitter amplifier

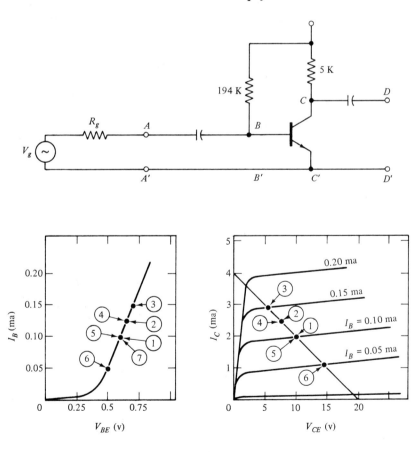

FIGURE 2–9
CE amplifier circuit for analysis along with transistor curves

(a) Total voltage at A-A'
(input signal voltage)

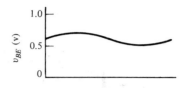

(b) Total voltage at B-B'
(dc component and ac component)

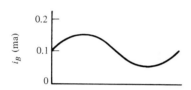

(c) Total base current
(dc component plus signal or
ac component)

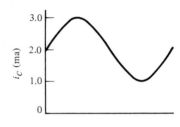

(d) Total collector current
(dc plus signal component)

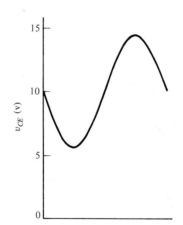

(e) Total voltage at C-C'

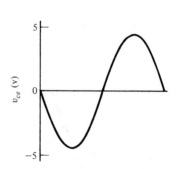

(f) Total voltage at D-D'

FIGURE 2–10
Current and voltage relations in the CE amplifier

that this swing of V_{BE} will cause I_B to swing from its quiescent value of 0.10 ma, upward to 0.15 ma and then downward to 0.05 ma in each cycle.

If values of I_B are read from the current wave shown in Part (c) of Figure 2–10 and used to find the corresponding instantaneous operating points on the load line in Figure 2–9, the resulting values of collector-to-emitter voltage V_{CE} may be obtained. For example, the value of I_B at point (1) is 0.1 ma. The load line shows that when $I_B = 0.1$ ma, $V_{CE} = 10$ v. Next, the value of I_B at point (2) is 0.125 ma. This is halfway between the 0.10 and 0.15 curves on the collector characteristics, and the corresponding value of V_{CE} is about 7.8 v. Following this procedure, Table 2–1 may be filled in.

TABLE 2–1

A Load Line Analysis

Point	V_{BE}	I_B	I_C	V_{CE} (read from load line)	V_{CE} (using load line value of I_C) $V_{CE} = V_{CC} - I_C R_L$	V_{out} (voltage at terminals D-D') $V_{out} = V_{CE} - 10$
	(v)	(ma)	(ma)	(v)	(v)	(v)
1	0.6	0.1	2.0	10	$20 - 10 = 10$	0
2	0.65	0.125	2.45	7.8	$20 - 12.25 = 7.75$	-2.2
3	0.7	0.15	2.9	5.5	$20 - 14.5 = 5.5$	-4.5
4	0.65	0.125	2.45	7.8	$20 - 12.25 = 7.75$	-2.2
5	0.6	0.1	2.0	10	$20 - 10 = 10$	0
6	0.5	0.05	1.1	14.5	$20 - 5.5 = 14.5$	$+4.5$
7	0.6	0.1	2.0	10	$20 - 10 = 10$	0

The results show that the collector current swings from a minimum of 1.1 ma to a maximum of 2.9 ma while the collector voltage swings from a minimum of 5.5 to a maximum of 14.5 v. Note also that the ac component of the collector voltage is 180° out of phase with the ac component of the base-emitter voltage; i.e., that V_{CE} is at its negative peak when V_{BE} is at its positive peak, and vice versa. This must logically occur, since a rise of V_{BE} causes a rise in I_B and therefore in I_C; and a rise in I_C must obviously cause a fall in V_{CE} according to the equation

$$V_{CE} = V_{CC} - I_C R_L$$

The load line of course shows this directly.

It should also be noted that the value of the *ac component* at any given instant is the amount by which the *total* varying quantity at that instant differs from the *dc component*. For example, at point (2), V_{CE} is 7.5 v, or 2.5 v *below* the dc value of 10 v. The value of the signal component at this instant is therefore -2.5 v. At point (6), the instantaneous value of V_{CE} is 15 v, or 5.0 v *above* the quiescent value, so that the instantaneous value of the ac component here is $+5$ v. The value of the ac component in other words may be obtained by subtracting the dc value from the total. The blocking capacitor in the output lead does just this — it blocks the dc, or subtracts it from the total. The last column in Table 2–1 shows the voltage V_{out}, at terminals D-D', as the ac component, or the total voltage minus the dc component, due to the action of the output coupling capacitor.

2.9 Notation

At this point it would be well to introduce some methods of notation which are generally accepted and which help to eliminate confusion in distinguishing between ac and dc components, average and root mean square (rms) values, and the like.

Figure 2–11 illustrates a combination of dc and ac voltage with the various

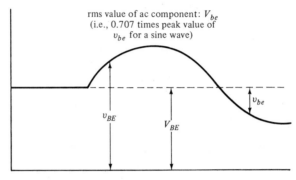

FIGURE 2–11
Some standard notation

components marked. Notice that rms and dc values are indicated by capital V (or I) while instantaneous values are shown by lowercase letters. Notice also that in the case of the *subscripts*, when the total or composite is referred to, capital letters are used, while the lowercase subscripts are reserved for the ac component only. (*Example: v_{be} refers to instantaneous value of ac component, but V_{be} refers to rms value of ac component.*)

2.10 Introduction to Amplifier Equivalent Circuit Analysis

In the amplifier discussed so far, an input signal component of voltage caused an input signal component current, an output signal component current, and — as a result of the output signal current flowing in resistor R_c — an output signal component voltage.

The occurrence of an input signal current resulting from the application of a signal voltage permits defining an input signal resistance. In general,

$$R_i = \frac{\Delta v_{IN}}{\Delta i_{IN}} = \frac{V_{in}}{I_{in}}$$

and in the case of the *CE* amplifier

$$R_i = \frac{\Delta v_{BE}}{\Delta i_B} = \frac{V_{be}}{I_b}$$

Observe the notation indicating rms values of the ac components of voltage and current in the terms on the extreme right.

An amplifier can then be considered in rather general form, as illustrated in Figure 2–12, if only the ac components, or signal components, are of con-

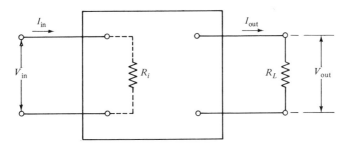

FIGURE 2–12
Simple generalized form for an amplifier

cern. The resistor designated R_L includes the effect of whatever electrical *load* or circuit the output signal is being applied to. It might be anything from a loudspeaker to a recording device or the input resistance of another amplifier. In the amplifiers discussed so far the only load has been the collector circuit resistor R_c. But when talking about amplifiers in a general way, it is quite common to designate the load resistance as R_L, to indicate the presence of other resistance in addition to, or in place of, R_c.

Now,

$$V_{in} = I_{in} R_i$$
$$V_{out} = I_{out} R_L$$

and the voltage gain is

$$A_v = \frac{V_{out}}{V_{in}} = \frac{I_{out} R_L}{I_{in} R_i}$$

But since the current gain is

$$A_i = \frac{I_{out}}{I_{in}}$$

Then,

$$A_v = A_i \frac{R_L}{R_i} \qquad (2\text{–}3)$$

This equation shows that the current gain and the voltage gain of an amplifier are not directly related. For example, a particular amplifier having an input signal resistance of 1000 ohms, might have a current gain of 30 with a load resistance of 2500 ohms. The voltage gain would be

$$A_v = A_i \frac{R_L}{R_I} = (30)\left(\frac{2500}{1000}\right)$$
$$A_v = 75$$

However, another transistor, capable of providing the same current gain but having twice the input resistance, would have only half that voltage gain:

$$A_v = (30)\left(\frac{2500}{2000}\right) = 37.5$$

This illustrates the importance of the input resistance in a transistor amplifier.

The equation used above, of course, applies to *any amplifier* providing that the amplifier is the kind for which an input resistance can be defined. More will be said concerning this later, but for the present it is sufficient that transistor amplifiers are certainly in this category.

The approximate signal input resistance in the amplifier example of Section 2.8 can be calculated from the input characteristic curve of Figure 2–1 or Figure 2–9. For the input signal involved it is

$$R_i \cong \frac{\Delta v_{BE}}{\Delta i_B}$$

$$R_i \cong \frac{0.1}{(0.05)(10^{-3})} = 2000 \text{ ohms}$$

The use of the input characteristic in this way is a somewhat simplified approach, and is being employed here for the purpose of making a useful approximation. The exact value of input resistance of a transistor amplifier may differ somewhat from the value given by the static input curve as above, because in an amplifier the collector voltage has some influence on the input. The relation as used above more properly defines a quantity often referred to as the "input resistance with the output short-circuited" and designated by the symbol h_{ie}:

$$h_{ie} = \frac{\Delta v_{BE}}{\Delta i_B}\bigg|_{v_{CE} \text{ constant}}$$

The value of h_{ie} is usually quite close to the actual value of input resistance of the operating amplifier circuit. It is a convenient approximation to use for the input resistance, since it is often given in the published specifications for a transistor.

The term A_i in Equation (2–3) above can also be approximated by a conveniently available figure. This is the transistor's h_{fe} — its current gain with the output short-circuited. Note, in Figure 2–9, that the actual current gain A_i as revealed by the load line, is only slightly less than the value of h_{fe} in the region near the quiescent point. The current gain measures approximately 18, while $h_{fe} = 20$. In many cases the two values are even closer. So h_{fe} is often used as an approximation for A_i.

Examination of Figure 2–9 shows that a steeper load line — corresponding to a smaller load resistance — would give A_i closer in value to h_{fe}. In general, then, this approximation may be expected to be valid when R_L is small, and might be dangerous to use when R_L is very large.

Now we have two gain equations which are very useful because they involve only simple combinations of two transistor parameters: *the current gain equation:*

$$A_i \cong h_{fe} \tag{2-4}$$

and, from Equation (2–3) with A_i and R_i replaced by h_{fe} and h_{ie}, *the voltage gain equation:*

$$A_v \cong \frac{h_{fe}}{h_{ie}} R_L \tag{2-5}$$

The generalized form of the amplifier shown in Figure 2–12 can now be drawn somewhat differently, for the *CE* circuit. Figure 2–13 depicts the ampli-

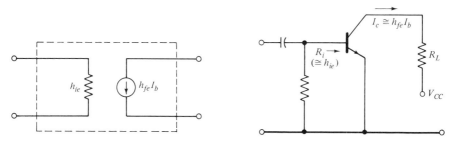

FIGURE 2–13
Approximate equivalent circuit and actual circuit

fier as having an input resistance equal to h_{ie} and an output current equal to $h_{fe}I_b$. This arrangement constitutes a simplified equivalent circuit, valid for analyzing the *signal component* action in an amplifier. The equivalent current generator symbol marked $h_{fe}I_b$ serves as an indication that in this equivalent circuit, I_c is always equal to $h_{fe}I_b$ — but it should be remembered that this is only an approximation. Later we will consider more accurate equivalent circuits.

Note that in the amplifier circuit shown in Figure 2–13, the input and output have a common "return" line (shown as a heavy line). This side of such circuits — to which all the circuits are "returned," and in which there is no intervening series resistance or impedance — is in fact often called the "common." (Whence comes the name common emitter.) Because of this, the equivalent circuit is usually shown as in Figure 2–14.

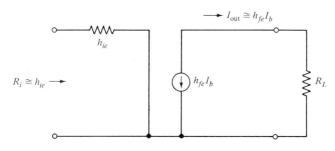

FIGURE 2–14
Final form of the approximate CE equivalent circuit

As examples of the practical use of the above gain equations and equivalent circuit, consider the following:

1. A transistor is being sought for possible use in a *CE* amplifier circuit employing a small value of load resistance. The expected load is to be about 2000 ohms. Two transistors that seem suitable are the 2N464 and the 2N334A. The specifications for these transistors (see Appendix B) list the following as "typical" values:

TABLE 2–2

h_{fe}		h_{ie}
2N464	26	900 ohms
2N334A	38	1700 ohms

Since the 2N334A has higher h_{fe}, the approximate current gain equation, $A_i \cong h_{fe}$, indicates better current gain for this transistor. But the 2N464 can be expected to have better voltage gain, as indicated by the approximate A_v equation:

$$\text{2N464:} \quad A_v \cong \frac{h_{fe}}{h_{ie}} R_L = \left(\frac{26}{900}\right)(2000) \cong 58$$

$$\text{2N334A:} \quad A_v \cong \frac{h_{fe}}{h_{ie}} R_L = \left(\frac{38}{1700}\right)(2000) \cong 45$$

Thus the 2N464 might well be preferred, depending upon the application.

2. An inexpensive tachometer is to be built. It will utilize a transducer which will generate a voltage proportional to frequency. This voltage will be amplified sufficiently to actuate a meter which will be calibrated in terms of frequency.

At the maximum frequency to be measured, the open-circuit output voltage of the transducer will be 15 mv. This will of course be the maximum voltage since the transducer output voltage is proportional to frequency. The transducer's output resistance (that is, its source resistance) is 500 ohms. The indicator is to be an ammeter with a full-scale sensitivity of 1 ma and an internal resistance of 50 ohms. If a transistor having $h_{ie} = 1000$ ohms is used, approximately what value of h_{fe} must it have, in order for the meter to read full scale at the maximum expected frequency?

The circuit arrangement will be as shown in Figure 2–15. (This is a simpli-

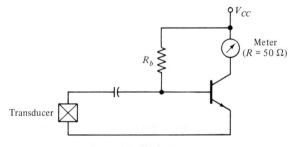

FIGURE 2–15
Transducer and amplifier arrangement

fied version. Practical circuits containing certain necessary additional features will be studied later.) The equivalent circuit is shown in Figure 2–16. This circuit shows that when the transducer is providing its maximum output of 15 mv, the amplifier input current will be

$$I_b \cong \frac{V_g}{R_o + h_{ie}}$$

$$I_b \cong \frac{0.015}{500 + 1000} = 10^{-5} \text{ amp}$$

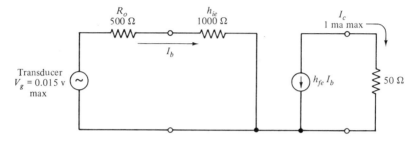

FIGURE 2–16
An equivalent circuit

Now the output current and input current are related by

$$I_c = h_{fe}I_b$$

and in order to have $I_c = 1$ ma under the above condition, we must have

$$0.001 \cong (h_{fe})(10^{-5})$$

so that the required h_{fe} is

$$h_{fe} \cong \frac{0.001}{10^{-5}}$$

$$h_{fe} \cong 100$$

2.11   The ac Load

Figure 2–17 shows a typical amplifier circuit with a blocking capacitor as introduced in Section 2.7. C_c serves to connect the amplifier to its load without disturbing the dc conditions. When two circuits are connected together, they

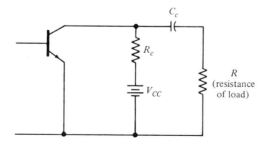

FIGURE 2–17
Typical output circuit in RC coupling

are said to be "coupled," and the capacitor connecting them is therefore often referred to as a "coupling capacitor." Because of the use of the collector resistor R_c and the coupling capacitor C_c, these amplifiers are known as *RC* coupled amplifiers.

The supply voltage V_{CC} shown in Figure 2–17 normally presents a very low impedance to signal frequency currents. For example, when the supply is a rectifier-filter type, the filter capacitor across its output has such a low reactance that the signal frequency component of the collector current, flowing through R_c and into the supply, produces very little ac voltage drop within the power supply. Consequently, R_c may be considered connected to ground for signal components. (This is sometimes referred to as being at "ac ground.") Figure 2–18 illustrates this.

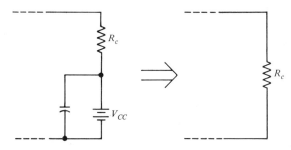

FIGURE 2–18
Effect of well-bypassed supply voltage on circuit seen by signal components

The coupling capacitor C_c of Figure 2–17 is usually made large enough so that there is negligible signal voltage drop across it also. Thus, the signal voltage drop across R in Figure 2–17 must be approximately equal to that across R_c and the two resistors may be considered to be in parallel as far as signal components are concerned, as illustrated in Figure 2–19. The equivalent circuit for such an amplifier can then be shown as in Figure 2–20(a) or 2–20(b). In (b), the resistance R_L is the parallel combination of R_c and R. It is evident that the parallel combination of R_c and R is the actual *signal* load on the amplifier, and determines the gain of the amplifier.

Since C_c is a very high reactance at very low frequency and *thus prevents R*

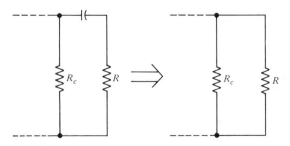

FIGURE 2–19
Effect of coupling capacitor on circuit as seen by signal components

from being in parallel with R_c as far as dc is concerned, the parallel combination of R_c and R is often called the "ac load" while R_c is referred to as the "dc load."

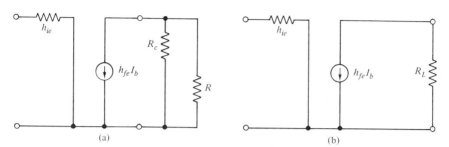

(a)   (b)

FIGURE 2–20
Equivalent circuit for RC-coupled amplifier

There is apt to be some confusion arising from the fact that the designation R_L is used sometimes to refer to the final "load" to which the signal is being fed, and sometimes to the total effective load on the amplifier as in Figure 2–20(b). When a single resistor is shown as the load in basic amplifier analysis (as in Section 2.10 above), it should be understood that it represents the parallel combination of any resistances such as R_c and R. Also the term R_L in any gain equation should be given the value of whatever the total effective load is, as seen by the amplifier.

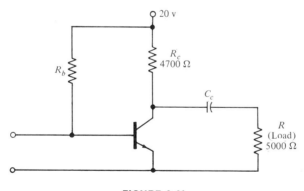

FIGURE 2–21
An example of a circuit

Example 2–1

The 2N464 transistor is used in the circuit of Figure 2–21. The voltage gain equation is

$$A_v \cong \frac{h_{fe}}{h_{ie}} R_L$$

where

$$R_L = \frac{(4700)(5000)}{4700 + 5000} \cong 2420 \text{ ohms}$$

Therefore

$$A_v \cong \frac{(26)(2420)}{900} \cong 70$$

In this circuit, the ac load is approximately 2420 ohms. DC signals (that is, voltage or current changes that occur very slowly, or are of very long time duration, such as a slow change of collector current from 2.0 ma to 2.9 ma which then stays at 2.9 ma for a long time) would be blocked by C_c. That is, the impedance in parallel with R_c at frequencies approaching dc would be almost infinite so that the effective load would be essentially equal to R_c. Thus, while the ac load in the above circuit is 2420 ohms, the dc load is R_c, or 4700 ohms.

2.12 The ac Load Line

In the example above, the dc load differed considerably from the ac load. The load line analysis of such circuits must take these effects into account. The quiescent operating point, and the quiescent values of collector current and collector voltage are found by load line construction using the value of R_c — since the quiescent values are the steady, dc values. However, the application of a signal to the input of the amplifier causes signal frequency fluctuations above and below the quiescent values. The amplifier load resistance for the signal components is the parallel combination of R_c and R. Thus, any load line which is to show signal variations must be drawn on the basis of this value of load resistance, and not R_c.

Since the signal variations occur about the quiescent operating point, the technique for such load line construction is to first draw the dc load line — that is, the load line for R_c — and establish the quiescent operating point, as in Section 2.2. Then, through the quiescent operating point, the ac load line is drawn for the load

$$R_L = \frac{R_c R}{R_c + R}$$

This is illustrated in Figure 2–22.

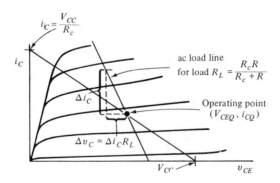

FIGURE 2–22
Construction of ac load line

A convenient technique for determining the slope of the ac load line may be based upon the following reasoning. At signal frequencies

$$\Delta v_{CE} = \Delta i_C R_L = \Delta i_C \left[\frac{R_c R}{R_c + R}\right]$$

As this relation indicates, any point along the ac load line must have v_{CE}, i_C

values such that the value of v_{CE} at the point is the quiescent value plus or minus $\Delta i_C R_L$. (A more compact way to say this is

$$v_{CE} = V_{CEQ} - \Delta i_C R_L$$

in which v_{CE} and i_C stand for instantaneous total values, and the Q subscript indicates the quiescent value.)

Therefore the ac load line may be found as follows. Choose a convenient increment of collector current Δi and calculate the change in voltage Δv_{CE} that would result from such a change of current occurring *in the ac load R_L.* From the dc load line's operating point, measure parallel to the current axis by the amount Δi_C and parallel to the voltage axis by the amount Δv_{CE}. If Δi_C is chosen as an increase in current then the Δv_{CE} should be in the negative direction.

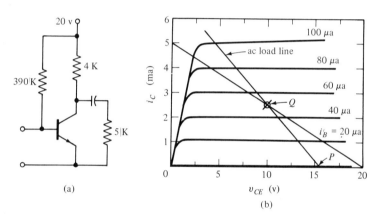

(a)   (b)

FIGURE 2–23
AC load line example

Example 2–2

In Figure 2–23, part (a) shows an amplifier circuit, and part (b) gives the graphical output characteristics for the transistor used.

1. The dc load line is shown drawn between the point $I_C = 0$, $V_{CE} = 20$, and the point $V_{CE} = 0$, $I_C = 20/4000 = 5$ ma.
2. The operating point is where the base bias sets it:

$$I_B \cong \frac{20 - 0.3}{390,000} \cong 50.5 \ \mu a$$

   This is marked Q on the diagram.
3. Since the quiescent point is at $I_C \cong 2.5$ ma, 2.5 ma is a convenient value to choose for Δi_C.
4. Then

$$\Delta v_{CE} = \Delta i_C R_L$$
$$\Delta v_{CE} = (2.5 \times 10^{-3})\left[\frac{(5000)(4000)}{9000}\right]$$
$$\Delta v_{CE} \cong 5.56 \ v$$

5. From Q drop *down* 2.5 ma and *to the right* 5.56 v (since a *decrease* in i_C must cause an *increase* in v_{CE}). This point is marked P on the diagram.

6.   Draw a straight line from this point through Q and as far up as desired.

Note that the increment of collector current that was chosen was equal to the quiescent value of the current. This is often the most convenient value since *decreasing* this current by that amount simply means that you can drop down to the voltage axis. Then the necessary increase in v_{CE} is obtained simply by moving to the right along the voltage axis from the quiescent V_{CE} value.

PROBLEMS

2-1.   Answer the following questions about the transistor and circuit shown, using load line construction as necessary.

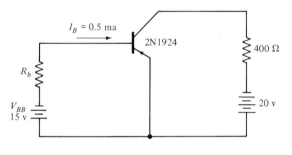

FIGURE P2-1

(a)   What are the quiescent values of collector current and collector-emitter voltage?

(b)   If the base current is changed from 0.5 to 0.4 ma, what is the new value of the collector current? What is the new value of collector voltage?

(c)   What are the increments of base current, collector current, and collector voltage (ΔI_B, ΔI_C, ΔV_{CE}) in the above case?

(d)   What is the value of the current gain indicated in the above case?

(e)   If the voltage increment that caused the base current increment of (b) above was 0.02 v, what is the voltage gain?

(f)   When the base current decreased, did the collector current increase or decrease?

(g)   When the base-emitter voltage decreased, did the base current increase or decrease? Did this cause the collector voltage to increase or decrease?

2-2.   (a)   On the basis of the *CE* input characteristics given for the 2N1924 in Appendix B, what is the approximate value of R_b needed to provide the quiescent base current of 0.5 ma in the above circuit?

(b)   If the value of V_{BE} is omitted from the above calculation, how much error will be introduced? What will be the resulting value of R_b?

(c)   Suppose the value of the base supply voltage V_{BB} in the above problem were 5 v instead of the given value. How much error would be introduced by using the approximate method of calculation which omits V_{BE}?

2-3.   A germanium small-signal transistor is to be operated with a quiescent base current of 100 μa. The bias supply voltage is to be 5 v. Without the manu-facturer's $V_{BE} - I_B$ information, what is the most accurate approximation you can make as to the required bias resistor?

2-4. A germanium small-signal transistor is to be operated at a base bias current of 50 μa, from a supply voltage of 20 v. Approximately what value of bias resistor is required?

2-5. A silicon small-signal transistor is to be operated with a quiescent base current of 0.25 ma, from a supply voltage of 10 v. For accuracy within 5 percent, what value of bias resistor must be used?

2-6. Draw the load line and locate the operating point for the following circuit.

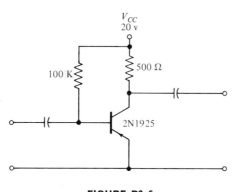

FIGURE P2-6

2-7. Assume that an input signal is applied to the above amplifier so as to produce a sine wave of base current. The peak value of the base current sine wave is 0.1 ma; that is, the base current rises 0.1 ma above the quiescent value, and falls the same amount below quiescent, during the cycle.

(a) Find the maximum and minimum values of total collector current that occur during the signal cycle.

(b) Find the maximum and minimum values of *total* collector-emitter voltage during the cycle.

(c) Find the instantaneous values of total collector current and voltage that occur when the total instantaneous base current is at the values:

(1) 0.15 ma
(2) 0.25 ma

(d) Find the instantaneous value of the total collector current that occurs when the *signal* component of the base current is:

(1) +0.05 ma
(2) −0.05 ma

(e) Find the instantaneous value of the *signal* component of the collector current that corresponds to the values of base current in (d) above.

(f) Make a neat sketch of the graph of the total base current, total collector current, and total collector-emitter voltage of the above problem. Mark the values of the quiescent currents and voltages, and the maximum and minimum current and voltages on the sketch.

(g) What is the phase relation between the base current and the collector current? Between the collector current and the collector voltage? What do you conclude is the phase relation between base voltage and collector voltage? Does this agree with the relations shown in Figure 2–10 in the text?

2–8. The general equation for the relation between the collector voltage and the collector current in a circuit such as the above is:

$$v_{CE} = V_{CC} - i_C R_L$$

List the parts of this equation which correspond to the following:

           (a)   Total instantaneous collector voltage
           (b)   Collector supply voltage
           (c)   Total instantaneous collector current
           (d)   AC component of collector voltage

2–9. On the current and voltage sketches which you drew for Problem 2–7 above, identify all of the following except (e), (i), and (m), using the letter designation shown below. For all items listed below, give the standard notation as given in the text.

    (a)   Quiescent base current
    (b)   Total instantaneous base current
    (c)   DC component of base current
    (d)   AC component of base current (instant.)
    (e)   AC component of base current (rms)
    (f)   Quiescent collector current
    (g)   Total instantaneous collector current
    (h)   AC component of collector current (instant.)
    (i)   AC component of collector current (rms)
    (j)   DC component of collector-emitter voltage
    (k)   Total instantaneous collector voltage
    (l)   AC component of collector voltage (instant.)
    (m)   AC component of collector voltage (rms)

2–10. A certain transistor is being used as an amplifier. When $v_{BE} = 0.50$ v, $i_B = 10$ ma. When $v_{BE} = 0.51$ v, $i_B = 10.4$ ma. What is the value of the input signal resistance R_i?

2–11. The following graph is the input characteristic of a particular transistor in an amplifier circuit under actual operating conditions. What is the amplifier's signal input resistance when biased to $I_B = 1.5$ ma?

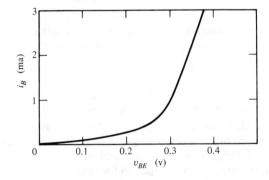

FIGURE P2–11

2–12. According to the manufacturer's data sheet, what is the input signal resistance of the 2N1926 when operated at a quiescent base current of 2 ma, and a collector-emitter voltage of 1 v?

2–13. The following information is available concerning the operation of a transistor amplifier:

$$I_{in} = 1 \text{ ma} \qquad R_i = 25 \text{ ohms}$$
$$I_{out} = 23 \text{ ma} \qquad R_L = 420 \text{ ohms}$$

What is the value of the voltage gain?

2–14. Approximately what are the values of the current gain and voltage gain for the following amplifier?

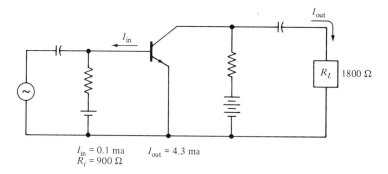

$I_{in} = 0.1 \text{ ma}$ $I_{out} = 4.3 \text{ ma}$
$R_i = 900 \ \Omega$

FIGURE P2–14

2–15. Approximately what are the values of current gain and voltage gain for the following amplifier?

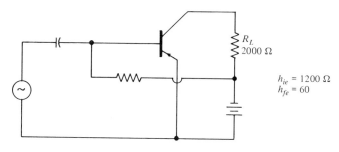

R_L
$2000 \ \Omega$

$h_{ie} = 1200 \ \Omega$
$h_{fe} = 60$

FIGURE P2–15

2–16. Draw the approximate equivalent circuit for the following amplifiers, assuming that the coupling capacitor is large enough in value that it has negligible reactance at signal frequencies. Show your work.

2–17. Assuming that the transistor in 2–16(a) above has $h_{fe} = 46$ and $h_{ie} = 750$ ohms, and that $R_C = 10,000$ ohms and $R = 5000$ ohms, what is the approximate voltage gain? What is the approximate current gain from base to collector?

2–18. The transistor in 2–16(b) has $h_{fe} = 28$ and $h_{ie} = 1200$ ohms. What is the approximate voltage gain? What is the approximate current gain from base to collector?

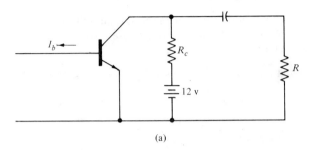

(a)

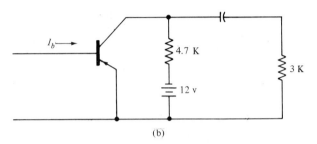

(b)

FIGURE P2–16

2–19. If I_b (that is, the rms value of the *signal* current in the base lead) is 0.03 ma in Problem 2–17, what is the approximate value of the signal current in the collector lead? What is the approximate value of the signal current in the *load resistor R*?

2–20. Assume the following transistor output curves apply to the transistor of Problem 2–16(b), and that the quiescent base current is 40 μa. Draw the dc load line and the ac load line.

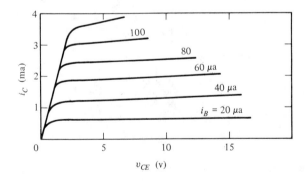

FIGURE P2–20

2–21. On the output curves given below, draw the dc load line and the ac load line for the circuit shown here. Locate the maximum and minimum values of v_{CE} on the load line for an input signal of 0.1 ma peak value.

2–22. On the curves given below, find the maximum and minimum values of i_C and v_{CE} for a peak input signal current of 50 μa in the accompanying circuit.

AC Load Line

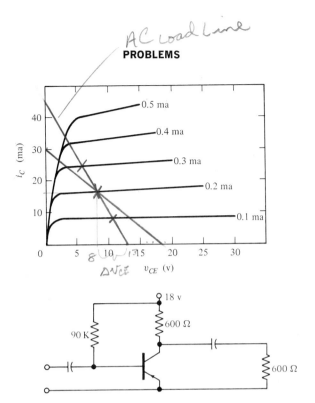

8 *ΔV_CE*

FIGURE P2–21

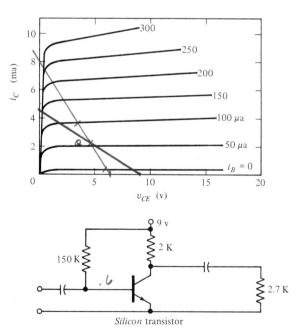

Silicon transistor

FIGURE P2–22

CHAPTER 3

Biasing Transistors

3.1 Introduction

Transistors are subject to variations in their characteristics which create several problems, one of which is the need for a better method of biasing than the simple scheme of the previous chapter. That bias method would be ideal if the relationship between base current and collector current were constant — that is, if $I_C = KI_B$. However, recall that instead,

$$I_C = h_{FE}I_B + (h_{FE} + 1)I_{CBO} \qquad \text{(1–12a)}$$

In this equation the term $(h_{FE} + 1)I_{CBO}$ is the common emitter, cutoff current called I_{CEO} — that is, the current from collector to emitter when the base current is zero, or the transistor is "cutoff."

$$I_{CEO} = (h_{FE} + 1)I_{CBO} \qquad \text{(1–11a)}$$

Equation (1–12a) indicates that changes in either h_{FE} (the dc or large-signal short circuit current gain) or I_{CBO} (the collector-to-base cutoff, or leakage, current) will cause changes in the quiescent collector current, in spite of a constant base bias current.

Both of these transistor parameters are greatly subject to change. They vary considerably from unit to unit, due to manufacturing variations, and they change with temperature. If such effects could not be eliminated, unit-to-unit variations would require the manufacturer of electronic equipment to individually adjust each of thousands of units to achieve approximately uniform operating characteristics. This might be done economically on a mass production basis, but the repair of such equipment after it was in use would then pose a problem. The replacement of a transistor with another of the same type might result in undesirable changes in the performance of the equipment.

70

Temperature effects may create even more serious difficulties. A civilian radio must often be capable of operating in temperatures ranging from the sub-zero of an unheated automobile or aircraft to the 100°+ temperatures encountered by a portable lying in the sun at the beach. Military equipment may encounter even more severe conditions. Shifts in the operating point due to such large temperature changes may be sufficient to completely halt the operation of such equipment.

3.2 Variations in the dc Operating Point

An understanding of the effects of variations in h_{FE} and I_{CBO} is important to an understanding of the techniques for minimizing such effects. Figure 3–1(a) illustrates the effect on a transistor's graphical characteristics of a

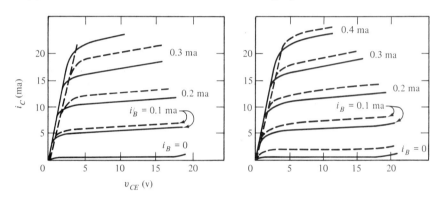

FIGURE 3–1
Collector characteristic curves showing the effects of variations in
h_{FE} *and* I_{CBO}

change in the value of h_{FE}. This might be the effect of temperature on a single transistor (in which case the dashed lines are for the higher temperature), or it might represent simply the differences between different transistors of the same type number. Part (b) of the figure shows the effect of a change in I_{CBO}. In both cases the result is that the value of I_C produced by a given value of I_B changes considerably. In actual practice both effects may occur at the same time, of course. They are shown separately here only for clarity.

In Figure 3–2 the possible consequences of such variations are illustrated by means of a load line. In this example the operating point has been set by a biasing circuit that produces a constant dc base current of 0.2 ma. In part (a) of this figure the quiescent collector current is about 11 ma, and the maximum allowable input signal, of 0.2 ma peak value, causes a collector current swing of about 10 ma peak value (that is, from 11 to 21 ma, then down to about 1 ma). The collector current sine wave resulting from a base current sine wave is shown to the left.

Part (b) shows the effect of about a 50 percent increase in the quiescent

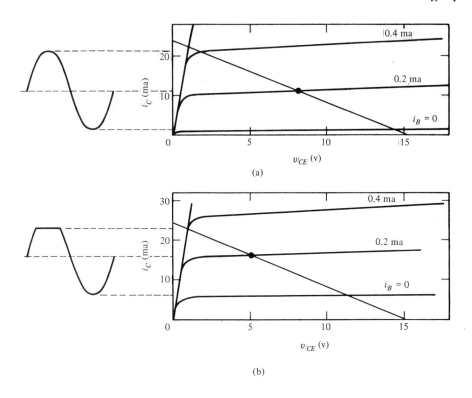

FIGURE 3–2

Distortion resulting from shift of a transistor's operating point

collector current due to temperature effects on I_{CBO}. The same quiescent base current now causes a quiescent collector current of 16 ma, and the same input signal of 0.2 ma peak causes the collector current to swing downward to about 6 ma, for a negative peak current of 10 ma — but on the upward swing the collector current stops at 23 ma, for a positive peak of only about 7 ma. In other words, at the time the input signal raises the base current to about 0.34 ma, the load line intersects the saturation portion of the curves, and the collector current can rise no further. Since the collector current is approximately constant during the time the base current is rising from 0.34 to its peak value of 0.4 and then falling back down, the collector current wave shape will show a clipped appearance at the top.

It is also worthwhile to note at this time that under the conditions described above, a small amount of increase of the quiescent collector current would have been permissible. The peak of the I_C wave in part (a) of Figure 3–2 is at 21 ma, but since the saturation line is not encountered until $I_C \cong 23$ ma, a rise of approximately 2 ma could have occurred before the clipping started. Methods of restricting the shift of operating point to certain permissible amounts — sometimes determined in the same way as the 2 ma above — will be considered in the latter part of this chapter.

Another and very important kind of problem, created by operating point movement due to temperature effects, is illustrated in Figure 3–3. This depicts a transistor with a collector-dissipation rating of 250 mw, biased so that the collector dissipation is approximately 160 mw. The 250 mw-collector dissipation curve is shown on the graph. Assuming a load line indicated by the solid

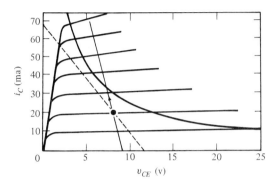

FIGURE 3–3
Effect of temperature upon the operating point

line, a rise in temperature can cause the operating point to rise into the danger area above the P_C curve. If it goes far enough, the transistor will be damaged. The operating point may of course be chosen low enough so that the increase in I_C, if caused only by the expected external temperature in which it is to be used, (the "ambient" temperature), would still leave it below the danger zone. However, an initial rise in current due to a high ambient temperature will cause additional heating of the transistor from its own power dissipation. Such self-heating of course makes the transistor hotter than it would be solely from the combination of normal current and ambient temperature. This may then cause enough further current increase to make the current-rise and temperature-rise a self-sustaining process, until the transistor destroys itself. This process is known as *thermal runaway*.

If the load line were located according to the dashed line instead of the solid line, the operating point would not move into the danger area. However, if there were enough self-heating, it would continue up the load line all the way to the saturation line, at which point the transistor would be useless as an amplifier.

3.3 Typical Parameter Values and Variations
Collector Cutoff Current

Germanium and silicon transistors differ greatly with regard to I_{CBO}, with the germanium units often having 10 to 100 times greater cutoff current than silicon units. Representative values of I_{CBO} at 25°C, (the figure most often used for "normal room temperature") for small-signal transistors such as might be operated with quiescent collector currents in the range of 1 to 10 ma are:

silicon	0.01 μa to 1 μa
germanium	2 to 15 μa

The variation of I_{CBO} with temperature also differs between the two types, but not so strongly. A rough rule of thumb for germanium is that I_{CBO} approximately doubles with each 8° to 10°C rise, while in the case of silicon it approximately doubles with each 12°C rise. A convenient figure suitable for both types for many practical situations, when specific information is not given by the transistor manufacturer, is approximately doubling for each 10°C rise.

These figures indicate how severe the problem of operating point stability could very well be. As an example, a small-signal germanium transistor with $I_{CBO} = 5$ μa, $h_{FE} = 40$, and operated at a quiescent I_C of 2.0 ma, would have collector-emitter cutoff current equal to about one-tenth the collector quiescent current, as indicated by Equation 1–11a:

$$I_{CEO} = (h_{FE} + 1)I_{CBO}$$
$$I_{CEO} = (40 + 1)(5 \ \mu a) = 0.205 \text{ ma}$$

Now if the temperature of the transistor should rise 30°C, that is, from 25°C to 55°C, the cutoff current could be expected to rise to about 8 times the above value, or about 1.6 ma. Thus the *quiescent collector current* would have risen to about 3.6 ma, or about 80 percent above its original value.

A silicon transistor would provide much better performance in this respect: a typical I_{CBO} of 0.1μamp would give

$$I_{CEO} = (41)(0.1 \ \mu a) = 4.1\mu \text{amp}$$

and a 30° rise would cause I_{CEO} to increase to about 8 times this or about 33 μa. Thus, for a typical silicon small-signal transistor under the same conditions (and assuming the same value of h_{FE}) the increase in quiescent current due to the temperature would have been less than 2 percent.

Unit-to-unit variations in I_{CBO} can also be expected to be great. The 2N1924, for example, a germanium transistor, is listed as having a typical I_{CBO} of 4 μa, but the maximum value is shown as 10 μa.

The Current Gain Factor h_{FE}

Variations in h_{FE} with temperature are not as uniform as the I_{CBO} variations, so that there is no convenient rule. Manufacturer's specifications should be consulted in each case. Figure 3–4 illustrates some curves found in such specifications.

Note that the ordinate of this graph is in percentage of the 25°C value. This is a common way to show parameters which are subject to variations. The value of the parameter under normal conditions, or under some specified condition, is listed in the main body of the specification, and the values to be expected when the operating conditions change are given in graphs or tables which show them as percentages (or fractions or multiples) of the normal or reference value.

For example, in the case of the 2N1924 transistor having a typical h_{FE} of 50 at 25°C, a graph such as Figure 3–4 would indicate that at 55°C the value would be 150 percent of its 25° value, or $(1.50)(50) \cong 75$.

Sometimes the scale will be entitled "normalized to the 25°C value;" then the value of 1.0 will correspond to the 25° value. This kind of scale, if used in the above example, would give the "normalized" value of h_{FE} at 70°, as 1.3; and the actual value would be (1.3)(85) = 110.

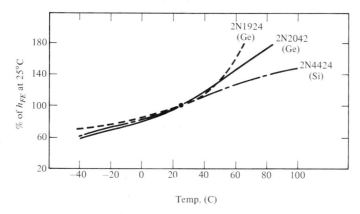

FIGURE 3–4
Typical variation of h_{FE} with temperature

Unit-to-unit h_{FE} variations are usually expressed in the manufacturer's specifications by listing the minimum and maximum values to be expected, with the typical value (that value which occurs most frequently, or the average value) often listed also. When the typical value is not specified, it may be roughly estimated by averaging the minimum and maximum values listed. The *variation* between the minimum and the maximum may be quite extreme in some cases, and it is not at all consistent, depending upon type of transistor, cost, intended use and the like. A good rule of thumb for general purpose transistors, however, is to expect at least a 3 to 1 variation. This, of course, is entirely separate from variations due to temperature effects.

Base-Emitter Voltage

Typical values of quiescent base-emitter voltage for small-signal transistors are:

silicon	0.6 to 0.7 v
germanium	0.2 to 0.3 v

Unit-to-unit variations in V_{BE} are not great, but variations due to temperature can be significant. Typically, V_{BE} for a given current decreases as temperature increases, at a rate of approximately 2.5 mv per degree centigrade.

3.4   Stabilizing the Operating Point With an Emitter Resistor

The effects of these parameter variations on the dc operating point may be minimized by several techniques. Figure 3–5 shows perhaps one of the most common; this method is sometimes called emitter resistance stabilizing.

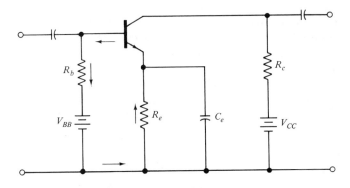

FIGURE 3–5

Bias stabilization by means of a resistance in series with the emitter

The stabilizing of the operating point occurs as a result of the resistance R_e in series with the bias supply voltage and the base-emitter junction. Consideration of the equation for voltage drops around the base-emitter circuit (indicated by the arrows in the figure) will reveal the basic principle. The equation is

$$V_{BB} = I_B R_b + V_{BE} + I_E R_e \qquad (3\text{–}1)$$

This shows that if the emitter current should start to increase, for any of the reasons discussed in Section 3.3, the resulting increase in the voltage drop $I_E R_e$ will leave less voltage available for forward-biasing of the junction, if V_{BB} and I_B are fixed. Thus, the initial rise in I_E causes a decrease of forward-bias, which opposes further increase of emitter current. The result is that the emitter current increase due to heating effects and the like, is much less in this type of circuit than in a circuit which contains no stabilizing provision.

The stabilizing action can perhaps be best summarized by comparing the effects on the currents in unstabilized and stabilized circuits as a transistor is heated. In an unstabilized circuit, as the temperature rises, I_B remains essentially constant while I_C and I_E rise. In the stabilized circuit under the same conditions, I_B would fall steadily (due to the decreasing forward-bias described above) while I_C and I_E would remain almost constant — rising actually only a very small amount.

Figure 3–6 illustrates this comparison on a set of collector curves with a dc load line drawn. Part (a) shows conditions at room temperature with the solid dot indicating the operating point. In part (b) the temperature has risen. Here the solid dot shows the new location of the operating point in the unstabilized circuit. Note that the base current is still the same value (0.03 ma) and that the collector current for this base current is much higher due to the increase in I_{CEO} and h_{FE} caused by the heat. But the small square shows what would happen in a stabilized circuit. I_B is decreased from its original 0.03 ma by the stabilizing action, and the quiescent value of I_C ends up only slightly greater than its original unheated value.

Bypassing the Emitter Resistance

At this point it might appear that desired *signal* fluctuations of I_C would also be decreased by this circuit. They would be, if it were not for the presence of the capacitance C_e bypassing R_e. This capacitance is made great enough so that the impedance of the parallel combination of X_C and R_e is negligible at signal frequencies. Thus, appreciable voltage drop is developed across R_e only by the dc component of the emitter current and not by the ac component. Temperature effects and transistor replacements are of course slow changing or long-time-duration "signals," and may be considered essentially dc.

Optimum Relation Between R_e and R_b

Emitter resistance stabilizing is most effective if R_e is made large, and R_b is made small. The reason for this is again revealed in the bias equation:

$$V_{BB} = I_B R_b + V_{BE} + I_E R_e \qquad (3\text{--}1)$$

Since it is the change in $I_E R_e$ which produces the compensating change in the bias conditions $(I_B R_b + V_{BE})$, the larger R_e is, the greater the compensating voltage change for a given change in I_E will be. In addition, for any given value of I_B, the smaller R_b is, the smaller the value of $I_B R_b$ and V_{BB}. This will mean that a given change in $I_E R_e$ will be a greater percentage of the available bias voltage.

Use of a Voltage Divider for the Bias

In order to obtain a low value of R_B, for a given I_B, one would have to use a low value of V_{BB}. In view of the fact that it is usually desirable to be able to use a single supply for both V_{CC} and V_{BB}, the low value of resistance in the base circuit for both V_{CC} and V_{BB}, the low value of resistance in the base circuit is

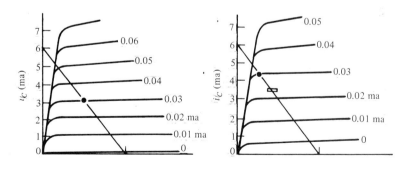

FIGURE 3–6
Comparison of stabilized and unstabilized circuits

usually obtained by employing a voltage divider as shown in Figure 3–7.

The bleeder current (that is, the current flowing in both R_1 and R_2 in addition to the base current in R_1) causes a voltage drop in R_1 which increases the

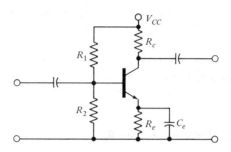

FIGURE 3–7
Emitter resistance stabilizing with bias voltage divider

drop over that produced by I_B alone — so smaller values of resistance can be used. If we Thevenize the bias circuit looking from the base into the $R_1 - R_2$ combination, we see that we have a source resistance $R = R_1R_2/(R_1 + R_2)$ and a source voltage equivalent which is equal to $[R_2/(R_1 + R_2)]V_{CC}$.

The *equivalent* circuit then is like that shown in Figure 3–8. The equivalent

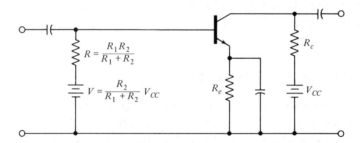

FIGURE 3–8
Emitter resistance stabilizing showing Thevenin equivalent for bias divider portion

resistance, R, can be made as small as desired — up to the point of shunting too much input signal current away from the base. This will be considered in later discussions.

The Effect of R_e on the dc Load Line

The presence of the resistance R_e must be taken into account in constructing the dc load line. This resistance is in series with the dc load R_c and the supply voltage V_{CC} in the collector-emitter loop. *Thus the total resistance in the output circuit for dc conditions is $R_e + R_c$, and the maximum dc current for load line purposes is $I_C = V_{CC}/(R_e + R_c)$.* This is illustrated in Figure 3–9.

The Effect of R_e on the ac Load Line and on the Equivalent Circuit

C_e is placed across R_e in order to prevent R_e from affecting the ac performance. It does this by causing the parallel combination of R_e and C_e to have very low impedance at the signal frequency. C is usually chosen large enough

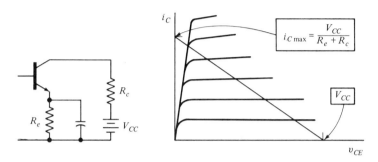

FIGURE 3–9
DC load line construction when emitter resistance is used

that X_C may for all practical purposes be considered to be zero compared to other impedances in the circuit. *Therefore, at the signal frequency the emitter may be considered to be connected directly to ground or common, just as though R_e were not being used.*

The ac load line is constructed as before, its slope being determined by the ac load impedance. For the same reason the emitter resistor will not appear in the equivalent circuit.

In the case of both the ac load line and the equivalent circuit, of course, it should be understood that at unusually low-signal frequencies the bypass capacitor's reactance may be great enough so that it does not provide good bypassing. In such a case, the parallel combination of R_e and C_e will affect the ac load line as well as the equivalent circuit, and would be included. Such effects will be considered in later chapters. For the present, whenever we analyze an amplifier's performance, it will be assumed that normal "mid-range" signal frequencies are intended, so that the bypassing may be considered fully effective, or $X_C \cong 0$.

3.5 Stabilizing the Operating Point by Means of Collector Feedback, or "Self-bias"

Another popular and effective stabilizing circuit is shown in Figure 3–10, in which the base-emitter bias current is obtained by connecting resistance R from base to collector (instead of to V_{CC} as in simple fixed biasing). The result is that the bias current is dependent upon the collector voltage, which is not a constant. Consider the effect when the quiescent collector current starts to rise due to temperature. This causes an increase in the voltage drop $I_C R_c$ and thus a de-

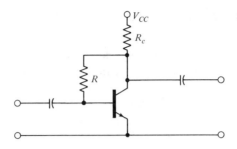

FIGURE 3-10
Collector feedback stabilization

crease in V_{CE}. But since V_{CE} in this circuit is the bias supply, the bias current would decrease, and the increase in I_C would therefore not be as great as it would have been with fixed bias.

Again, as in emitter resistance stabilizing, signal fluctuations of I_C would also be decreased by this circuit. Both of these stabilizing arrangements result in what is known as "negative feedback." The output is connected back to the input in such a way as to effectively cause a decrease in the actual input signal and therefore a decrease in the output signal amplitude. In effect, there is a loss of amplification for the circuit, or "signal degeneration."

In the case of emitter resistance stabilizing, a capacitor was placed across the resistor providing the feedback, so that the feedback was effective only for dc, or very long-term changes. For collector feedback stabilizing, a similar measure can be used. But in this case, bypassing the feedback resistor would increase the feedback for the signal frequencies. Instead, a low-pass filter must be placed between the collector and the base — so that the feedback will be effective for dc and negligible for signal frequencies. In order to accomplish this, the arrangement of Figure 3–11 can be used. R_1 can usually be made large enough so that it does not seriously affect the collector load conditions, and the reactance of C_1 can be made small enough so that the R_1-C_1 voltage divider prevents significant ac voltage from being applied to the base from the collector. DC, or very-long-term changes at the collector, however, will still be applied as feedback to the base.

3.6 Signal Current Paths in the Typical Amplifier Circuit

At this point it might be well to make sure there is a good understanding of the paths taken by the ac components in an amplifier circuit. Figure 3–12 illustrates a typical amplifier, but for simplicity in the initial discussion, shows a single resistor and separate supply for biasing, instead of the more usual voltage divider. The single resistor and separate supply is, of course, the Thevenin equivalent of the voltage divider and V_{CC} combination introduced in Section 3.4.

In addition to a bypass capacitor across the emitter resistor, there is also a capacitor shown bypassing the collector power supply, as described in Chapter

2. This is designated as C_f in Figure 3–12. As explained in Chapter 2, the reactance of C_f at the signal frequencies is normally very small compared to R_c. Thus, the output signal voltage is essentially the ac voltage drop across R_c alone

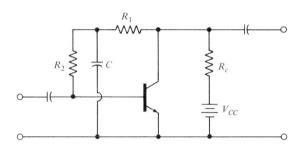

FIGURE 3–11
Bypassing of feedback resistor to avoid signal degeneration

because the signal voltage developed across the supply should be negligible. The junction of R_c and C_f is considered to be at "signal ground" or "ac ground."

Now examine the dc and ac current paths. The solid arrows designate the paths for the dc components while the dashed arrows designate the ac component paths. Note that in the input circuit the series combination of V_{BB} and R_b, *in parallel* with the series combination of the transistor's input resistance and C_e, act as a load for the signal source V_g. But in addition, the transistor input resistance and R_e act as a dc load for V_{BB}.

In the output circuit the dc path is from V_{CC} through R_e, the transistor, and R_c. The ac path, assuming perfect bypassing, is through R_e and C_f, and also through the load in parallel with R_c and C_f, then through C_e and the transistor. Note that the voltage V_{CC} is the source for the dc component while the transistor acts as the source for the signal component.

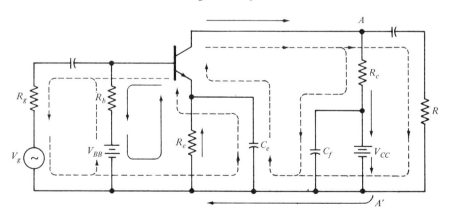

FIGURE 3–12
dc and ac current paths

Now refer to Figure 3–13, in which the same type of circuit is presented, but with a voltage divider bias circuit, and drawn in the form in which the power supplies are not explicitly shown. In this form of presentation some of

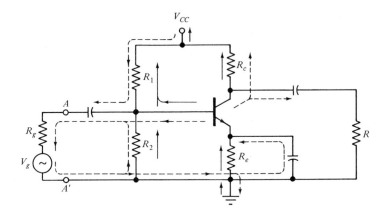

FIGURE 3–13
dc and ac current paths

the current paths are not so evident. But they can be traced readily if the dc voltage source (and its associated bypass capacitor) are mentally visualized as connected in place between the indicated supply terminal and the ground terminal or common.

For example, in this circuit, the dc current flow in the bias circuit is (for electron flow direction) out of the N-terminal of the power supply (i.e., out of the ground) through R_2 and the emitter-base junction of the transistor in parallel, and then through R_1 to the P-terminal of the supply.

The ac currents in the input are indicated by the dashed lines. Note that R_2 is in parallel with the transistor input as a load on the signal source, similarly to R_b of Figure 3–12. *But note that R_1 is also in parallel with the transistor input for signal components. Since R_1 is connected from the signal lead (the base lead) to V_{CC}, and V_{CC} is at "ac ground" due to its bypass capacitor, R_1 is effectively connected from the base lead to ground (i.e., at the bottom end of R_2 as shown in the diagram) as far as the signal is concerned.* To see this better, consider the ac current flow. Coming from terminal A' of the signal source, it not only flows into R_2 and into C_e (to the emitter), but also flows into ground or common (to which A' is connected), through the V_{CC} bypass capacitor to the positive terminal of V_{CC}, thence through R_1 to its junction with R_2. All of these ac current paths are shown by the dashed lines in Figure 3–13.

In the collector circuit the signal component of current flows out of the collector, dividing to go through R_c and R in parallel. That portion going through R_c returns to the emitter by way of the supply bypass capacitor to ground, and then through C_e to the emitter.

3.7 Simplified Design of Emitter-Resistor Stabilizing Circuit

A method for detailed design of an emitter-resistor-stabilized bias circuit will be presented in Section 3.11. It will permit designing a circuit for specified limits on drift of the operating point when the expected variations in leakage current, h_{FE}, and V_{BE} are known.

However, there are many applications in which such exact results are not needed. These include circuits which will be operated in protected environments, and which will not be manufactured in quantities. For example, experimental versions of new circuits are likely to be modified after initial testing, and detailed attention often is not given to the bias design until the rest of the design had been judged satisfactory.

A bias design which will usually give satisfactory results for such purposes may be based upon the following arbitrary relation between the effective parallel resistance R of the bias divider, defined as in Figures 3–7 and 3–8, and the emitter resistor R_e:

$$R \leqq 20R_e \tag{3–2}$$

If the temperature and interchangeability requirements are only slight, R can be made the maximum value indicated above (or even greater). If more protection is felt desirable, the value of R can be made smaller.

One way to approach the design is to first choose a value for R_e based on how much supply voltage can be invested in the IR drop in this resistor. It is not uncommon to find anywhere from 5 to 20 percent of V_{CC} used here. Then the required value for R is found from Equation (3–2). Finally, the values for R_1 and R_2, which will provide the required forward-bias voltage (i.e., the required base current) and at the same time have the required parallel resistance R, may either be calculated or adjusted experimentally.

Example 3–1

The simplified bias design method is to be used to determine the bias resistances for an amplifier that is to be operated at a quiescent collector current of 5 ma. The supply voltage is 15 v. A fair amount of interchangeability and temperature immunity is desired, so $R = 10R_e$ will be used. An $I_E R_e$ drop of roughly one volt will be used as a starting point.

Now at approximately 5-ma quiescent current, a 220-ohm resistor would cause slightly over one volt drop. Let this be our initial choice for R_e. Then,

$$R = 10R_e$$
$$R = 2200 \text{ ohms}$$

This is the parallel resistance of the bias divider. If this value is lower than you wish to have shunting the input of the amplifier, a larger value could be chosen for R_e (at the expense of using up more of the supply voltage), or you could try a higher ratio of R to R_e and see if the stability proved to be good enough.

Experimental Adjustment of the Bias Divider

Although the required values for the elements of the bias divider, R_1 and R_2, may be calculated (See Section 3.11), perhaps the most convenient approach for "one-of-a-kind" circuits is to breadboard the amplifier (i.e., construct it in temporary form for preliminary test and adjustment) using potentiometers or resistance decades and an adjustable power supply.

The values of the various resistances can then be adjusted experimentally until the desired quiescent collector or emitter current is obtained with values of R_1, R_2, and R_e that meet the requirements set above. In the example being considered here, a 220-ohm resistor might be inserted for R_e, and the values of R_1 and R_2 adjusted until the voltage across R_e was approximately 1.1 v (indicating that the desired quiescent emitter current of 5 ma was flowing), and the parallel combination of R_1 and R_2 at the same time was approximately 2200 ohms.

3.8 Stability Factors

As an aid in analyzing and designing bias circuits, the effects of each of the parameters that are subject to variation may be separately examined. For this purpose it has been quite common to define stability factors, which express the amount of change of dc collector current per unit change of the parameter concerned.

The Leakage Current Stability Factor

For example, the *leakage current stability factor* is defined as the ratio of the change in I_C caused by a change in leakage current, to the change in I_{CBO}:

$$S = \frac{\Delta I_C}{\Delta I_{CBO}} \tag{3-3}$$

Obviously in an unstabilized amplifier the value of S is high, since the leakage current variations cause large changes in collector current, while a stabilized circuit results in a lower value of S.

The S value for an unstabilized CE circuit may be found from the dc current equation for this circuit:

$$I_C = h_{FE}I_B + (h_{FE} + 1)I_{CBO} \tag{1-12a}$$

When I_{CBO} changes by an amount ΔI_{CBO}, I_C will change by an amount ΔI_C, and the equation must then be:

$$I_C + \Delta I_C = h_{FE}I_B + (h_{FE} + 1)(I_{CBO} + \Delta I_{CBO})$$

Solving for ΔI_C then gives

$$\Delta I_C \parallel (h_{FE} + 1)(\Delta I_{CBO})$$

So that

$$S = \frac{\Delta I_C}{\Delta I_{CBO}} = \frac{(h_{FE} + 1)(\Delta I_{CBO})}{\Delta I_{CBO}}$$

giving

$$S = h_{FE} + 1$$

For example, consider a germanium transistor, having an h_{FE} of 50 and $I_{CBO} = 10\ \mu a$ at 25°C, to be operated in an ambient temperature that may rise as high as 55°C. The value of I_{CBO} can be expected to increase to about (8) (10 μa) = 80 μa when the transistor temperature rises to 55°C (recall that I_{CBO} roughly doubles for each 10° rise). Thus the change in I_{CBO} would be (80 − 10)μa, or 70 μa.

Now,

$$S = h_{FE} + 1 = 50 + 1 = 51$$

Also,

$$S = \frac{\Delta I_C}{\Delta I_{CBO}} \tag{3-3}$$

Therefore,

$$\Delta I_C = S\Delta I_{CBO}$$
$$\Delta I_C = (51)(70\ \mu a)$$
$$\Delta I_C = 3.57\ ma$$

In other words the quiescent value of I_C, i.e., the operating point, could be expected to rise about 3.57 ma in such circumstances. This would be unacceptable in an amplifier intended to operate at a quiescent current in the vicinity of 1 or 2 ma, or even one designed for 5 or 10 ma. A stabilized bias circuit with $S = 5$, on the other hand, would give:

$$\Delta I_C = S\Delta I_{CBO} = (5)(70\ \mu a)$$
$$\Delta I_C = 0.35\ ma$$

which might be acceptable.

An equation for the stability factor for either type of bias stabilizing arrangement discussed above can be derived from the equation of the bias loop for the particular circuit (for example, Equation 3-1) in conjunction with the basic equation that relates I_C, I_B, and I_{CBO} to each other.

For the emitter resistance stabilizing circuit the resulting expression for S is

$$S = \frac{h_{FE} + 1}{h_{FE}\left(\dfrac{R_e}{R + R_e}\right) + 1} \tag{3-4}$$

in which R is the parallel equivalent of the bias divider resistors, as shown in Figure 3-8.

This equation shows that for S to be small, R_e should be large, and R should be small. This is what we found in the earlier consideration of the circuit. The smallest possible value of S, it should be noted, is 1 for as R_E becomes very much larger than R, $R_E/(R + R_E) \to 1$ and $S \to (h_{FE} + 1)/(h_{FE} + 1)$.

The stability factor equation for collector feedback stabilization has the same form:

$$S = \frac{h_{FE} + 1}{h_{FE}\left(\dfrac{R_c}{R + R_c}\right) + 1} \tag{3-5}$$

in which R is as shown in Figure 3-10. Here, the equation shows that to obtain a small value of S, R_c should be large, and R should be small.

An amplifier circuit can use both collector feedback and emitter resistor feedback stabilizing, as shown in Figure 3–14. In this case the S equation is

$$S = \frac{h_{FE} + 1}{h_{FE}\left[\dfrac{R_e + R_c}{R + R_e + R_c}\right] + 1}$$

(3–6)

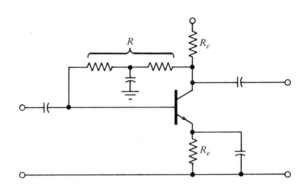

FIGURE 3–14
Amplifier with both R_e and collector feedback stabilization

Again this is of the same form as the others. Where the previous expressions contained either R_e or R_c, this contains both. The conclusion that may be drawn is that it makes no difference, for a given S, how the resistance is split up between R_c or R_e as long as the total ($R_c + R_e$) is kept the same. If R_c is zero (as would be the case, approximately, for transformer-coupled amplifiers), the results would be the same as if R were connected directly to V_{CC} — that is, as if using emitter resistor stabilizing only.

On the other hand, if there is a large enough resistance being used for R_c — as would usually be the case with RC-coupled amplifiers — collector feedback would give the required stability with a smaller R_e. The supply voltage required would then be smaller, which may be an advantage in some cases. But if the supply voltage value is not critical, the use of both types of stabilization may be considered too expensive, since it requires two bypass capacitors.

Other Stability Factors

The above discussion concerned the use of the leakage current stability factor. Other stability factors are often useful, and are listed here for reference.

$$M = \frac{\Delta I_C}{\Delta V_{BE}}$$

(3–7)

$$N = \frac{\Delta I_C}{\Delta h_{FE}}$$

(3–8)

Each of the stability factors may be used to predict the amount of change in I_C due to changes in the indicated variable.

That is,
$$(\Delta I_C)_S = S(\Delta I_{CBO})$$
$$(\Delta I_C)_M = M(\Delta V_{BE})$$
$$(\Delta I_C)_N = N(\Delta h_{FE})$$

so that the total change in collector current is

$$\Delta I_C = S\Delta I_{CBO} + M\Delta V_{BE} + N\Delta h_{FE} \tag{3-9}$$

This equation is valid only if the increments involved are small. In particular, the stability factors depend upon the value of h_{FE} (recall Equations (3–3), (3–4), and (3–5) for example) so that appreciable changes in h_{FE} will change the values of S, M, and N in Equation (3–9). But Equation (3–9) can serve as a guide, with proper awareness of its limitations.

3.9 Analysis of Circuit Conditions in the Stabilized Amplifier

It is desirable to be able to analyze dc conditions in an amplifier circuit. Such analysis is often necessary in verifying circuit details in an experimental design, in evaluating the effects of variations in component values, or in diagnosing circuit troubles. Figure 3–15, the diagram of an emitter resistor

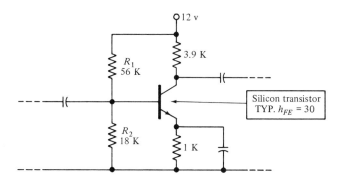

FIGURE 3–15
Circuit to be used for operating point calculations

stabilized amplifier, will be used as an example of the general approach to such calculations.

If collector characteristic curves for the transistor are available, a load line could be drawn, but then the dc base current would still have to be calculated before the dc collector current and collector voltage could be found on the graph. Frequently, such curves are not included in the transistor specifications, while h_{FE} is very commonly included. Thus this example will assume only the latter.

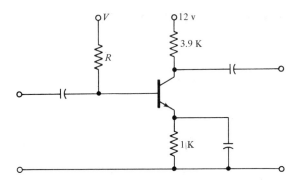

FIGURE 3–16
Simplified bias circuitry

Perhaps the simplest way to approach the problem is to recall that this circuit simplifies, by Thevenizing the bias network, to that shown in Figure 3–16. The Thevenin equivalent voltage V has the value

$$V = \left[\frac{R_2}{R_1 + R_2}\right]V_{CC}$$

$$V = \frac{18,000}{(56 + 18)(10^3)} (12) = 2.92 \text{ v}$$

The Thevenin equivalent bias resistor R is

$$R = \frac{R_1 R_2}{R_1 + R_2}$$

$$R = \frac{(18)(56)(10^6)}{(74)(10^3)} \cong 13.6 \text{ kilohms}$$

The voltage drop equation can be written for the bias loop in Figure 3–16:

$$V = I_B R + V_{BE} + I_E R_e$$

But

$$I_E = (h_{FE} + 1)I_B + I_{CEO}$$

And since I_{CEO} can be expected to be very small (this is a silicon transistor),

$$I_E \cong (h_{FE} + 1)I_B$$

Leading to

$$V = I_B R + V_{BE} + (h_{FE} + 1)I_B R_e$$

Now known values can be used, and the equation solved for I_B. The value of V_{BE} can be approximated as 0.7 v.

$$I_B = \frac{V - V_{BE}}{R + (h_{FE} + 1)R_e}$$

$$I_B \cong \frac{2.92 - 0.7}{13,600 + (31)(1000)} = \frac{2.22}{44,600}$$

$$I_B \cong 49.8 \times 10^{-6} \cong 50 \ \mu a$$

Now when I_{CEO} is small as it is here,

$$I_C \cong h_{FE}I_B$$

So, $$I_C \cong (30)(50)(10^{-6}) \cong 1.5 \text{ ma}$$

From this, the collector-to-ground voltage V_{CN}, the emitter-to-ground voltage V_{EN}, and the collector-to-emitter voltage V_{CE} may be calculated:

$$V_{CN} = V_{CC} - I_C R_c$$
$$\cong 12 - (1.5)(10^{-3})(3.9)(10^3)$$
$$V_{CN} \cong 12 - 5.85 = 6.15 \text{ v}$$
$$V_{EN} = I_E R_e = (I_C + I_B)R_e$$
$$\cong (1.55)(10^{-3})(10^3)$$
$$V_{EN} \cong 1.55 \text{ v}$$
$$V_{CE} = V_{CN} - V_{EN}$$
$$\cong 6.15 - 1.55$$
$$V_{CE} \cong 4.6 \text{ v}$$

If it were desirable to know the dc base-to-ground voltage, it can be obtained from the fact that it is the sum of the base-emitter voltage V_{BE} and the emitter-to-ground voltage V_{EN}:

$$V_{BN} = V_{BE} + V_{EN}$$
$$\cong 0.7 + 1.55$$
$$V_{BN} \cong 2.25 \text{ v}$$

From this and the base current, the bias divider currents can be calculated if needed:

$$I_2 = \frac{V_{BN}}{R_2}$$
$$I_2 \cong \frac{2.2}{18,000} \cong 122 \text{ } \mu a$$
$$I_1 = \frac{V_{CC} - V_{BN}}{R_1}$$
$$I_1 = \frac{12 - 2.22}{56,000} = \frac{9.78}{56,000}$$
$$I_1 \cong 175 \text{ } \mu a$$

Of course, approximately 50 μa of this 175 μa in the upper resistor of the bias divider, is the base current.

In the above calculations, the collector cutoff current could have been included if it were not small enough to ignore, but how great it would need to be to make it necessary to include it, would depend upon the circumstances. Other variations in the circuit may very well exceed the error contributed by ignoring the leakage current. For example, a bias circuit might be designed for reasonably good stability, but not necessarily for great precision in location of operating point. Such a circuit might employ 10 percent tolerance resistors, and errors of less than 1 percent might not be significant in its analysis. On the other hand, circuits requiring great accuracy would be built using precision components, and the circuit variations due to component tolerances might be small enough to make the leakage current value significant in the calculations.

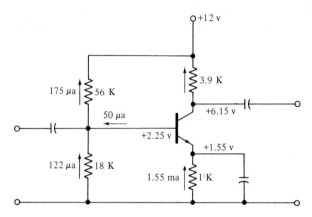

FIGURE 3–17
Amplifier circuit showing calculated dc voltages and currents

Figure 3–15 (Figure 3–17) is now repeated here with the voltage and current values, found in the above calculations shown on the diagram. Arrows indicate electron flow directions.

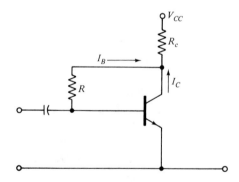

FIGURE 3–18
Basic collector feedback circuit in considering dc analysis

dc Analysis in Circuits Involving Collector Feedback

The dc analysis of circuits involving collector feedback bias stabilizing is done in a manner similar to that of the emitter resistor stabilized circuits. Here, however, it should be observed that the dc base current flows in R_c along with the collector current. Refer to Figure 3–18.

The base circuit equation is

$$V_{CC} = (I_C + I_B)R_c + I_B R + V_{BE}$$

so that $\qquad\quad V_{CC} = (h_{FE} + 1)I_B R_c + I_B R + V_{BE}$

and knowing V_{CC}, h_{FE}, R_c, and R, and using an estimated V_{BE}, permits solving for I_B. I_C is then equal to $h_{FE}I_B$, and the necessary voltages can be found from the appropriate IR drops.

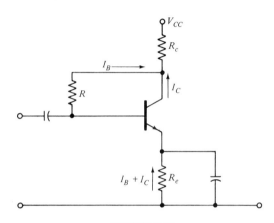

FIGURE 3–19
Combination of emitter resistor and collector feedback stabilizing

When the circuit involves both collector feedback and emitter resistor stabilizing, as in Figure 3–19, R_c and R_e *both* carry $I_B + I_C$. The bias equation then is

$$V_{CC} = (I_C + I_B)R_c + I_B R + (I_C + I_B)R_e + V_{BE}$$

or $\qquad V_{CC} = (h_{FE} + 1)I_B R_c + I_B R + (h_{FE} + 1)I_B R_e + V_{BE}$

which can be solved for I_B.

3.10 Additional Stabilizing Circuits

The value of R as determined by the stability requirement in a collector feedback stabilizing arrangement may not produce the desired quiescent base current. When the value of R is such as to cause I_B to be smaller than called for, R may be reduced to the value as determined by the desired bias. The relationship between R and I_B is

$$R = \frac{V_R}{I_B} = \frac{V_{CE} - V_{BE}}{I_B}$$

Reducing R will simply make the stability better than required. (It may also, of course, create a problem in the form of excessive shunting of the output, since it is effectively in parallel with R_c at the collector.)

On the other hand, R as determined by the stability requirement may produce greater dc base current than desired. In such a case a voltage divider could be used as shown in Figure 3–20.

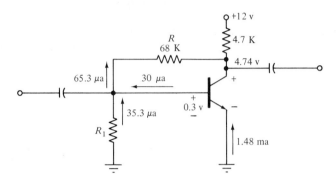

FIGURE 3–20
Use of a bias divider in collector feedback stabilizing

To illustrate the use of this arrangement, suppose that the stability requirement dictates the use of 68 kilohms or less as the feedback resistor, and that the values of V_{CE} and V_{BE} are 4.74 v and 0.3 v as shown. Then the voltage across the 68 kilohms is $4.74 - 0.3 = 4.44$ v and $I_B \cong 4.44/68,000 \cong 65.3$ μa. If this *were* the value of the desired quiescent base current, resistor R_1 would not be needed.

However, let us suppose that the desired operating point is such that the necessary base current is 30 μa. Then R_1 is needed to carry the additional 35.3 μa.

$$R_1 = \frac{0.3}{(35.3)(10^{-6})} \cong 8500 \text{ ohms}$$

This value of resistance shunting the input may be too low from the point of view of its shunting effect on the signal at the amplifier input. If so, R_1 may be

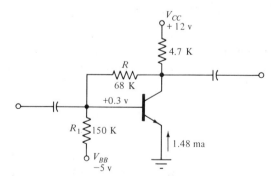

FIGURE 3–21
Use of additional supply voltage in collector feedback stabilizing

connected to a negative supply voltage, thus permitting a larger value. Thus in Figure 3–21, $R_1 = 5.3/(35.3)(10^{-6}) \cong 150$ kilohms.

In determining the necessary value of R_1 above, we were illustrating the *design* of such a circuit. The voltage V_{CE} and the current I_C, defining the desired operating point, were assumed known as part of the design problem. But in the dc analysis of an existing circuit these would not initially be known. In addition, the base bias circuit has two unknown currents — the base current and the current I_{BL} through R_1.

For the circuit of Figure 3–20, a rough approximation of dc conditions may be obtained by using an estimated value of V_{BE} to solve for I_{BL}:

$$I_{BL} \cong \frac{V_{BE}}{R_1}$$

Then the bias loop equation is

$$V_{CC} = (I_{BL} + I_B + I_C)R_c + (I_{BL} + I_B)R + V_{BE}$$
$$V_{CC} = (I_{BL} + I_B + h_{FE}I_B)R_c + (I_{BL} + I_B)R + V_{BE}$$

which may be solved for I_B.

This is a rough approximation since the use of an estimated value for V_{BE} here involves possible error in I_{BL} directly proportional to the error in estimating V_{BE}. In our earlier use of such estimates, this error was reduced because V_{BE} was only a small part of the total voltage producing I_B.

However, the stabilizing action of the circuit helps to minimize the effects of these errors. In addition, if input characteristics are available for the transistor, V_{BE} can be more closely approximated if the requirements of the problem justify the additional work.

In circuits such as that of Figure 3–21, the error in approximating V_{BE} becomes negligible for practical work, since here the total voltage across R_1, determining the bleeder current, is $V_{BB} + V_{BE}$. Thus

$$I_{BL} = \frac{V_{BB} + V_{BE}}{R_1}$$

and the estimated portion (V_{BE}) is a relatively small part of the total voltage.

3.11 Design of the Bias Circuit

Stability factors such as those discussed in Section 3.7 are very useful in analyzing operating point stability problems. They serve to show which variables may be causing the major portion of the drift, and which may be contributing little or no effect, in any particular case. They provide general indications concerning the circuit relations necessary for good stability, and permit comparing transistors and circuits with respect to dc stability.

But in the design of specific circuits, general indications and comparisons are often not sufficient. It is time consuming to try different values, evaluating and comparing the results until finally the desired goal is achieved. In other words, it is often helpful to have a method of *design* rather than simply a method of analysis. By design is meant a means of finding out the specific circuit values that will provide a given objective.

In the case of bias circuits, the objective is a particular operating point with known limits on the amount of change or drift of the operating point under expected operating conditions.

Design techniques will vary according to the goal, and according to the constraints, or given conditions. As an introduction to such methods, a simple design for the ordinary emitter-resistance-stabilized amplifier will be considered here. Figure 3–22(a) will serve as a starting point. This shows the basic

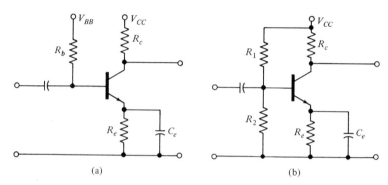

(a)   (b)

FIGURE 3–22
General circuit used in considering bias design method

circuit using an emitter resistor and a single base-bias resistor, with a separate bias supply. The resistor R_b and supply V_{BB} can be used to represent either an actual circuit, or the Thevenin equivalent of the voltage divider arrangement so often used, as depicted in part (b) of the figure. In the following discussion the circuit of (a) will be used to design for the desired stability, and will then be converted to that of (b) to provide the correct operating point.

The design method is derived from a Kirchhoff's voltage equation for the total bias circuit. Thus, from Figure 3–22(a) we have

$$V_{BB} = I_B R_b + V_{BE} + I_E R_e \tag{3–1}$$

But
$$I_E = I_C + I_B$$

And
$$I_C = h_{FE} I_B + I_{CEO} \tag{1–7a}$$

By using these relations Equation (3–1) may be manipulated into

$$V_{BB} = \left(\frac{R_b}{h_{FE} + 1} + R_e \right) I_E + V_{BE} - I_{CBO} R_b \tag{3–10}$$

which relates the quiescent current I_E to the supply voltage, the bias resistors R_b and R_e, and the transistor characteristics.

Now if the maximum and minimum values of h_{FE}, V_{BE}, and I_{CBO}, due to temperature and manufacturing variations, are substituted into this equation, the following two "worst case" equations result:

Worst case in one direction:

$$V_{BB} = \left(\frac{R_b}{h_{FE\ max} + 1} + R_e\right)I_{E\ max} + V_{BE\ min} - I_{CBO\ max}\ R_b \qquad (3\text{--}11)$$

Worst case in the other direction:

$$V_{BB} = \left(\frac{R_b}{h_{FE\ min} + 1} + R_e\right)I_{E\ min} + V_{BE\ max} - I_{CBO\ min}\ R_b \qquad (3\text{--}12)$$

On the assumption that V_{BB} and the resistance values are constant, these two equations can be solved simultaneously for R_b. With $I_{CBO\ min}$ omitted because it is usually quite small compared with the other factors, the result is

$$R_b = \frac{(I_{E\ max} - I_{E\ min})R_e + V_{BE\ min} - V_{BE\ max}}{I_{CBO\ max} - \dfrac{I_{E\ max}}{h_{FE\ max} + 1} + \dfrac{I_{E\ min}}{h_{FE\ min} + 1}} \qquad (3\text{--}13)$$

Now the desired limits, $I_{E\ max}$ and $I_{E\ min}$, as determined by the desired operating point stability, may be put into this equation along with information from the transistor data sheet, or from tests, as to the expected maximum and minimum values of V_{BE}, I_{CBO}, and h_{FE}, and the equation can be solved for R_b in terms of R_e. (Recall from Equation [3–4] that the stability factor S depended upon the *relation* between these two.) A certain amount of choice in the values of R_b and R_e is then available, depending upon other aspects of the amplifier's design which might be affected by these resistances.

R_e may be assigned a small value, for example, to keep the required value of V_{CC} from being too great. But this may in some cases result in a value of R_b which is too small, excessively shunting the amplifier input. In such a case, a choice might have to be made between adopting a higher value of V_{CC}, or using an additional stage of amplification to make up for the loss due to the shunting effect of R_b.

Example 3–2

The circuit of Figure 3–22(b) is to be used for an amplifier. The value of R_c is to be 4700 ohms. The quiescent emitter current is not to fall below 1.6 ma or rise above 2.4 ma due to transistor replacement or due to temperature over the range of 0 to 60°C. The transistor specifications are found in Table 3–1.

TABLE 3–1

	At 25°C			Value at 0 and 60°C relative to value at 25°C	
	Min	Typ	Max	0°C	60°C
I_{CBO}			1.0 μa	0.1	10
h_{FE}	50		150	0.8	1.25
V_{BE}		0.62	v	1.1	0.85

The temperature limits are often not given so explicitly in data sheets. When this is the case, approximations based on the typical variations as given in Section 3.3 will prove satisfactory for many applications. Often the transistor manufacturer will supply additional data concerning these characteristics. In addition, circuit and equipment manufacturers often perform tests themselves to determine these values.

When the figures shown above are used to find the minimum and maximum values required by Equation (3–13), the results are as follows:

$$
\begin{array}{ll}
I_{E \text{ max}} & 2.4 \text{ ma} \\
I_{E \text{ min}} & 1.6 \text{ ma} \\
V_{BE \text{ min}} & (0.85)(0.62) = 0.527 \text{ v} \\
V_{BE \text{ max}} & (1.1)(0.62) = 0.671 \text{ v} \\
I_{CBO \text{ max}} & (10)(1 \ \mu a) = 10 \ \mu a \\
h_{FE \text{ max}} & (1.25)(150) = 187.5 \\
h_{FE \text{ min}} & (0.8)(50) = 40
\end{array}
$$

These values then give

$$
R_b = \frac{(0.0024 - 0.0016)R_e + 0.527 - 0.671}{(10)(10^{-6}) - \dfrac{0.0024}{188.5} + \dfrac{0.0016}{41}}
$$

$$
R_b \cong 22 \ R_e - 3960
$$

The resistances R_b and R_e may now be chosen to suit the individual circumstances. The relationship indicated here is that which will give the required dc stability; larger R_e (or smaller R_b) will result in better stability. Since R_e is in series with the transistor and V_{CC}, the larger the value of R_e, the greater will be the required supply voltage V_{CC}. This might indicate that R_e should be chosen small. But this will then require R_b to be small. Since R_b is effectively in parallel with the output of the previous stage and the input of this stage, small values of R_b result in low voltage gain (due to the low effective load resistance for the preceding stage) or low current gain (due to excessive signal current losses in this shunt resistance). Thus the choice of R_e and R_b will involve compromises, and the method of deciding upon the values may vary considerably with individual circumstances.

In this example, let us assume that R_b is to be chosen at least large enough so that the signal current in it will not exceed 10 percent of the signal current going to the transistor input. Assume the input resistance of the amplifier, at the base of the transistor, is 800 ohms. The value of R_b then must be ten times this, or 8000 ohms, if it is to take no more than one-tenth of the base signal current. We then have

$$
8000 \cong 22 \ R_e - 3960
$$

$$
R_e \cong \frac{8000 + 3960}{22}
$$

$$
R_e \cong 544 \text{ ohms}
$$

and the nearest standard value of 560 ohms might be used.

The value of R_b chosen above was not converted to the nearest standard value because we intend to change R_b into a two-resistor voltage divider of the form shown in Figure 3–22(b), as discussed earlier. This may be done in the following fashion.

The original statement of the problem indicated that the desired nominal emitter current was to be 2 ma. Assume that the nominal collector-to-emitter voltage is to be 5 v. Assuming that the nominal room temperature value of h_{FE} is the average of the minimum and maximum values given, we have

$$h_{FE} = 100$$

and since

$$I_E = I_C + I_B$$

we have

$$I_E = h_{FE}I_B + (h_{FE} + 1)I_{CBO} + I_B$$

and

$$I_E = (h_{FE} + 1)I_B + (h_{FE} + 1)I_{CBO}$$

This equation is solved for I_B:

$$I_B = \frac{I_E - (h_{FE} + 1)I_{CBO}}{h_{FE} + 1}$$

Often, I_{CBO} is small enough so that it may be ignored, giving

$$I_B \cong \frac{I_E}{h_{FE} + 1}$$

In this example this results in

$$I_B \cong (2)(10^{-3})/101$$
$$I_B \cong 19.8 \ \mu a$$

as the approximate value of base current necessary for this circuit.

Using the values of resistances determined above, or

$$R_b = 8000 \text{ ohms}$$
$$R_e = 560 \text{ ohms}$$

we then have for the required equivalent supply voltage V_{BB} as defined by Figure 3–22(a):

$$V_{BB} \cong I_B R_b + V_{BE} + I_E R_e$$
$$V_{BB} \cong (19.8)(10^{-6})(8000) + 0.62 + (2)(10^{-3})(560)$$
$$V_{BB} \cong 1.9 \text{ v}$$

while the necessary value of V_{CC} is

$$V_{CC} \cong I_C R_c + V_{CE} + I_E R_e$$
$$V_{CC} \cong (1.98)(10^{-3})(4700) + 5 + (2)(10^{-3})(560)$$
$$V_{CC} \cong 15.42 \text{ v}$$

In practice this required value of collector supply voltage might be modified, perhaps by adjusting some of the design values in the circuit, in order to achieve a value of V_{CC} that fits with other circuits in the same equipment. In this example we shall assume that the calculated value of 15.4 v is to be used "as is."

Design of the Voltage Divider

The necessary voltage divider ratio may be obtained from the fact that V_{BB} is the Thevenin source voltage, obtained from V_{CC} and the divider, as originally shown in Figure 3–8. Thus

$$\frac{R_2}{R_1 + R_2} = \frac{V_{BB}}{V_{CC}}$$

$$\frac{R_2}{R_1 + R_2} \cong \frac{1.9}{15.4} \cong 0.123$$

Now R_1 and R_2 must be chosen so as to give this divider ratio and at the same time have a parallel resistance of 8000 ohms. Simultaneous solution of these two equations will provide the necessary values:

$$\frac{R_2}{R_1 + R_2} \cong 0.123$$

$$\frac{R_1 R_2}{R_1 + R_2} \cong 8000$$

The results are

$$R_1 \cong 65{,}000 \text{ ohms}$$
$$R_2 \cong 9100 \text{ ohms}$$

Since both of these are not standard values, some readjustment of values may be necessary, with the associated necessary checking of the results to make sure that the design is not hurt by any compromises that are made.

3.12 Troubleshooting Amplifier Circuits

The ways in which an amplifier's performance can be affected by circuit failures are extremely limited. There may be lack of signal output (or weak output), distorted output, undesired signal (noise or interference), or oscillation. But the individual faults or defects which can create these symptoms are quite numerous. Each component in an amplifier stage can suffer any of several troubles (short-circuit, open-circuit, change in value, and the like), and practical circuits may contain many components. In addition, all connections between components are subject to failure.

Efficient troubleshooting consists of using measurements of circuit conditions coupled with a knowledge of the general operating principles of the circuits to make logical deductions concerning the nature and location of the fault. A diagnosis of the trouble made in this way is usually much more efficient than the tedious process of individually testing each component and each connection, especially since individual component checking often requires unsoldering many of the circuit connections.

Equipment manufacturers often supply information which helps greatly in troubleshooting. Such information usually includes the dc and ac voltage levels at a number of points in the circuit for normal conditions. Comparisons can then be made between the defective equipment and the normal equipment in order to facilitate diagnosis. But even with such information, making logical deductions concerning the condition of a circuit requires a good knowledge of circuit operation and of troubleshooting principles. When the manufacturer's troubleshooting notes are not available, such general principles become even more important.

Amplifier malfunctions may be of such a nature as to affect the ac performance only, or may affect both the dc and the ac conditions. An example of faults that would affect ac conditions without disturbing dc conditions would be an open-circuit occurring in a blocking capacitor or bypass capacitor, as at C_{c1}, C_{c2}, or C_e, in Figure 3–23. Since these capacitors already (in normal

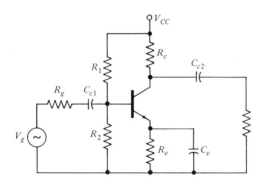

FIGURE 3–23

Basic RC-coupled amplifier illustrating the effect of circuit faults

operation) act as open-circuits for dc, this kind of fault does not change dc conditions. But the effect on the ac signal is of course drastic. In the case of C_{c1} and C_{c2} such a fault serves to block the signal. In the case of C_e it leaves the emitter resistor unbypassed and may therefore reduce the voltage gain drastically.

Normally, however, in *RC*-coupled amplifiers most defects will disturb dc conditions as well as signal conditions. In addition, dc measurements will often provide more information as to the nature and location of the trouble than will ac measurements. For example, in Figure 3–23, breaks in either R_1, R_2, R_e, or R_c, or shorts across R_1, R_c, or R_e, would all produce approximately the same symptom as far as signal conditions are concerned. There would be input signal but little or no output signal. But dc voltage measurements would indicate where the fault was, because the short-circuits or open-circuits would cause changes in the dc voltages directly related to the location of the short or open. Consequently, a quick and convenient way to diagnose an amplifier's condition when trouble develops is to check the dc voltages.

Shorts and Opens in Simple Resistive Circuits

In order to understand the usefulness of dc measurements for diagnosis, consider Figure 3–24. Note the effects of breaks (open-circuits), and of short-circuits, on the voltage distribution in the simple series circuit illustrated in (a), (b), and (c).

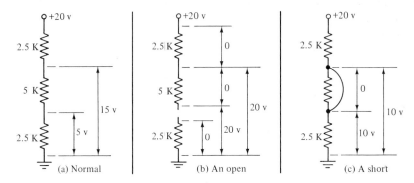

FIGURE 3–24
Effects of shorts and opens in simple series circuit

Opens cause the current to go to zero, so there can be no *IR* drop in any of the series elements. The voltage from ground or common to any of the circuit points *below* the break must therefore be zero. But voltage from ground to any point *above* the break must be equal to the supply voltage. Thus, there is a *jump* in voltage, equal to the supply voltage, across the break. Note the effect of the circuit break upon the voltages in part (b) of the figure.

A shorted component changes the voltage distribution in a somewhat less dramatic way. The voltage drop is eliminated only in the shorted component. The voltage drops across other components are changed but often not so obviously. The revealing measurement is the one which shows that the voltage is the same at both ends of the component, as illustrated in part (c) of the figure. (This type of fault is of course not readily detected by dc voltage measurement if it occurs in a component that normally has a very small dc voltage drop across it — as in the case of low resistance transformer windings.)

Shorts and Opens in Transistor Circuits

In circuits involving a transistor, the effects of shorts and opens may be detected by similar measurements. Note the collector-circuit symptoms illustrated in Figure 3–25. Observe, however, that the voltage *below* the break, at the collector, will not quite be zero (in contrast with the simple series resistive circuit) because of the effect of the bias divider $R_1 - R_2$ in forward-biasing the collector-base junction.

Shorts and Opens in the Emitter-to-Ground Circuit

An open-circuit in this portion of the amplifier produces simple effects. The collector current is cut off, and the collector potential is therefore approximately equal to V_{CC} except for the small IR drop due to I_{CBO}. Thus, an open emitter-to-ground circuit will cause approximate V_{CC} voltage along the entire collector-to-V_{CC} circuit, similar to the effect of a shorted collector resistor.

A short from emitter to ground removes some of the circuit's reverse-bias and causes an increase in forward-bias. The collector current will be very high (the transistor may be in saturation), and consequently the collector-to-emitter voltage will be very low.

Effect of Shorts and Opens in the Bias Divider

If the resistor $R2$ of the bias divider in Figure 3–25 is shorted, the base will be grounded. It will be left without forward-bias, and the transistor will be cut off. DC voltage at the collector will be equal almost to V_{CC}. Only the small IR drop due to collector leakage current in R_c will be evident. Signal output will be zero because of the short across the input signal path.

If $R2$ is open, the forward-bias will be very high; collector current will be very high (the transistor will probably be in saturation), and the collector-to-emitter voltage will be very low. However, collector-to-ground voltage may not be decisively low because of the large IR drop in R_e. Collector-to-*emitter* voltage is the decisive test here, and will probably be less than a volt in a small-signal amplifier. The stage may exhibit a small amount of gain but will exhibit severe limiting as one attempts to increase the output signal beyond a fraction of a volt.

If R_1 is shorted, the transistor will be in saturation due to the excessive forward-bias. The base will of course be at V_{CC}. The emitter will be only slightly below V_{CC}. Due to being hard into saturation, the transistor's gain should be exceedingly low, and extreme limiting should be evident.

If R_1 is open, the transistor will be cut off due to the lack of forward-bias. The dc and signal conditions will be similar to those prevailing in the case of the shorted R_2, described above, except that there may be a slight output signal, since the input signal path will not be shorted.

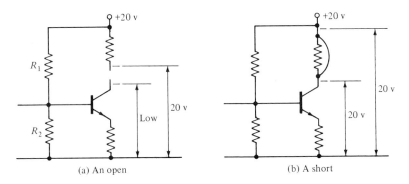

FIGURE 3–25
Effects of shorts and opens in simple amplifier circuit

Ohmmeter Measurements

A diagnosis of the suspected trouble is only that — a diagnosis. In some cases, depending upon the circumstances and the ability of the individual, it is at best an educated guess. Therefore, it should be verified by direct check of the suspected component before rushing into circuit repairs.

The ohmmeter may often be used to good advantage for this while components are still in the circuit. But ohmmeter measurements "in-circuit" should be made with caution and with due regard for possible parallel paths through other resistances. When such paths do exist and where the circuit construction is of a type to permit it, one end of the component to be checked should be disconnected from the rest of the circuit in order to prevent such shunting effects from causing misleading measurements.

Figure 3–26 illustrates a relatively simple example of such a situation.

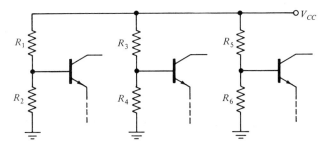

FIGURE 3–26
Parallel paths causing error when making in-circuit resistance measurements

In this circuit any attempt to measure $R3$ or $R4$ would be drastically affected by the presence of shunt paths such as $R1$-$R2$ and $R5$-$R6$. Disconnecting one end of the resistor being checked would, however, eliminate the shunt paths.

PROBLEMS

3–1. Write the equation that relates collector current to base current and collector cutoff current in the *CE* connection of the transistor.

3–2. Write the equation that relates I_{CEO} to I_{CBO}.

3–3. A transistor data sheet lists typical h_{FE} as 40, and typical I_{CBO} as 5 μa. If the transistor is operated with a quiescent base current of 100 μa, what quiescent collector current should you expect (typically)? $4,205 \times 10^{-3}$ amp.

3–4. If the minimum and maximum values of h_{FE} due to production variations (i.e., the "unit-to-unit" variations at fixed temperature) are 20 and 60, what minimum and maximum values of quiescent collector current would you expect (assuming I_{CBO} stays at its typical value of 5 μa) in the transistor of Problem 3–3, operated with 100 μa of base current?

3–5. If, *in addition to the h_{FE} variation*, the production variations in I_{CBO} for the above transistor are 0 to 20 μa, what limits might you expect for quiescent collector current when operated in the same way?

3–6. A transistor data sheet lists TYP h_{FE} at room temperature as 40, and also shows that h_{FE} varies from 0.8 times its room temperature value to 1.7 times its room temperature value over the temperature range of − 20°C to +60°C. If the quiescent base current is held constant at 100 μa and the collector leakage current is negligible, what will the typical quiescent collector current variation be when the temperature of the transistor changes between these limits?

3–7. Suppose that the above transistor *also* has production variations in h_{FE} of 20 to 60. What would the possible variation in I_C be over the above temperature range, when considering many transistors of this type?

3–8. What are the *normalized* values of h_{FE} for the 2N1926 at − 40°C and +60°C?

3–9. What are the *actual typ.* values of h_{FE} for the 2N1926 operated at I_C = 100 ma at the temperatures of Problem 3–8?

3–10. What is the typical value of h_{FE} for the 2N1924 at a temperature of 50°C?

3–11. What is the maximum value of I_{CBO}, at room temperature, for the 2N1925?

3–12. What is the possible maximum value of I_{CBO} for the 2N1925 at 55°C, as given on the manufacturer's data sheet? How does this compare with the "rule of thumb" given in the text?

3–13. The same transistor is being used in both of the following circuits. At 25°C both have the same operating point.
   (a) As the temperature of the transistors rises, why does the quiescent collector current of circuit (b) rise less than that of (a)?
   (b) If the bias stability of circuit (b) needed to be improved, should R_e be increased or decreased in value?
   (c) How might R_b be changed to improve the stability?

3–14. What is the purpose of C_e in circuit (b) above?

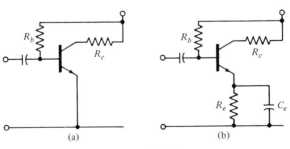

(a) (b)

FIGURE P3–13

3–15. With a signal applied to the input of circuit (b) above, assuming C_e is large enough, what will the voltage across R_e be, principally?

dc plus ac component?
dc only?
ac only?

3–16. (a)   Why is the circuit shown here usually used instead of that in figure (b) of Problem 3–13?

(b)   Redraw the above circuit with the single-resistor Thevenin equivalent in place of the voltage-divider portion of the circuit. Show the *value* of each portion of the new circuit in terms of the resistance and voltage designations in the original.

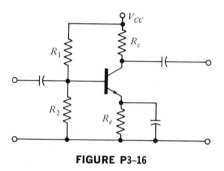

FIGURE P3–16

3–17. The following circuit is operated initially with the currents and voltages indicated.

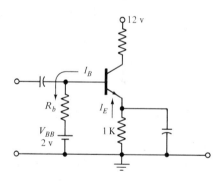

$I_E = 1$ ma
$I_B = 0.05$ ma
I_{CEO} is negligible
dc voltage from emitter to ground $(V_{EN}) = 1$ v
$V_{BE} = 0.7$ v

FIGURE P3–17(a, b, c)

(a)   What is the value of V_{BN}?

(b)   What is the value of the dc IR drop across R_b? *Hint:*

$$V_{BB} = I_b R_b + V_{BE} + I_E R_E$$

(c)   What is the value of the base resistor, R_b?

(d)   Suppose that now the transistor is replaced with another of the same type, but has about twice the h_{FE} value. If I_B could remain at its original value, what effect would doubling the h_{FE} in this way have on I_E (assuming negligible I_{CEO})?

What would this do to the value of the voltage V_{EN}? (*Remember:* $V_{EN} = I_E R_E$.) Is this possible in this circuit? By several trial-and-error calculations, try out several values of I_E between 1 and 2 ma, dividing each by the *new* value of h_{FE} to get the corresponding new value of I_B. Then read the value of V_{BE} from the following $I_B - V_{BE}$ curve of the transistor and substitute the appropriate values in the equation:

$$V_{BB} = I_B R_B + V_{BE} + I_E R_E$$

until you get a value of I_E (with its corresponding I_B) which seems to approximately satisfy the equation — i.e., to approximately be able to exist in the circuit.

About how much increase of I_E does this circuit seem to permit in this case? Compare this with the amount it would have increased in an un-stabilized (i.e., constant I_B) circuit. How much did I_B decrease in order to provide this stabilizing effect?

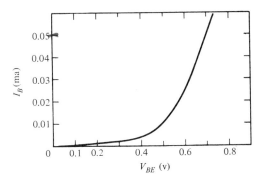

FIGURE P3–17(d)

3–18. An amplifier is to be built using the circuit of Figure 3–7. The transistor has the characteristics shown below.

$$R_c = 6000 \text{ ohms}$$
$$R_e = 2000 \text{ ohms}$$
$$V_{CC} = 24 \text{ v}$$
$$I_B = 0.04 \text{ ma}$$

Draw the dc load line and the ac load line.

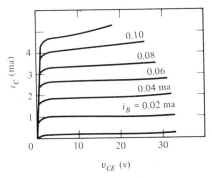

FIGURE P3–18

3–19. Using the simplified design method, design the bias stabilizing circuitry for a transistor to be operated at a quiescent collector current of 10 ma, and collector supply voltage of 30 v.

3–20. Using the simplified method, design the bias stabilizing circuitry for a transistor to be operated at a quiescent collector current of 100 ma, and collector supply voltage of 12 v.

3–21. Calculate the stability factor S for the following circuits. h_{FE} is 45 in each case.

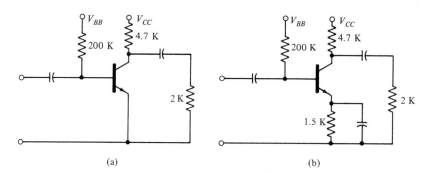

FIGURE P3-21

3–22. Compare the four values of S from the above problem, and discuss the circuit reasons for the significant differences between them.

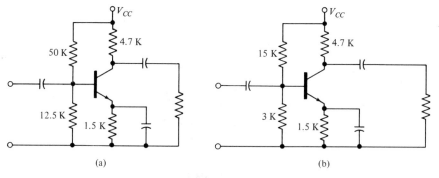

FIGURE P3-23

3–23. What is the value of the stability factor for each of the following circuits? $h_{FE} = 45$.

3–24. Explain why the circuit of Problem 3–23(a) provides the same stability factor as that of 3–21(c), and why that of 3–23(b) provides a better value of S.

3–25. What is the approximate value of the quiescent base current in the following circuit, assuming that I_{CEO} is negligible?

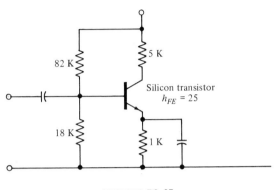

FIGURE P3–25

3–26. Find the approximate value of all dc currents and voltages in the circuit of Problem 3–25 above.

3–27. In the following circuit, a dc collector voltage of 4 v is desired. The required value of I_B is 40 μa.

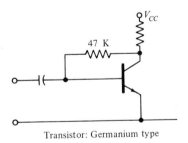

Transistor: Germanium type

FIGURE P3–27

(a) Will the circuit as shown give the required value of I_B?

(b) If the circuit does not give the required value of I_B, what value of resistance connected from base to ground will be necessary?

(c) Assume that the resistance from base to ground in (b) above is too small, so that it shunts the input excessively. A larger resistance, in conjunction with a negative supply voltage, is to be used. What value of resistance would be needed with a − 6 v supply? Draw the final circuit.

3–28. An *RC*-coupled amplifier stage is not providing normal output signal. The normal circuit of the amplifier is as follows:

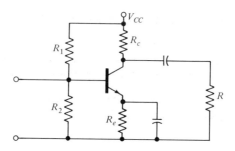

FIGURE P3-28

(a) If this were an amplifier that you had just built, what do you think would be the most logical check to make first?

(b) If this were a circuit in equipment that had been operating satisfactorily up until now, what would be the most logical check to make first?

(c) What dc voltages should be checked?

3–29. (a) Assume that in the troubleshooting problem described in 3–28 above, the collector voltage when checked is approximately equal to V_{CC}. What possible trouble does this indicate? (*Hint:* There are several types of faults that could cause this symptom.)

(b) In view of the possibilities listed in your answer to (a), what voltages should be checked next?

3–30. (a) Suppose that, after finding the symptom described in 3–29(a), you check the voltage from emitter to ground and find it to be apparently zero, on the lowest range of your voltmeter (a 1 v range). What possibilities would this indicate?

(b) Would a check of the voltage at the junction of R_1 and R_2 help you to decide which of the possible defects is causing the symptom in this case?

(c) Suppose the voltage at the junction of R_1 and R_2 seems normal, and an ohmmeter check shows that the emitter is not shorted to ground. What should you now suspect?

3–31. Suppose that, *instead* of the symptom described in 3–29(a) above, the voltage at the collector of the transistor had been very low — perhaps only a fraction of a volt. What possibilities exist?

CHAPTER 4

Equivalent Circuits

4.1 Introduction

The use of equivalent circuit analysis for amplifiers is based upon the approximate linearity of amplifying devices. The curvature of characteristics is usually moderate enough, in the normal operating region, so that the relation between output and input can be considered approximately constant for small increments of voltage or current. Thus the parameters of the equivalent circuit are considered valid as long as the signal is small. The term "small-signal equivalent circuit" is often used to emphasize this restriction.

Although small changes of voltage or current do not cause significant changes in the parameters, large changes do. Consequently, the parameter values are specified for a particular operating point. If operation is to be at a different point, analysis must include correction for the difference.

In Chapter 2 an approximate equivalent circuit was derived. In this chapter more complete representations will be presented, which will adequately portray the small-signal performance under most normal operating conditions. Two major effects create the differences between the approximations of Chapter 2 and the more accurate equivalent circuits. One of these is that the output current is affected by the value of load resistance, rather than being constant at the value $h_{fe}I_b$. The other is that the output voltage has an effect on the input circuit, so that changes in the output cause changes in the input. This is known as *feedback*. Because of these effects (and others), equivalent circuits sometimes become quite complicated.

Several possibilities exist for the representation of devices such as transistors. Figure 4–1 illustrates some of these. The effects of internal capacitances, usually negligible at low frequencies, will be considered in later sections.

Part (a) of this figure shows what is often called the equivalent-tee representation. The effect of the output on the input is taken into account by the

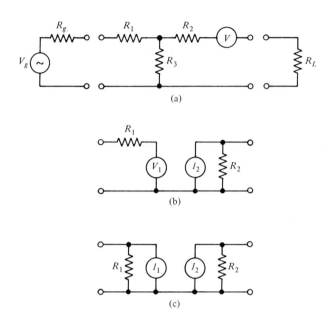

FIGURE 4–1
Several forms of amplifier equivalent circuits

resistance $R3$, since both output and input currents flow in this "mutual" impedance.

The equivalent circuit form in part (b) is called the hybrid equivalent because its input portion is a Thevenin equivalent, or voltage generator with series resistance, while its output side is a Norton equivalent, or current generator with shunt resistance. Thus it is a mixture, or a hybrid. The effect of the output upon the input is represented here by the equivalent generator (V_1). The value of V_1 depends directly upon the output signal voltage. This form of equivalent circuit has become the most commonly used for general purpose, low-frequency (i.e., audio frequency) transistor amplifiers. A major reason for this is the relative ease with which the transistor parameters defined by this circuit can be measured.

4.2 The Hybrid Equivalent Circuit, or "h-Parameter" Equivalent

The equivalent circuit of an amplifying device is merely an expression, in circuit form, of equations which can be written relating the voltages and currents at the input and output of the device. The coefficients in these equations — the quantities involved in the relation between V and I — are of course resistances (or impedances) or their reciprocals, conductances (or admittances). Thus each portion of the equivalent circuit could be defined by proper manipulation of the equations without recourse to the circuit. However, we shall define each parameter by examination of circuit conditions, in order to provide more familiarity with the use of the equivalent circuit.

Figure 4–2 shows the hybrid equivalent with the designations R_1, R_2, V_1, I_2 that were used in Figure 4–1 replaced by the symbols customarily employed

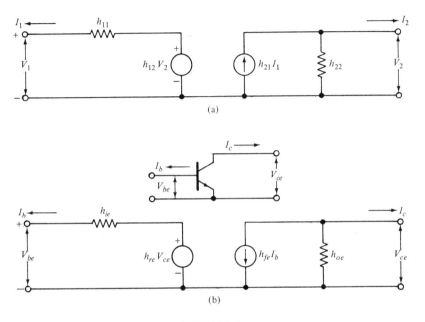

(a)

(b)

FIGURE 4-2
The hybrid equivalent circuit

in this circuit. Note the use of the letter h (for hybrid) for each parameter, with the different parameters distinguished by different subscripts. Part (a) of the figure illustrates a notation used in general circuit analysis. The first number in the double subscript designates the circuit in which the effect takes place, and the second number designates the circuit from which the effect comes. For example, h_{21} is the short-circuit forward current gain, or the ratio of the current in the output ("circuit 2") to the current in the input ("circuit 1"). This notation will often be encountered in general discussions of amplifier equivalents.

Part (b) illustrates the notation that is generally accepted for representing the *CE* configuration of the transistor. The first letter in the double subscript designates the parameter, while the second letter indicates the element which is grounded or common. For example, h_{fe} is the *forward* current gain, h_{ie} is the *input* resistance — and the e in both cases indicates the common *emitter* configuration.

The following is a brief discussion of the meaning of each portion of the h-parameter equivalent circuit, followed by the equation defining the parameter in each case. Remember that the parameters used in amplifier equivalent circuits are valid only for ac components, or signal components. Their definitions are given in terms of ac quantities or increments of dc quantities, where in either case it is understood that the amplitude of the signal or increment is quite small.

$h_{re}V_{ce}$

This is the voltage feedback — the equivalent signal voltage in the input representing the effect of the output voltage V_{ce}. The h_{re} portion of this term is the coefficient which tells how much signal voltage appears in the input circuit per unit of signal voltage in the output.

As the equivalent circuit shows, $h_{re}V_{ce}$ can be measured only if there is no voltage drop across the resistance h_{ie}, that is, only if $I_b = 0$. This is due to the fact that $h_{re}V_{ce}$ can only be measured at the terminals of the device, and the only way to eliminate the voltage drop $I_b h_{ie}$ from such a measurement is to make $I_b = 0$, or make the total current i_B constant.

Thus h_{re} can be defined as the ratio of the incremental input voltage to the incremental output voltage when the incremental input current is zero. It is commonly called the voltage feedback ratio, or the reverse voltage ratio.

The definitions of the amplifier equivalent circuit parameters will appear variously in Δ form, in rms signal component form, and in partial derivative form, so each of these notations will be used here. Thus, in the case of h_{re}:

$$h_{re} = \frac{\Delta v_{BE}}{\Delta v_{CE}}\bigg|_{\Delta i_B = 0} = \frac{V_{be}}{V_{ce}}\bigg|_{i_b = 0} = \frac{\partial v_{BE}}{\partial v_{CE}}$$

Figure 4–3 shows the graphical interpretation of h_{re}, and the circuit for

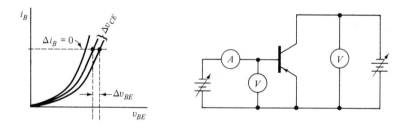

FIGURE 4–3
Graphical interpretation of h_{re}, and static test

making the static measurement. The desired operating point at which h_{re} is to be evaluated is set by means of the supply voltages V_{CE} and V_{BE}. I_B is noted, and then one of the voltages is changed a small amount, and the other voltage is changed just enough to restore i_B to its original value, that is, to meet the requirement that $\Delta i_B = 0$. The ratio of the base-emitter voltage change to the collector-emitter voltage change is, then, the value of h_{re}.

h_{ie}

This is the input resistance with the output shorted — that is, the ratio of input signal voltage to input signal current when there is no output signal voltage to affect the input. As the equivalent circuit shows, it can be measured only when $h_{re}V_{ce} = 0$, and this can happen only if $V_{ce} = 0$, or V_{CE} is held constant.

$$h_{ie} = \left.\frac{\Delta v_{BE}}{\Delta i_B}\right|_{\Delta v_{CE} = 0} = \left.\frac{V_{be}}{I_b}\right|_{V_{ce} = 0} = \frac{\partial v_{BE}}{\partial i_B}$$

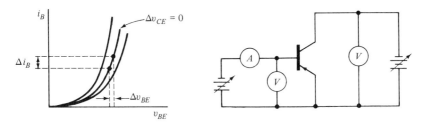

FIGURE 4–4
Graphical interpretation of h_{ie}, and static test

For the graphical interpretation, and the static test, see Figure 4–4. V_{CE} is held constant with a fixed power supply, V_{BE} is changed a small amount, and the resulting change in I_B is recorded.

h_{fe}I_b

This is the equivalent current generator in the output representing the output signal current flowing as a consequence of the input signal current. The h_{fe} in this term is the coefficient which tells how much signal current appears in the output per unit of signal current in the input. The equivalent circuit shows that $h_{fe}I_b$ can be measured at the output terminals only if none of it flows through h_{oe}; all of it must flow through the output. To achieve this, the voltage across h_{oe} must be zero; that is, $V_{ce} = 0$, or V_{CE} be held constant. Under amplifying conditions with ac signal, the output signal voltage V_{ce} will be zero only if the load resistance R_L is zero. *Thus h_{fe} is called the short-circuit current gain — the current gain which would result only if any load resistance were shorted out.* This value is always greater than the current gain in an amplifier circuit containing some load resistance, although the difference is often very slight. This was illustrated in Figure 1–39.

From all this we see that *h_{fe} can be defined as the ratio of the output signal current to the input signal current when the output is shorted* (i.e., *when R_L = 0*).

$$h_{fe} = \left.\frac{\Delta i_C}{\Delta i_B}\right|_{\Delta v_{CE} = 0} = \left.\frac{I_c}{I_b}\right|_{V_{ce} = 0} = \frac{\partial i_C}{\partial i_B}$$

The graphical interpretation and the static test method are shown in Figure 4–5.

h_{oe}

This is used to express the source impedance, or output impedance, and is in the position of the familiar Norton equivalent source impedance. However, because shunt elements are customarily expressed as admittances in circuit

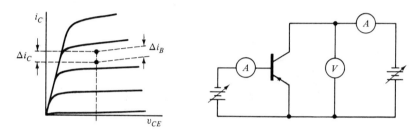

FIGURE 4–5
Graphical interpretation of h_{fe}, and static test

analysis work, h_{oe} is an admittance, or the ratio of the current to the voltage. It can be measured by measuring the current that flows in the output for a given voltage — but only if there is no other current flowing in the output. Therefore $h_{fe}I_b$ must be zero for this measurement; this can only be achieved by making $I_b = 0$.

Thus h_{oe} can be defined as the ratio of the output signal current to the output signal voltage when the input signal current is zero:

$$h_{oe} = \frac{\Delta i_C}{\Delta v_{CE}}\bigg|_{\Delta i_B = 0} = \frac{I_c}{V_{ce}}\bigg|_{I_b = 0} = \frac{\partial i_C}{\partial v_{CE}}$$

Figure 4–6 illustrates the graphical interpretation of h_{oe} and the static test circuit.

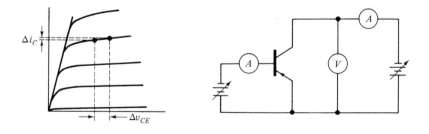

FIGURE 4–6
Graphical interpretation of h_{oe}, and static test

4.3 Amplifier Performance Equations Obtained from the *h*-Parameter Equivalent Circuit

General equations for gain, input resistance, and output resistance can be derived from the amplifier equivalent circuit. These equations will be more exact than those derived in Chapter 2, and will provide accurate information for conditions in which the Chapter 2 approximations are either very inaccurate or wholly useless.

There are, however, significant limitations on the use of even these more complete equations. First, the values of the hybrid parameters are subject to considerable variation — unit-to-unit variation, variation due to change of temperature, and variation due to change of operating point. In predicting an amplifier's performance, care must be taken to use *h*-parameter values that are correct for the quiescent voltages and currents being used, and to recognize the variations in performance that can occur with extremes of temperature, or simply as a deviation from the average. In building a prototype or a test model of a new design, for example, it is a common practice to test a number of transistors in order to select one which does happen to have "average" *h*-parameter values, so that the test circuit will represent average performance. Transistors having minimum or maximum values are also often used in order to have actual tests of "worst case" conditions.

Secondly, the equivalent circuit method is valid only for small signals, as a consequence of the variations described above. The use of specified parameter values becomes inaccurate when the signal is so large that the current and voltage-increment, during the signal cycle, cover a large portion of the transistor's normal operating region. The decision as to whether equivalent circuit methods are accurate enough, in the case of signals of intermediate amplitude, is a matter of experience and judgement. When large-signal operation involving considerable nonlinearity is called for, graphical analysis based on the load-line technique is used.

In the following material, only the current gain equation will be derived, in order to establish some familiarity and confidence with the relationship between physical performance and mathematical analysis. Keep in mind that the parameters which are being manipulated in the equations are aspects of transistors which can be actually measured.

In Figure 4–7 a typical *RC*-coupled *CE* amplifier is shown along with its *h*-parameter equivalent. The voltage polarities indicated are arbitrary reference polarities and will be accounted for in writing any equations. Note that the base-bias divider resistances are not shown in the equivalent circuit. The input to the amplifier will for the present be considered to be the base lead into the transistor, and the shunting resistance of the bias divider, in conjunction with the generator output resistance R_g, will form a signal source resistance R_s for the equivalent circuit. The effective load resistance R_L for the equivalent circuit will be the parallel combination of R_c and R. Thus, the current gain of the amplifier will be considered to be the ratio of the current in the collector lead (I_c) to the current in the base lead (I_b).

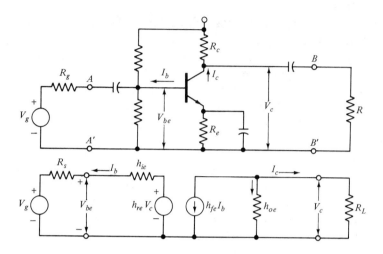

FIGURE 4-7
Typical amplifier and its equivalent circuit

The resistor R_e does not appear in the equivalent circuit because it is assumed to be effectively bypassed for signal frequencies.

Current Gain

On the basis of the above, we may write for the current gain:

$$A_i = \frac{I_c}{I_b}$$

and recognize that the current I_c is some fraction of the current $h_{fe}I_b$ — the fraction being determined by the relative magnitudes of the two resistances in parallel: $1/h_{oe}$ and R_L. Thus,

$$I_c = \left(\frac{1/h_{oe}}{\frac{1}{h_{oe}} + R_L}\right)h_{fe}I_b$$

$$I_c = \left[\frac{1}{1 + h_{oe}R_L}\right]h_{fe}I_b$$

So
$$A_i = \frac{I_c}{I_b} = \frac{h_{fe}}{1 + h_{oe}R_L} \qquad\qquad \textbf{(4–1)}$$

In other words, the current gain simply depends upon h_{fe} and the size of the current shunt R_L, in parallel with the internal resistance $1/h_{oe}$. Often, it is easier to think of $1/h_{oe}$ and R_L in parallel being fed by $h_{fe}I_b$, than to recall the equation for A_i. Thus, if $R_L \cong 1/4\,(1/h_{oe})$, then the load current $\cong 4$ times the current in h_{oe}, and $I_L = (4/5)h_{fe}I_b$ — so that A_i must be about $(4/5)h_{fe}$.

This same parallel circuit method can be used to determine the validity of the current gain approximation

$$A_i \cong h_{fe} \qquad\qquad \textbf{(2–4)}$$

That is, if $R_L \ll 1/h_{oe}$, then most of the current $h_{fe}I_b$ goes to R_L and very little to $1/h_{oe}$. Of course the inequality

$$R_L \ll 1/h_{oe}$$

is equivalent to

$$R_L h_{oe} \ll 1$$

which is the condition required to make Equation (4–1) into Equation (2–4).

Input Resistance

The input resistance of an amplifier is an important aspect of its performance because it indicates what kind of load the amplifier presents to the signal source. In the *CE* amplifier the input resistance is not just h_{ie}. Since it is the ratio of the total input voltage to the input current, it must include the feedback voltage $h_{re}V_{ce}$. That is, in Figure 4–7,

$$R_i = \frac{V_{be}}{I_b} = \frac{I_b h_{ie} + h_{re}V_c}{I_b} \tag{4-2}$$

From the relation expressed in Equation (4–2), an equation for the input resistance in terms of the *h*-parameters and the circuit resistance in the output may be obtained. Two forms in which this equation frequently appears are:

$$R_i = h_{ie} - \frac{h_{re}h_{fe}R_L}{1 + h_{oe}R_L} \tag{4-3a}$$

and

$$R_i = \frac{h_{ie} + \Delta^{he}R_L}{1 + h_{oe}R_L} \tag{4-3b}$$

The symbol Δ^{he} in Equation (4–3b) represents a combination of the *h*-parameters which occurs in several equations:

$$\Delta^{he} = h_{ie}h_{oe} - h_{re}h_{fe} \qquad \times$$

Fortunately, the feedback effect $h_{re}V_c$ in Equation (4–2) is usually small compared to the effect of h_{ie}, so that for most routine practical work the input equation can usually be written, as a practical approximation,

$$R_i = \frac{V_{be}}{I_b} \cong \frac{I_b h_{ie}}{I_b}$$

so that

$$R_i \cong h_{ie} \tag{4-4}$$

This of course is the approximation which was introduced in Chapter 2. This approximation will prove extremely useful because of its simplicity.

Voltage Gain

The exact voltage gain equation, derived from the equivalent circuit of Figure 4–7, is

$$A_v = -\frac{h_{fe}R_L}{h_{ie} + \Delta^{he}R_L} \tag{4-5}$$

but here again an approximation is extremely useful. In Chapter 2 we showed that $A_v = A_i(R_L/R_i)$, and that when the approximations $A_i \cong h_{fe}$ and $R_i \cong h_{ie}$ are valid, then

$$A_v \cong \frac{h_{fe}R_L}{h_{ie}} \qquad\qquad\qquad \textbf{(2–5)}$$

This approximation should be avoided whenever the load resistance is large enough compared with $1/h_{oe}$ to introduce excessive error into the $A_i \cong h_{fe}$ approximation. For example, if $h_{oe} = 20$ μmhos, so that $1/h_{oe} = 50$ kilohms, then a 5 kilohm load would cause almost 10 percent error in $A_i \cong h_{fe}$ (since 50 kilohms would shunt $1/11$ of the total current away from R_L).

Output Resistance

The output resistance equation obtained from the equivalent circuit is

$$R_o = \frac{R_g + h_{ie}}{R_g h_{oe} + \Delta^{he}} \qquad\qquad\qquad \textbf{(4–6)}$$

This resistance is large enough that it often may be neglected in amplifier performance calculations.

Power Gain

Several definitions involving power gain have been found useful in amplifier work, and will be discussed in later chapters. At the present time we shall simply consider the power gain from base to collector — the ratio of signal power developed in the entire collector load to the signal power input to the base of the transistor. This is expressed as

$$A_p = \frac{P_o}{P_i}$$

but since

$$P_o = V_o I_o$$

and

$$P_i = V_i I_i$$

we have

$$A_p = \frac{V_o I_o}{V_i I_i}$$

so that

$$A_p = A_v A_i \qquad\qquad\qquad \textbf{(4–6)}$$

and we see that the power gain is the product of the voltage gain and the current gain.

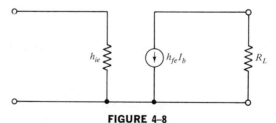

FIGURE 4–8

Simplified equivalent circuit of common-emitter amplifier

Summary of Simplified Equivalent Circuit and Approximate Performance Equations

The simplified equivalent circuit is repeated here as it was presented originally in Chapter 2. (See Figure 4–8.) The approximate equations are:

$$A_i \cong h_{fe} \tag{2-4}$$
$$R_i \cong h_{ie} \tag{4-4}$$
$$A_v \cong \frac{h_{fe}R_L}{h_{ie}} \tag{2-5}$$

4.4 Conversion From CB to CE Parameters

Our principal concern so far has been with the *CE* form of the transistor amplifier because that is the most frequently used circuit. However, manufacturer's data sheets sometimes list common base values. When this is encountered it may be necessary to convert. The following set of equations can be used to convert between *CB* values and *CE* values.

$$h_{ie} = \frac{h_{ib}}{1 + h_{fb}} = h_{ib}(h_{fe} + 1) \tag{4-7}$$

$$h_{re} \cong \frac{h_{ib}h_{ob}}{1 + h_{fb}} - h_{rb} = h_{ib}h_{ob}(h_{fe} + 1) - h_{rb} \tag{4-8}$$

$$h_{fe} \cong \frac{-h_{fb}}{1 + h_{fb}} \tag{4-9}$$

$$h_{oe} \cong \frac{h_{ob}}{1 + h_{fb}} = h_{ob}(h_{fe} + 1) \tag{4-10}$$

4.5 Application of the Equivalent Circuit Equations

Example 4–1

Consider the use of the 2N334A transistor in a low-frequency amplifier in which the quiescent emitter current is to be 1 ma and the quiescent collector voltage about 5 v. The manufacturer's specifications list the typical parameters for low-frequency operation as follows: $I_{eq} = 1\,ma$

$$V_C = 5\,v$$

$$h_{fe} = 38$$
$$h_{ie} = 1700 \text{ ohms}$$
$$h_{oe} = 6.0 \times 10^{-6} \text{ mhos}$$
$$h_{re} = 1.3 \times 10^{-4}$$

$R_L = 2000\,\Omega$

$R_g = 100\,\Omega$

The load resistance is to be 2000 ohms, and the signal source has an output resistance of 100 ohms.

Calculate A_i, R_i, A_v, A_p, and R_o.

$$\Delta^{he} = h_{ie}h_{oe} - h_{re}h_{fe}$$

$$\Delta^{he} = (1700)(6 \times 10^{-6}) - (1.3 \times 10^{-4})(38)$$

$$\Delta^{he} = (102 \times 10^{-4}) - (49.4 \times 10^{-4})$$

$$\Delta^{he} \cong 53 \times 10^{-4}$$

$$R_i = \frac{h_{ie} + \Delta^{he}R_L}{1 + h_{oe}R_L}$$

$$R_i = \frac{1700 + (53 \times 10^{-4})(2 \times 10^3)}{1 + (6 \times 10^{-6})(2 \times 10^3)} = \frac{1700 + 10.6}{1 + 0.012}$$

$$R_i = 1690 \text{ ohms}$$

$$R_o = \frac{R_g + h_{ie}}{R_g h_{oe} + \Delta^{he}}$$

$$R_o = \frac{100 + 1700}{(100)(6 \times 10^{-6}) + (53 \times 10^{-4})} = \frac{1800}{(59)(10^{-4})}$$

$$R_o = 305,000 \text{ ohms}$$

$$A_i = \frac{h_{fe}}{1 + h_{oe}R_L}$$

$$A_i = \frac{38}{1.012} \cong 37.6$$

$$A_v = -\frac{h_{fe}R_L}{h_{ie} + \Delta^{he}R_L}$$

$$A_v = -\frac{(38)(2 \times 10^3)}{1700 + (53 \times 10^{-4})(2 \times 10^3)} = -\frac{76 \times 10^3}{1710.6}$$

$$A_v \cong -44.4$$

$$A_p = A_i A_v$$

$$A_p \cong (37.6)(44.4)$$

$$A_p \cong 1670$$

Note that in this example, due to the low value of R_L, we do indeed have $R_i \cong h_{ie}$, $A_i \cong h_{fe}$, $A_v \cong h_{fe}R_L/h_{ie}$, and R_o large enough to be ignored, as discussed earlier.

Example 4–2

Assume that the same transistor, signal source, and effective load resistance are to be used, but that the quiescent emitter current is to be 10 ma. Since the manufacturer's specifications for this transistor list the h-parameter values at 1 ma, it will be necessary to consider any possible difference in values at 10 ma. The specifications provide curves of h-parameter values versus current, but these show mostly common base values. It will be necessary to find the *CB* values for the current level being used, and then convert to common emitter values.

At 10 ma the curves (See Appendix B) show approximately the following values relative to the 1 ma values:

$$h_{fe} \cong 0.37$$
$$h_{ib} \cong 0.18$$
$$h_{ob} \cong 9.5$$
$$h_{rb} \cong 1.2$$

Thus, the 10 ma values will be

$$h_{fe} \cong (0.37)(38) \cong 14.1$$
$$h_{ib} \cong (0.18)(40) \cong 7.2 \text{ ohms}$$
$$h_{ob} \cong (9.5)(0.18 \times 10^{-6}) \cong 1.71 \times 10^{-6} \text{ ohms}$$
$$h_{rb} \cong (1.2)(1.2 \times 10^{-4}) \cong 1.44 \times 10^{-4}$$

The *CB* values above are converted to *CE* values by using the relations from Section 4.4.

$$h_{ie} = h_{ib}(h_{fe} + 1)$$
$$h_{ie} \cong (7.2)(14.1 + 1) \cong 109 \text{ ohms}$$
$$h_{oe} = h_{ob}(h_{fe} + 1)$$
$$h_{oe} \cong (1.71 \times 10^{-6})(15.1) \cong 25.8 \times 10^{-6} \text{ ohms}$$
$$h_{re} = (h_{ib}h_{ob})(h_{fe} + 1) - h_{rb}$$
$$\cong (7.2)(1.71 \times 10^{-6})(15.1) - (1.44 \times 10^{-4})$$
$$h_{re} \cong 0.42 \times 10^{-4}$$

The gains and terminal resistances computed with these values then are

$$\Delta^{he} = h_{ie}h_{oe} - h_{re}h_{fe}$$
$$\cong (109)(25.8 \times 10^{-6}) - (0.42 \times 10^{-4})(14.1)$$
$$\cong (28.1 \times 10^{-4}) - (5.91 \times 10^{-4})$$
$$\Delta^{he} \cong 22.2 \times 10^{-4}$$

$$R_i = \frac{h_{ie} + \Delta^{he}R_L}{1 + h_{oe}R_L}$$
$$R_i \cong \frac{109 + (22.2 \times 10^{-4})(2 \times 10^3)}{1 + (25.8 \times 10^{-6})(2 \times 10^3)}$$
$$\cong \frac{109 + 4.44}{1 + 0.032}$$
$$R_i \cong 110 \text{ ohms}$$

Similarly,

$$R_o \cong 43.6 \text{ kilohms}$$
$$A_i \cong 13.7$$
$$A_v \cong -248$$
$$A_p \cong 3400$$

When these results, obtained for an amplifier operated at a quiescent emitter current of 10 ma, are compared with the figures for the same amplifier biased to operate at a quiescent emitter current of 1 ma (Example 4–1) the differences are dramatic:

TABLE 4–1

	At $I_E = 1$ ma	At $I_E = 10$ ma
R_i	1690	110
R_o	305,000	43,600
A_i	37.6	13.7
A_v	-44.4	-248
A_p	1670	3400

It is of practical interest to note that again in the 10 ma case, just as in the 1 ma case, the performance calculations done by the approximate equations are not greatly different from the exact calculations. The approximate calculations give

$$R_i \cong h_{ie} \cong 109 \text{ ohms}$$
$$A_i \cong h_{fe} \cong 14.1$$
$$A_v \cong \frac{h_{fe}R_L}{h_{ie}} \cong 259$$

and R_o at 43,600 ohms is still large enough to be ignored compared with the 2000 ohm load.

4.6 High-Frequency Effects in Transistors

At low signal frequencies the hybrid equivalent circuit is a very useful representation of the transistor. Its parameters are easy to measure, and easy to use in circuit analysis. But as the signal frequency is increased, the effects of the transistor's internal capacitances become significant, and the short-circuit current gain decreases and acquires a phase angle.

At frequencies which are not too great, these effects can often be represented by the addition of simple shunt capacitances to the input and output of the hybrid equivalent. At higher frequencies, however, such methods become inadequate. The internal mechanism of the transistor is quite complicated, and the effective current gain and output impedance change with frequency in a way which a simple single generator and single resistance-capacitance combination cannot represent. In order to use this type of circuit it becomes necessary to publish actual measurements of the values of the equivalent circuit elements showing the way in which they change with frequency over the useful frequency range. Such information is often given in the form of graphs.

Such measurements are difficult to make if the equivalent circuit is the *h*-parameter type, because it requires that the input be open-circuited. This is a condition that is impractical at high frequencies because the presence of normal amounts of shunt capacitance, difficult to eliminate from any practical circuit, results in quite low reactance at such frequencies. A low value shunt reactance, of course, prevents having an open-circuit.

Consequently, other types of equivalent circuits have been used to represent the transistor in high-frequency use. One approach that has proved profitable in the past has been to attempt to depict the internal action of the transistor physically. The elements of the equivalent circuit and their arrangement are chosen so that even though their values remain fixed, the arrangement is complex enough to provide approximately the correct terminal characteristics. This type of representation has the advantage of providing a "feel" for the action of the transistor, because the action within the equivalent circuit is an approximation of the physical action within the transistor. Thus, an examination of relationships in the equivalent circuit provides an understanding of expected frequency effects. However, the effects within the transistor represented by the elements of these equivalent circuits are difficult to measure accurately, and since the equivalent circuit in addition is only approximate, the results are not highly accurate over an extended frequency range.

A nother approach has been the use of circuits similar to the h-parameter circuit, but using parameters of a type which do not require open circuits for their measurement. Although these do not provide a feel for the physical action, they do permit circuit calculations based upon accurate parameter measurements. The manufacturer publishes data, usually in the form of curves, giving the parameter values over the entire frequency range.

Of the various high-frequency equivalent circuits only a few will be presented here, and these will be discussed only briefly at this time. The principal objective will be to provide familiarity with the concepts and an introduction to some of the problems of high-frequency operation.

4.7   Variation of h_{fe} and h_{fb} with Frequency

The transistor's junction capacitances are related to the storage and the movement of charges across the junctions. (See Chapter 1). The effects of these phenomena at high frequencies are to cause the current gain to decrease. In essence, this decrease in current gain at high frequencies is a consequence of the slowness of the charges in moving through the transistor, and could be described as a failure of the output current to respond immediately to input current changes.

Although this high-frequency effect can be represented by capacitances, it has also been found convenient to be able to express it in terms of the current gain "cutoff frequency" — the frequency at which the current gain has fallen a specified amount. Transistors can then be compared for high-frequency ability by comparing their current gain cutoff frequencies.

The manufacturer of a transistor will often state the "alpha cutoff frequency," which is that frequency at which the CB short-circuit current gain has fallen 3 decibels (db), or to 0.707 times its low-frequency value. Three frequently encountered symbols for this are f_α, f_{ab} and f_{hfb}. Or he may specify the "beta cutoff frequency" — the frequency at which h_{fe} is down 3 db. Notation for this may be f_β, f_{ae}, or f_{hfe}. In the case of transistors intended for high-frequency use, the data sheets will more frequently list f_T, the frequency at which h_{fe} has fallen to a value of one, or will show the frequency at which h_{fe} has fallen to some other arbitrary value. If the data sheet parameter does not happen to be the one needed by the user, it is necessary to have a knowledge of the relations between the various expressions in order to be able to make an evaluation.

The value of h_{fb} varies with frequency approximately in accordance with the equation

$$h_{fb} \cong \frac{h_{fbo}}{1 + j(f/f_{hfb})} \qquad (4\text{--}11)$$

in which h_{fbo} stands for the low-frequency value of h_{fb}, and f_{hfb} is the frequency at which h_{fb} has decreased by 3 db. This approximation is not very accurate for transistors having graded base regions, as in diffused-base transistors intended for high frequency use. More accurate expressions are available.

The CE current gain factor h_{fe} is more likely to be the parameter needed, as the CE amplifier is more widely used. The variation of h_{fe} is essentially the same form:

$$h_{fe} \cong \frac{h_{feo}}{1 + j(f/f_{hfe})} \qquad (4\text{--}12)$$

However, the CE cutoff frequency is much lower than that for h_{fb}, and is given approximately by

$$f_{hfe} = \frac{K_\theta f_{hfb}}{h_{feo} + 1} \qquad (4\text{--}13)$$

in which K_θ is a factor that depends upon the type of transistor. Table 4–2 gives approximate values of K_θ for several transistor types.

TABLE 4–2
Approximate Values of K_θ

Transistor Type	K_θ
Alloy junction	0.82
Germanium mesa	0.90 − 1.0
Ge. epitaxial mesa	0.80
Ge. non-epitaxial mesa	0.70
Silicon annular and planar	0.80 − 1.0
MADT	0.60

*Adapted from *The Semiconductor Data Book*, Second Edition, Motorola, Inc.

The variation of h_{fe} with frequency, as given by Equation (4–12), is illustrated in Figure 4–9. This graph shows how the *magnitude* of h_{fe} — indicated by the symbol $|h_{fe}|$ — varies relative to its low-frequency value h_{feo}. Thus, the vertical scale in part (a) of the figure is the ratio of $|h_{fe}|$ (at each frequency) to the reference value h_{feo}. This ratio is obtained by taking the magnitude of the complex number which is the denominator in Equation (4–12) and dividing through by h_{feo}:

$$|h_{fe}| \cong \frac{h_{feo}}{\sqrt{1 + (f/f_{hfe})^2}}$$

$$\frac{|h_{fe}|}{h_{feo}} = \frac{1}{\sqrt{1 + (f/f_{hfe})^2}} \qquad (4\text{--}14)$$

Part (b) of Figure 4–9 is the above ratio plotted in decibels. This is obtained by taking 20 log $[|h_{fe}|/h_{feo}]$:

$$\left.\frac{|h_{fe}|}{h_{feo}}\right|_{\text{in db}} = 20\log\frac{1}{\sqrt{1+(f/f_{hfe})^2}}$$

Equation (4–13) indicates that the *CE* connection provides considerably poorer high-frequency characteristics than the *CB*. For example, consider the 2N1924. The specifications in Appendix B list f_{hfb} as 3.0 megaHertz (MHz) and h_{fe} as 44. This transistor is an alloy type, so that K_θ can be considered to be approximately 0.82. Equation (4–3) then gives

$$f_{hfe} \cong \frac{(0.82)(3\times10^6)}{44+1} \cong 54.6 \text{ kHz}$$

as the typical value for this transistor's "beta cutoff" frequency.

The Current-Gain-Bandwidth Product f_T

Another way of describing a transistor's high-frequency capability is to specify the frequency at which its short-circuit current gain, h_{fe}, falls to a value of one. This frequency is usually indicated by the notation f_T. It is also known as the current-gain-bandwidth product.

At frequencies well above f_β, the value of h_{fe} falls at a rate such that the product of the current gain and the frequency is approximately constant and numerically equal to f_T. This relationship is indicated in Figure 4–9(b). Examination of this graph reveals that it gets quite straight at frequencies considerably higher than f_{hfe}, and in this straight region it falls about 6 db per

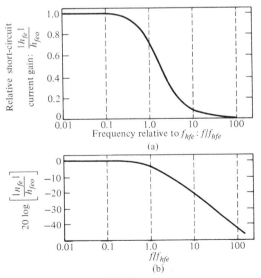

FIGURE 4–9
Curves of h_{fe} versus frequency

octave. That is, each time the frequency is doubled, h_{fe} reduces by one-half, or by 6 db. Thus the product of the current gain and the frequency is constant. That this product must have the value f_T is made clear by the following reasoning. Since f_T is the frequency at which $h_{fe} = 1$, the product $h_{fe}f_T = f_T$ at this frequency. At one-half this frequency, h_{fe} is doubled, or 2, and the product is $(2)(f_T/2) = f_T$. At one-half of this frequency, h_{fe} doubles again, and the product is $(4)(f_T/4) = f_T$, and so on. That is,

$$h_{fe}f = f_T \qquad\qquad\text{(4–15)} \quad \times$$

This 6 db per octave characteristic permits evaluating h_{fe} anywhere in the very high-frequency region. For example, if a transistor's specification lists the frequency at which $h_{fe} = 2$, its f_T must be twice that frequency, and it may therefore be compared with another transistor for which f_T is listed. If the data lists the frequency at which $h_{fe} = 3$, then f_T is three times that frequency, and so on.

If a particular transistor has an f_T of 500 MHz and is to be used at 100 MHz, its h_{fe} at 100 MHz will be

$$h_{fe} = \frac{f_T}{f} = \frac{500}{100} = 5$$

4.8 The *h*-Parameter Circuit at High Frequencies

An equivalent circuit approach which has been used for the upper audio frequencies and lower radio frequencies consists of adding shunt capacitance at the input and output of the *h*-parameter circuit to represent the effects of the transistor's internal capacitances. Figure 4–10 illustrates the arrangement.

Transistor data sheets often list a *CB* output capacitance C_{ob}, and in some cases a *CB* input capacitance C_{ib}. Others may specify a collector-to-base

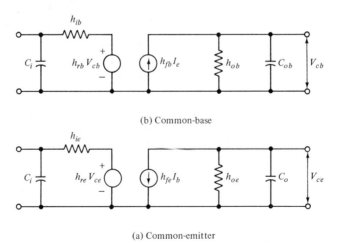

(b) Common-base

(a) Common-emitter

FIGURE 4–10
The h-parameter circuit modified for high frequencies

capacitance C_{cb}. These capacitances are primarily junction capacitances and therefore may vary considerably with current or voltage. The data sheet will usually specify the bias conditions under which they were measured, and sometimes will provide graphs showing the variation of the capacitance with bias. Occasionally *CE* input and output capacitances may also be found on data sheets.

Capacitances in the Small-Signal Amplifier

The most important capacitance from a practical standpoint in small-signal amplifiers is the *CB* output capacitance C_{ob}. Since the output capacitance is from collector to ground or common, in the *CB* arrangement the output capacitance is essentially the same as the capacitance from collector to base, often listed as C_{cb}, $C_{b'c}$, or C_c. The importance of this capacitance is in the fact that in the small-signal *CE* circuit, the effective input capacitance is predominantly due to feedback from the output through C_{cb}.

The total input capacitance is a combination of two major effects which for routine practical work may be expressed as

$$C_i \cong C_{be} + C_{cb}(1 + A_v) \tag{4–16a}$$

or

$$C_i \cong C_{be} + C_{ob}(1 + A_v) \tag{4–16b}$$

in which C_{be} is the diffusion capacitance associated with the forward-biased base-emitter junction, mentioned in Chapter 1, and $C_{cb}(1 + A_v)$ is the feedback capacitance. The feedback capacitance is also known as the Miller effect capacitance.

The diffusion capacitance C_{bc} is proportional to the current, and in small-signal amplifiers is therefore usually much smaller than the Miller effect capacitance. Consequently, the input capacitance in small-signal amplifiers may often be expressed as

$$C_i \cong C_{cb}(1 + A_v) \tag{4–17a}$$

or

$$C_i \cong C_{ob}(1 + A_v) \tag{4–17b}$$

The output capacitance for the *CE* circuit (C_o in Figure 4–10) is approximately equal to the *CB* output capacitance C_{ob}.

Capacitances in the Large-Signal Amplifier

Since the base-emitter capacitance, C_{be}, is proportional to the current, it becomes important in amplifiers operated at higher current levels. This capacitance is given approximately by

$$C_{be} \cong \frac{40I_E}{2\pi f_T} \tag{4–18}$$

in which I_E is the quiescent emitter current, and f_T is the gain-bandwidth product.

In a medium-high-frequency transistor operated at low current this capacitance is small. For example, the 2N3250 operated at 1 ma would give

$$C_{be} \cong \frac{(40)(10^{-3})}{(2\pi)(250)(10^{-6})}$$
$$C_{be} \cong 25.4 \text{ pf}$$

while the Miller effect capacitance, in a stage having a voltage gain of 50, would be

$$C_M = C_{ob}(1 + A_v)$$
$$C_M = 6(1 + 50) = 306 \text{ pf}$$

But operated at 50 ma, the value of C_{be} would be greater than 1000 pf.

Thus in large-signal amplifiers the input capacitance must be considered to be the sum of both C_{be} and the Miller effect, as was given in Equation (4–16):

$$C_i \cong C_{be} + C_{cb}(1 + A_v) \tag{4–16a}$$
$$C_i \cong C_{be} + C_{ob}(1 + A_v) \tag{4–16b}$$

4.9 Equivalent-Tee Circuits

An early form of equivalent circuit for the transistor was the equivalent-tee, one version of which is illustrated in Figure 4–11 for the *CB* connection. In this circuit, r_e represents the dynamic resistance of the base-emitter junc-

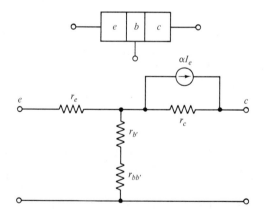

FIGURE 4–11
Single generator equivalent-tee representation of the transistor

tion, while $r_{b'}$ represents a feedback effect — the influence of the collector voltage upon the emitter current. The resistor $r_{bb'}$ represents the ohmic resistance of the base material. The resistor r_c is the collector resistance, or approximately the incremental ratio of collector voltage to collector current with constant emitter current.

When used to depict high-frequency operation, this circuit is modified to show the internal junction capacitances approximately where they occur. Thus, an emitter capacitance C_e and collector capacitance C_c are added to the T-equivalent as shown in Figure 4–12. The feedback effect is accounted for in this representation by the use of the equivalent generator μV_c.

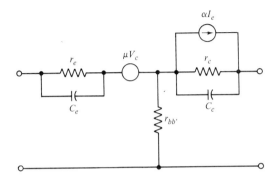

FIGURE 4–12
Equivalent-tee circuit modified for high frequencies

4.10   The Hybrid-π Circuit

A simplified representation of the principal resistances and capacitances of the transistor is shown in Figure 4–13. An equivalent circuit based on this representation which has proved very useful is the hybrid-π, or Giacoletto circuit. This is shown in Figure 4–14.

The resistor $r_{bb'}$ represents the ohmic resistance of the base material. The point b' stands for a fictitious terminal inside the base region, so as to permit separating the ohmic resistance from the base-emitter dynamic resistance. Thus $r_{bb'}$ is the resistance from the external base terminal up to the junction. The base-emitter dynamic resistance is represented by r_e (as before) when

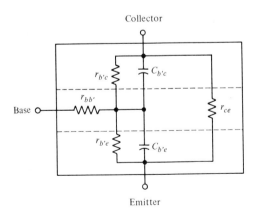

FIGURE 4–13
Physical picture of transistor resistances and capacitances

viewed looking into the emitter; but when viewed looking into the base, as the input for the *CE* circuit, this becomes $r_{b'e} = (h_{fe} + 1)r_e$, since for the same junction voltage the base current is smaller than the emitter current by the factor $(h_{fe} + 1)$. $C_{b'e}$ is principally the emitter capacitance C_{be} of Section 4.8.

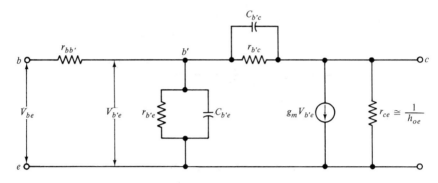

FIGURE 4-14
The hybrid-π equivalent

The current generator $g_m V_{b'e}$ is the constant current generator in the output resulting from the applied input voltage. The ratio of an *output current* to an *input voltage* is called *transconductance* (also sometimes called *mutual conductance*). g_m is defined by

$$g_m = \frac{\Delta i_C}{\Delta v_{B'E}}\bigg|_{\Delta v_{CE} = 0} = \frac{I_c}{V_{b'e}}\bigg|_{V_{ce} = 0}$$

The transconductance varies with the quiescent current and with the temperature. At room temperature it has the value

$$g_m = \frac{10^3 I_C}{26} \cong 40 I_C \tag{4-19}$$

The feedback within the transistor from output to input is accounted for by $C_{b'c}$ and $r_{b'c}$. $r_{b'c}$ is very large (in the range of megohms). $C_{b'c}$ will often lie in the range of 1 to 50 pf. The resistance r_{ce} is approximately equal to $1/h_{oe}$.

Relations Between Hybrid-π Values and h-Parameter Values

The resistance $r_{b'c}$ is very much larger than $r_{b'e}$, so that, at low frequencies where the capacitive effects are negligible, essentially all of the input current I_b flows through $r_{b'e}$. Thus, we can see that the effective input resistance is approximately equal to $r_{bb'} + r_{b'e}$ and that this is approximately the same as the input resistance of the *h*-parameter equivalent, h_{ie}. That is,

$$h_{ie} = r_{bb'} + r_{b'e} \tag{4-20}$$

In addition, $r_{bb'}$ is usually quite small (50 ohms or less), so that

$$h_{ie} \cong r_{b'e} \tag{4-21}$$

The resistance $r_{b'e}$ can be related to h_{fe} and g_m by the following reasoning:

$$V_{b'e} \cong I_b r_{b'e}$$

The short-circuit collector current is

$$I_c = g_m V_{b'e}$$

so that

$$I_c \Big|_{V_{ce} = 0} \cong g_m I_b r_{b'e}$$

giving

$$\frac{I_c}{I_b} \Big|_{V_{ce} = 0} \cong g_m r_{b'e}$$

But the short-circuit current gain h_{fe} is

$$h_{fe} = \frac{I_c}{I_b} \Big|_{V_{ce} = 0}$$

so that

$$h_{fe} \cong g_m r_{b'e}$$

giving

$$r_{b'e} \cong \frac{h_{fe}}{g_m} \tag{4-22}$$

Finally, another useful relationship, which we will not derive, is

$$g_m = \frac{1}{h_{ib}} \tag{4-23}$$

Summary of Hybrid-π Parameter Values

$$r_{bb'} \lesssim 50 \text{ ohms}$$

$$r_{b'c} = \text{megohms}$$

$$C_{b'e} \cong \frac{40 I_E}{2\pi f_T} \tag{4-18}$$

$$C_{b'c} = \text{in the range of 1 to 50 pf}$$

$$r_{ce} \cong \frac{1}{h_{oe}}$$

$$r_{b'e} \cong h_{ie} \tag{4-21}$$

$$r_{b'e} \cong \frac{h_{fe}}{g_m} \tag{4-22}$$

$$g_m \cong 40 I_C \tag{4-19}$$

$$g_m \cong \frac{1}{h_{ib}} \tag{4-23}$$

Simplified Hybrid-π Circuit

The resistance $r_{b'c}$ is so large that it may be omitted from the circuit for most purposes. In addition, the capacitance $C_{b'c}$ may be represented in terms of its effect (through feedback from the output) on the input circuit. This is the

Miller effect mentioned in Section 4.8 in connection with the h-parameter input capacitance C_i, and given first in Equations (4–16). It results in an effective input capacitance of $C_{b'c}(1 + A_v)$. Finally, $r_{bb'}$ may usually be omitted because it is quite small. This is especially true in the case of high-frequency transistors.

When these approximations are made, the hybrid-π circuit appears as in Figure 4–15. This circuit can be shown to be approximately the same as the

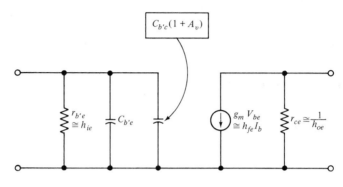

FIGURE 4–15
Simplified hybrid-π circuit

simplified h-parameter circuit with Miller effect capacitance added at the input. To see this, note that

$$g_m \cong \frac{h_{fe}}{r_{b'e}}$$

from Equation (4–22), and also that

$$V_{b'e} \cong I_b r_{b'e}$$

Consequently, the output current generator is seen to be

$$g_m V_{b'e} \cong h_{fe} I_b$$

Putting $h_{fe} I_b$ in place of $g_m V_{b'e}$, h_{oe} (or $1/h_{oe}$) in place of r_{ce}, and h_{ie} in place of $r_{b'e}$ results in the h-parameter circuit with capacitances added at the input.

PROBLEMS

4–1. A transistor is tested in the circuit shown in Figure 4–4. With the collector-to-emitter voltage v_{CE} held constant, a change of i_B of 10 μa is recorded when v_{BE} is changed 0.01 v. What is the value of h_{ie}?

4–2. The test circuit of Figure 4-5 is used to find the value of h_{fe} for a transistor.

With v_{CE} held constant, i_C changes by 1 ma when i_B is changed 20 μa. What is the value of h_{fe}?

4-3. What is the approximate value of h_{fe} at $v_{CE} = 10$ v in the region around $i_C = 5$ ma, for the transistor whose collector characteristics are shown here?

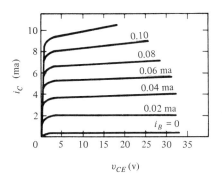

FIGURE P4-3

4-4. For the transistor of Problem 4–3, what is the value of h_{fe} at $v_{CE} = 5$ v, in the region between 1 and 2 ma?

4-5. According to the data sheet in Appendix B, what is the typical value for h_{fe} of the 2N1926 at an operating point of $I_C = 1$ ma, $V_{CE} = 5$ v, at 25°C? What are the minimum and maximum values of h_{fe} under these same conditions?

4-6. What is the approximate average value of h_{fe} for the 2N4875 at $V_{CE} = 10$ v, $I_C = 50$ ma?

4-7. (a) A *CE* transistor amplifier is operated with an effective load resistance of 20,000 ohms. The signal source feeding the input has an output resistance of 1000 ohms. The *h*-parameter values used at the operating point are:

$$h_{fe} = 26$$
$$h_{ie} = 1200$$
$$h_{oe} = 10 \times 10^{-6}$$
$$h_{re} = 1.2 \times 10^{-4}$$

Find the voltage gain and the current gain.

(b) How much error would have resulted if the approximate equations of Chapter 2 had been used in (a)?

4-8. What is the value of the input resistance in the amplifier of Problem 4–7?

4-9. Does the voltage gain equation $A_v = A_i \left[\dfrac{R_L}{R_i} \right]$ give the same result as the equivalent circuit equation you used in Problem 4–7? Should it?

4-10. The 2N1924 transistor is to be used in the following circuit. The operating point is at $I_C \cong 2$ ma, $V_{CE} \cong 5$ v. From the manufacturer's specifications in Appendix B, find the *CE* *h*-parameter values for this operating point.

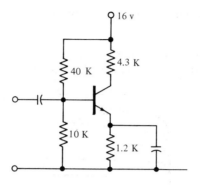

FIGURE P4–10

4–11. How would the voltage gain of a 2N1926, operated at a quiescent collector current of 2 ma and collector-emitter voltage of 5 v with an effective load of 2000 ohms, compare with its voltage gain when operated at $I_C = 1$ ma, $V_{CE} = 5$ v, and the same load?

4–12. A certain transistor has $h_{feo} = 50$, and $f_{hfe} = 200$ kHz. What is the value of $|h_{fe}|$ at 200 kHz? At 400 kHz?

4–13. A transistor has $h_{fe} = 100$ at 1 kHz, and $f_{ae} = 1$ MHz. What is the value of $|h_{fe}|$

    (a)   at 500 kHz?
    (b)   at 1 MHz?
    (c)   at 3 MHz?

4–14. Given $h_{feo} = 50$, $f_{hfb} = 10$ MHz:

    (a)   For an alloy transistor, what is the value of f_{hfe}?
    (b)   For an MADT, what is the value of f_{hfe}?

4–15. For the transistors of Problem 4–4, what is the value of $|h_{fe}|$ at 200 kHz?

4–16. If a transistor $f_T = 100$ MHz, what is the value of $|h_{fe}|$ at

    (a)   50 MHz?
    (b)   25 MHz?
    (c)   12.5 MHz?

4–17. (a)   A transistor having $C_{ob} = 5$ pf is to be used in a small-signal amplifier with an expected voltage gain of 50. What is the approximate input capacitance, assuming C_{be} is small enough to be neglected?

    (b)   If the total capacitance due to the load circuit is 7 pf, what is the approximate total output capacitance?

4–18. A transistor with $f_T = 500$ MHz and $C_{b'c} = 3$ pf is to be operated at $I_E = 10$ ma. The expected voltage gain is to be 50. What is the approximate input capacitance?

4–19. The 2N4874 transistor is to be operated at $I_E \cong 20$ ma. The voltage gain is to be 15. What is the approximate input capacitance?

4–20. Transform the following hybrid-π circuit to a simplified h-parameter equivalent valid for low frequencies.

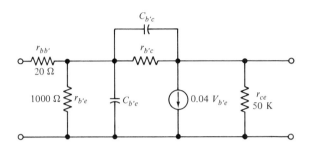

FIGURE P4–20

REFERENCES:

Belke, R. E., *et al. Transistor Manual.* Syracuse, New York: General Electric Company, 1964.

Manasse, F. K., *et al. Modern Transistor Electronics Analysis and Design.* Englewood Cliffs, New Jersey: Prentice-Hall, Inc., 1967.

CHAPTER 5

Frequency Response

5.1 Introduction

Although sine wave signals are convenient for testing amplifiers, and are frequently encountered in practice, the signals with which we must work are usually complex variations having little resemblance to a sine wave. However, harmonic analysis tells us that such complex signals may be expressed as a sum or combination of sine waves of various frequencies.

Speech, for example, may be analyzed into sine waves most of which fall between several hundred and 4000 or 5000 Hz, depending upon the individual characteristics. The content of music may range from below 50 Hz to above 10 kHz, depending upon the instrument and the composition. Many other kinds of signals are encountered in amplifiers, with frequencies ranging from less than one Hz to hundreds and thousands of MHz.

One important feature of an amplifier is its ability to amplify without distorting the signal. If a complex signal, containing many frequency components, is to retain its characteristics after amplification, it seems evident that the amount of amplification must be the same for each of the frequencies in the signal. When this is so, the amplifier is said to have *uniform frequency response* over that range of frequencies. Thus, frequency response is an important characteristic of amplifiers, in addition to the amount of gain or amplification.

It is characteristic of amplifiers that their gain is relatively uniform only over a restricted range of frequencies, and usually declines markedly at frequencies away from that range. For example, in Figure 5–1 the graph shows how gain typically varies with frequency in an audio amplifier (that is, one intended for speech and music signals). In order to be able to compare the quality of amplifiers with respect to their frequency response, it has been a common practice to indicate the frequencies at which the gain has declined

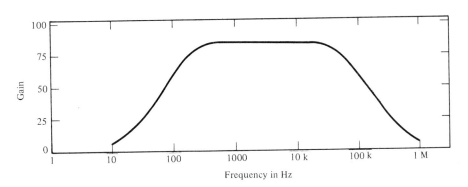

Frequency in Hz

FIGURE 5-1

Typical curves of gain versus frequency

to 70.7 percent of the gain at some reference frequency within the range. In audio amplifiers the reference frequency is very often 1000 Hz.

Thus, an audio amplifier having a gain of 85 at 1000 Hz, and in which the gain falls to $(0.707)(85) \cong 60$ at 100 Hz and 100 kHz as in Figure 5–1, is said to have a frequency range of 100 to 100,000 Hz. Another amplifier with 1000 Hz gain of only 50 but having its 70.7 percent response points at, say 20 Hz and 150 kHz would be considered to have better frequency response (even though lower gain). These 0.707 points are sometimes referred to as marking the *bandwidth* of the amplifier.

5.2   Decibels in Amplifier Work

Often in technical work the ratio of quantities is as important as the absolute values. The preceding chapters, for example, have been greatly concerned with voltage and current ratios as measures of amplifying ability. We have also encountered instances in which certain effects have been considered in terms of their values as percentages or fractions of some standard or reference value, or as multiples of these reference values. The most recent example is that in Section 5.1 above, in which the bandwidth is marked by the frequencies at which the gain has decreased to 0.707 times the 1000 Hz gain.

When dealing with ratios, logarithms are often convenient, and a unit based on logarithms which has become very commonly used is the decibel. The decibel was originally defined in terms of power ratios but has come to be used also to express voltage and current ratios.

In terms of the ratio of two powers, the number of decibels is

$$db = 10 \log \left[\frac{P_2}{P_1} \right] \qquad (5\text{–}1)$$

in which it is understood that the logarithm is to the base 10. Since

$$P = \frac{V^2}{R}$$

we have

$$db = 10 \log \left[\frac{V_2^2/R_2}{V_1^2/R_1} \right] \tag{5-2}$$

where R_1 and R_2 are the circuit resistances across which the powers P_1 and P_2 are developed respectively. This leads to

$$db = 10 \log \left[\frac{V_2^2}{R_2} \right] \left[\frac{R_1}{V_1^2} \right]$$

and if the resistances are equal,

$$db = 10 \log \left[\frac{V_2}{V_1} \right]^2$$

so that

$$db = 20 \log \left[\frac{V_2}{V_1} \right] \tag{5-3}$$

Similarly in the case of currents

$$db = 20 \log \left[\frac{I_2}{I_1} \right] \tag{5-4}$$

It has become an accepted practice to use the above two expressions for voltage and current ratios in electronics work even when the resistances are not equal. Thus, voltage gains may be expressed as

$$\text{Gain in db} = 20 \log \left[\frac{V_2}{V_1} \right] = 20 \log A_v$$

When it is desirable to express the change of a quantity relative to some fixed reference value, the change is often expressed in decibels — especially when it is in connection with amplifier work.

Thus, if the power gain of an amplifier under certain conditions is only one-half of its normal gain, it is often expressed as having a gain of

$$10 \log \left[\frac{P_2}{P_1} \right] = 10 \log 1/2 \cong -3 \text{ db}$$

relative to its normal gain or "down 3 db" from its normal gain.

Since negative logarithms are often awkward to handle, the calculation is very commonly made in such a way as to permit obtaining *positive* decibels, and the sign of the answer is handled separately.

Thus, in the above case, the smaller of the two powers being compared would have been placed in the denominator, giving

$$10 \log \left[\frac{P_1}{P_2} \right] = 10 \log 2 \cong 3 \text{ db}$$

and the person doing the calculating would supply the negative sign afterwards, by referring to the gain as "down 3 db" or "3 db below normal."

The output of a voltage divider or attenuator is smaller than the input, and the amount of "attenuation" is often expressed in decibels. Thus an attenuator in which the output voltage is $1/100$ of the input is said to have an attenuation of "100 times" or "100 to 1" or

$$\text{Attenuation} = 20 \log 100 = 40 \text{ db}$$

Since the logarithm of a product is the sum of the logarithms of the individual factors of the product, the use of decibels permits the great convenience of *adding* to obtain a total product. Thus, when two separate effects operate to cause increase or decrease of an amplifier's gain, the total effect may be expressed in decibels by *adding or subtracting* the decibel values for the individual effects. Suppose, for example, that one effect causes a 50 percent decrease in an amplifier's current gain while the other causes a 30 percent decrease. Expressed as a *ratio* this would give

$$A'_i = A_i(0.5)(0.7)$$

The decibel values of these effects are:

50 percent decrease: $-20 \log \left[\dfrac{1}{0.5}\right] = -20 \log 2 \cong -6 \text{ db}$

30 percent decrease: $-20 \log \left[\dfrac{1}{0.7}\right] \cong -20 \log 1.43 \cong -3.1 \text{ db}$

(*Note:* In each case the problem was handled so as to permit a ratio greater than 1, and therefore a positive log.) The overall result then would be:

$$A'_i(\text{in db}) = (A_i - 6 - 3.1) \text{ db}$$
$$A'_i \cong (A_i - 9.1) \text{ db}$$

In other words the two effects have reduced the gain by a total of 9.1 db.

On the other hand, suppose the amplifier's current gain is decreased 30 percent by one effect and *increased* 50 percent by a second effect. The overall result then would be:

$$A'_i = A_i - 20 \log \left[\dfrac{1}{0.7}\right] + 20 \log 1.5 \text{ decibels}$$
$$= A_i - 3.1 + 3.52 \text{ decibels}$$
$$= A_i + 0.42 \text{ decibels}$$

In this case the total effect is an increase of gain by 0.42 db.

5.3 Frequency Effects in RC-Coupled Amplifiers

In order to understand the variation of gain that may occur in an amplifier as the signal frequency is changed, consider the simple amplifier circuit of Figure 5-2(a) and its approximate equivalent circuit in part (b) of the figure.

Shunt Capacitance Effects

The capacitances C_{s1} and C_{s2} represent effects which are an unwanted but unavoidable part of every amplifier circuit: the stray capacitance between wires, terminals and the like, and the capacitance existing across the input and output of any amplifying device. C_{s1} represents the total of the stray capacitance of the circuit wiring connected to the input of the transistor plus the transistor's input capacitance, while C_{s2} is the total of the output circuit wiring stray capacitance and the transistor's output capacitance.

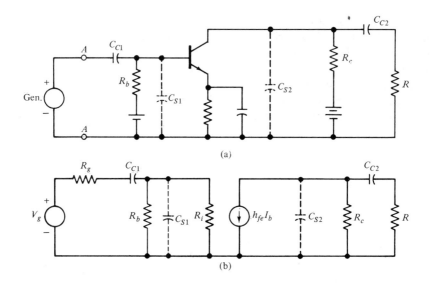

FIGURE 5-2
Amplifier circuit illustrating frequency dependency

The capacitance C_{s2} which is shown from collector to ground is effectively in parallel with the load resistance for signal components. It is *shunt capacitance* such as this which causes amplifier gain to decrease at high frequencies. The effective load for the amplifier is the parallel combination of R_c, R, and C_{s2}. At low frequencies the reactance of C_{s2} is usually so large compared to R_c and R that its effect is negligible. However, when the frequency becomes high enough, the reactance becomes small enough to make the impedance of the parallel combination significantly less than that of just R_c and R in parallel. Since voltage gain depends strongly on load resistance, or more correctly, on load impedance, we may expect a decrease of voltage gain at high frequencies, due to shunt capacitance. Current gain is affected in the same way, since the signal current into the load is directly proportional to the signal voltage. The capacitance C_{s1} from base to ground has a similar effect since it shunts R_i, which is the load for the signal source.

Coupling Capacitance Effects

The capacitors C_{c1} and C_{c2} are, of course, the coupling capacitors. Capacitance in series with the signal circuit like this causes a loss of amplification at the lower frequencies. Consider, for example, the output portion of the equivalent circuit in Figure 5–2(b). The resistance R is the load to which the signal is being coupled by C_{c2}. The series combination of C_{c2} and R acts as a voltage divider across the output of the amplifier. Throughout much of the range of frequencies which the amplifier is intended to handle, the reactance of C_{c2} is usually so small that essentially all of the signal voltage developed across R_c is impressed upon R. However, as the frequency is lowered, X_C

increases in value. At very low frequencies X_C may be large enough so that an appreciable fraction of the voltage developed across R_c is dropped across X_C, and much less appears across the load R. Thus, the presence of C_{c2} results in a reduction of effective voltage and current gain at the lower frequencies. The input coupling capacitor plays a similar role.

The Emitter-Bypass Capacitor

Also shown in the amplifier circuit in part (a) of Figure 5–2, but not in the equivalent circuit in (b), are the emitter resistor R_e and bypass capacitor C_e. In the preceding chapters we have assumed this capacitance to be a perfect bypass, that is, large enough so that the impedance of the $R_e - C_e$ combination is negligible. For this reason these two elements have not been shown in the equivalent circuit. But at the lower frequencies the reactance of C_e can become great enough so that the impedance is not negligible, and both current gain and voltage gain can be affected. The current gain is decreased because the increased impedance in series with the base-emitter junction causes a decrease of input current. The voltage gain is reduced because a large part of the input signal voltage is dropped across the $R_e - C_e$ combination, leaving less actually applied to the base-emitter junction.

General Approach to Analysis of Frequency Response

In analyzing and testing an amplifier in a chain of amplifiers, a single stage may be considered to be the circuit from the base of one transistor to the base of the next. Stage gain computations can then be made on the assumption that a constant amplitude signal is applied to the base, and *the output of the stage is the base of the next transistor.* Thus, it is quite common to consider only the circuit from the collector to the next base. Any effects associated with the input circuit can be included in the output of the preceding stage. Because of this, the general amplifier circuit for purposes of analysis is often shown as in Figure 5–3.

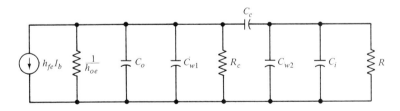

FIGURE 5–3
Equivalent circuit showing elements usually used in frequency response analysis

The resistance R in this circuit represents the final load, which may be the effective input resistance of the next stage, or the resistance of some device being operated by the amplifier's output signal.

C_o represents the output capacitance of the transistor; C_{w1} and C_{w2} are wiring capacitance (shown separately here rather than as a single capacitance representing the total stray wiring capacitance simply to emphasize that such capacitance exists throughout the circuit, therefore, on both sides of C_c). And C_i is the effective input capacitance of the next stage or of whatever load is being supplied with the output signal from the amplifier.

In the usual amplifier the low-frequency loss occurs well below 1000 Hz — usually below several hundred Hz, depending upon the quality and intended use of the amplifier — while the high-frequency effect does not begin until above several thousand Hz. Thus, there is usually an intervening frequency range of constant gain; this region is usually called the midfrequency region, or the midrange. It should be understood that the midfrequency region is not defined by one particular pair of frequencies. It is merely the region, between the low-frequency region and the high-frequency region, in which the gain is relatively unaffected by the frequency-sensitive elements of the circuit. Thus, an amplifier's frequency response may usually be divided into three well-defined regions: the low range, the midrange, and the high range. The analysis of the frequency response characteristics is usually carried out separately for each of these regions.

5.4 Analysis of Amplifier in Midrange

If the equivalent circuit of Figure 5–3 is reproduced without any of the circuit elements that cause loss of gain in the low range or the high range, the circuit of Figure 5–4 results.

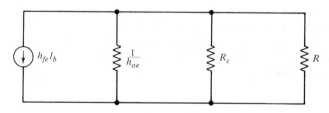

FIGURE 5–4
Midrange equivalent circuit

This is, of course, the same kind of circuit as we considered in the preceding chapters, in which the effective amplifier load was simply a resistance. In Figure 5–4 the effective load resistance is the parallel combination of R_C and R. That is,

$$A_v = \frac{-h_{fe}R_L}{h_{ie} + \Delta^h R_L} = -A_i \frac{R_L}{R_i} \cong h_{fe} \frac{R_L}{h_{ie}}$$

in which

$$R_L = \frac{R_c R}{R_c + R}$$

The current gain from the base to the load R differs from the base to collector current gain to the extent that the current divides up between R_c and R. This will be taken up in the next chapter as a basic problem in cascaded amplifier analysis.

5.5 Analysis of the Low-Frequency Response

In Figure 5–5 the equivalent circuit applicable to the low-frequency range is shown. Shunt capacitance elements do not appear in this circuit since their effect is negligible in this portion of the frequency range.

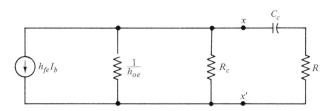

FIGURE 5–5
Low-frequency equivalent circuit

It is a common practice to analyze the frequency response by comparing the gain, or the output amplitude, at the frequencies of interest with that in the midrange. This is called the *relative response*. The advantage of relative response figures, in dealing with frequency effects, is illustrated in the following.

Amplifier A has a gain of 120 at midrange, and its gain drops to 96 at 30 Hz. Its relative response at 30 Hz is therefore 96/120 or 0.8 (or 80 percent). Amplifier B has a midrange gain of 70 and a 30 Hz gain of 35. Its relative response at 30 Hz is 35/70 or 0.5. If we wish to compare the low-frequency response of these two amplifiers using gain figures, we would have to say, "The gain of A drops from 120 at midrange to 96 at 30 Hz, while B drops from 70 to 35." This kind of statement still leaves us wondering how the two circuits compare on a *relative* basis. It is much more direct and convenient to simply say, "The response of A is 0.8 at 30 Hz, while that of B is 0.5." The gain at midrange can then be discussed separately, if desired.

It might be noted here that relative responses such as these are often expressed in db. Circuit A would be approximately 1.8 db down at 30 Hz, while B is 6 db down.

In the following material we will derive general equations which may be used to calculate relative response at any desired frequency.

A convenient way to obtain such an equation for the low-frequency case illustrated in Figure 5–5 is to find an expression for the voltage across R *as a function of frequency*, and divide this by the expression for this voltage *at midfrequency*. To do this, Figure 5–5 can be Thevenized at points X-X'. This will result in the output equivalent circuit shown in Figure 5–6.

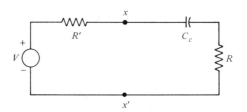

FIGURE 5-6

Voltage generator form of output circuit for low-frequency analysis

The equivalent source resistance R' is the parallel combination of the amplifier's source resistance R_o (Chapter 4) and R_c:

$$R' = \frac{R_o R_c}{R_o + R_c} \tag{5-5}$$

The Thevenin equivalent generator is then

$$V = h_{fe} I_b R'$$

This voltage generator is of constant amplitude since it is derived from h_{fe} and I_b. The latter is assumed constant, in accordance with the method of analysis described above, in which any input circuit variations are included as part of the output effects of the preceding stage, so that the input signals may be considered constant. (This kind of amplifier is usually tested with an input signal whose amplitude is held constant as the frequency is varied.) h_{fe} is considered constant because frequency has no effect on the short-circuit current gain in this range, and because temperature and operating point are assumed constant.

By voltage divider action in this circuit, the voltage across R at any frequency is

$$V_L = \left[\frac{R}{R + R' - j(1/\omega C_c)} \right] V$$

In the midfrequency range, however, the reactance of C_c is negligible, so that we can write

$$V_M = \left[\frac{R}{R + R'} \right] V$$

Then the ratio of the low-frequency output to the midfrequency output (which is the ratio of the voltage gains, since the input is held constant) is

$$\frac{V_L}{V_M} = \frac{A_{vL}}{A_{vM}} = \left[\frac{R}{R + R' - j1/\omega C_c} \right]\left[\frac{R + R'}{R} \right]$$

$$\frac{A_{vL}}{A_{vM}} = \frac{R + R'}{R + R' - j1/\omega C_c} \tag{5-6}$$

and

$$\left| \frac{A_{vL}}{A_{vM}} \right| = \frac{R + R'}{\sqrt{(R + R')^2 + X_C^2}} \tag{5-7}$$

These equations and the circuit of Figures 5–5 and 5–6 are important as expressions of the action of an RC-coupling circuit at low frequencies, and they deserve study. Note that the equation shows, through the X_C term in the denominator, a decline in A_{vL}/A_{vM} at low frequencies, as anticipated. On the other hand, as frequency is increased, X_C eventually becomes negligible compared to $R + R'$ so that $A_v/A_{vM} \rightarrow (R + R')/(R + R') = 1$. Figure 5–7 is a graph showing the low-frequency response, as computed from this equation, for an amplifier in which $R + R' = 4000$ ohms, and $C = 1\ \mu f$.

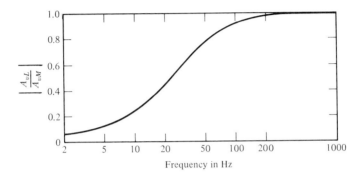

FIGURE 5–7
Low-frequency response example (computed from Equation [5–7])

Improvement of Low-Frequency Response

The equation also reveals that the low-frequency response may be improved by increasing either of the resistances, or by decreasing X_C.

Increasing the resistance results in a higher value for A_{vL}/A_{vM} at any given low frequency, since the resistance term is then larger relative to the reactance. Note carefully, however, that this does not necessarily imply an increase in midrange gain. Current gain, in fact, would be decreased by increasing the load resistance, although the relative response A_{vL}/A_{vM} would be improved.

Since the resistances are usually determined by other aspects of the circuit design, it is more commonly the coupling capacitor which is chosen to meet the low-frequency requirements. The larger the value of capacitance, the better the low-frequency response. For example, typical values for a small signal audio amplifier might be:

$$R' \cong 3000 \text{ ohms}$$
$$R \cong 1000 \text{ ohms}$$

If a 1 microfarad (μf) coupling capacitor were used with these resistances, the relative response at 50 Hz would be found as follows:

$$X_C = \frac{1}{2\pi f C} = \frac{159 \times 10^{-3}}{(50)(10^{-6})}$$
$$X_C \cong 3180 \text{ ohms}$$

Then the relative response at 50 Hz is

$$\frac{A_{vL}}{A_{vM}} = \frac{R + R'}{\sqrt{(R + R')^2 + X_C^2}} = \frac{4000}{\sqrt{(4.0^2 + 3.18^2)(10^6)}}$$

$$= \frac{4}{\sqrt{16 + 10.1}}$$

$$\frac{A_{vL}}{A_{vM}} \cong 0.785$$

This can also be expressed as

$$20 \log \frac{A_{vL}}{A_{vM}} = 20 \log 0.785 \cong -2.1$$

or approximately 2.1 db down at 50 Hz.

Thus, this circuit would have approximately 21 percent or 2.1 db loss of signal at 50 Hz. If this was considered excessive, C_c could be made larger in value. A 5-μf coupling capacitor would give

$$X_C \cong 640 \text{ ohms}$$

$$\frac{A_{vL}}{A_{vM}} \cong \frac{4000}{\sqrt{(16 + 0.642)(10^6)}} \cong \frac{4}{\sqrt{16.41}} \cong \frac{4}{4.05}$$

$$\frac{A_{vL}}{A_{vM}} \cong 0.99$$

5.6 The Low-Frequency 3-db Point

At the frequency at which the capacitive reactance equals the total resistance $R + R'$, the relative response is 0.707. To show this, we can substitute $R + R'$ for X_C in the relative response equation and calculate the response at this frequency (identifying this particular frequency as f_1):

$$\frac{A_{vL}}{A_{vM}} = \frac{R + R'}{\sqrt{(R + R')^2 + X_C^2}} \tag{5-7}$$

$$\frac{A_{vf1}}{A_{vM}} = \frac{R + R'}{\sqrt{(R + R')^2 + (R + R')^2}}$$

$$\frac{A_{vf1}}{A_{vM}} = \frac{1}{\sqrt{2}} = 0.707$$

The frequency f_1 is known as the 3-db frequency, or the half-power frequency. The 3-db designation comes from the fact that when expressed in decibels, a relative voltage response of 0.707 is $20 \log 0.707 = -3$ db; that is, the output at this frequency is 3 db below the midfrequency value. The term half-power frequency is used because when the voltage is down to 0.707 its midrange value, the power (proportional to V^2) is down to 0.707^2 or one-half of its midrange value.

A convenient way of comparing the response of two amplifiers, as mentioned earlier, is by comparing the frequencies at which the response falls to 0.707. Thus, low-frequency responses could be compared by noting the low-frequency 3-db points. A general equation for the 3-db frequency can be obtained from the condition stated above,

$$X_C = R + R'$$

Thus,

$$\frac{1}{2\pi f_1 C_c} = R + R' \tag{5-8}$$

$$f_1 = \frac{1}{2\pi C_c(R + R')} \tag{5-9}$$

In the example above, the 3-db point when using the 1-μf coupling capacitor would be

$$f_1 = \frac{1}{2\pi(R + R')C}$$

$$f_1 = \frac{(159)(10^{-3})}{(4000)(1)(10^{-6})} \cong 40 \text{ Hz}$$

While for the 5-μf capacitor it would be

$$f_1 \cong \frac{(159)(10^{-3})}{(4000)(5)(10^{-6})} \cong 8 \text{ Hz}$$

5.7　The Universal Response Curve

An expression for the relative response in terms of signal frequency and the half-power frequency can be derived from Equations (5–6) and (5–8). From Equation (5–6) we have

$$\frac{A_{vL}}{A_{vM}} = \frac{R + R'}{R + R' - j1/\omega C_c} = \frac{1}{1 - j\left[\dfrac{1}{2\pi f C_c(R + R')}\right]}$$

but since by Equation (5–8),

$$R + R' = \frac{1}{2\pi f_1 C_c} \tag{5-8}$$

We can substitute $1/2\pi f_1 C_c$ for $R + R'$ in the equation above and obtain

$$\frac{A_{vL}}{A_{vM}} = \frac{1}{1 - j\left[\dfrac{2\pi f_1 C_c}{2\pi f C_c}\right]}$$

so that

$$\frac{A_{vL}}{A_{vM}} = \frac{1}{1 - j(f_1/f)} \tag{5-10}$$

or

$$\frac{A_{vL}}{A_{vM}} = \frac{1}{\sqrt{1 + (f_1/f)^2}} \tag{5-11}$$

Equation (5–10) indicates a *general* aspect to the response of Figure 5–6; that is, the equation shows that the *shape* of the response curve is the same regardless of the values of resistance and capacitance. The only effect produced by changing the values of resistance and capacitance is to change the value of $f_1 = 1/2\pi(R + R')C_c$, i.e., to change the frequency at which the response goes through the 3-db point.

It is of interest to note that the *form* of the response would be identically the same for a circuit such as in Figure 5–8, which is the basic high-pass *RC* circuit.

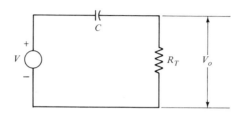

FIGURE 5–8
Basic high-pass RC *filter*

It can be readily verified that the relative response for this circuit is:

$$\frac{V_{oL}}{V_{oM}} = \frac{R_T}{R_T - j(1/\omega C)}$$

and that this leads to precisely the same Equation (5–10). The general nature of the f_1/f function of Equation (5–10) is simply an expression of the fact that all single-time-constant circuits have the same general frequency response characteristics.

The use of Equations such as (5–10) or (5–11) can be illustrated by the previous example, in which

$$R' = 3000 \text{ ohms}$$
$$R = 1000 \text{ ohms}$$
$$C_c = 1.0 \text{ } \mu\text{f}$$

The method is to first calculate the 3-db frequency f_1:

$$f_1 = \frac{1}{2\pi(R + R')C}$$
$$f_1 \cong 40 \text{ Hz}$$

This value for f_1 is then substituted in Equation (5–11) to get the following specific relation for the particular circuit of the example:

$$\left|\frac{A_{vL}}{A_{vM}}\right| = \frac{1}{\sqrt{1 + (40/f)^2}}$$

Any particular values of f may then be substituted in this equation in order to find the relative response at any frequency from midrange downward.

(The data for the graph of Figure 5–7 was obtained in this way.) For example, if the relative response at 20 Hz is needed, $f = 20$ is substituted in the equation:

$$\frac{A_{vL}}{A_{vM}} = \frac{1}{\sqrt{1 + (40/20)^2}} = \frac{1}{\sqrt{1 + 2^2}}$$

$$\frac{A_{vL}}{A_{vM}} \cong 0.448$$

Equation (5–11) is often presented in the form of a *universal response curve* as in Figure 5–9. Note that part (b) of this figure shows the relative response in db.

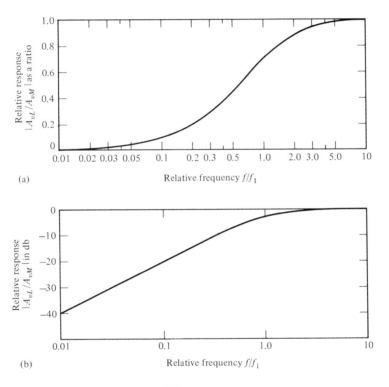

(a)

(b)

FIGURE 5–9
Universal (low-frequency) response curve

The horizontal scale for both curves is in terms of *frequency relative to* f_1. That is, in the above example, in which the circuit has an f_1 of 40 Hz, an f/f_1 value of one on the frequency scale indicates a frequency of 40 Hz; $f/f_1 = 0.1$ indicates 4 Hz, etc. Thus, at 40 Hz the relative response is -3 db; at 4 Hz it is -20 db, etc.

Another circuit, having a different value of f_1, could be compared at the same frequencies if desired. For example suppose a second circuit had $f_1 = 60$ Hz. This circuit's response at 40 Hz would be obtained by finding the relative frequency $f/f_1 = 40/60 \cong 0.67$, and reading the relative response for this frequency (approximately -5 db). At 4 Hz, $f/f_1 = 4/60 \cong 0.067$, and the response is approximately -23.8 db.

5.8 Effect of the Emitter-Bypass Capacitor on Low-Frequency Gain

In Section 5.5 only the low-frequency losses due to the coupling capacitance were considered, in order to simplify the discussion. But an equally important source of low-frequency loss is the emitter bypass capacitance.

Consider Figure 5–10, illustrating a typical CE circuit. If C_e were not used

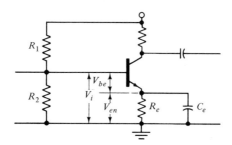

FIGURE 5–10

CE *amplifier circuit illustrating emitter bypassing*

as a bypass, the signal current flowing in R_e would cause a large signal voltage between emitter and ground. The effect of this signal voltage would be to decrease the amount of input signal actually applied to the base-emitter junction, and consequently to decrease the effective output of the amplifier.

The figure shows that the input signal V_i is the sum of V_{be} and V_{en}. Thus, the base-emitter junction voltage V_{be} must be less than V_i by the amount of any signal voltage developed across R_e. If V_{be} is reduced, the resulting current is reduced also. Consequently, the effective voltage gain and the effective current gain are both reduced. The fact that the output (collector) signal current flows in R_e as well as the input (base) signal current makes the signal voltage developed across it much greater than it would be if only the input current were involved.

The capacitance C_e is used to minimize this signal voltage, by making the impedance between emitter and ground very small. However, at low frequencies the increased reactance of C_e makes it more difficult to achieve this result. Thus, at the low-frequency end of the band, the effective stage gain may be reduced. Either this effect or the coupling capacitance loss may be the determining factor in the low-frequency response, depending upon the circuit values chosen.

There is a distinctive difference between the general low-frequency characteristic due to C_e and that described in Section 5.5 for the coupling capacitor.

The typical response curve due to C_e alone (that is, with a coupling capacitor so large that it causes no loss) is illustrated in Figure 5–11.

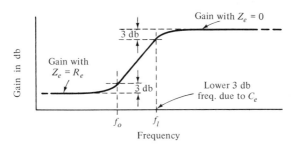

FIGURE 5–11
Low-frequency response due to emitter bypassing

The falling portion of this curve is due to the gradual increase of reactance of C_e as the frequency is lowered. However, instead of falling indefinitely, the gain levels off. This leveling off occurs when X_C becomes so large compared with R_e that the parallel combination is approximately equal to R_e — that is, further increase in X_C has no noticeable effect. With the impedance between emitter and ground constant, the loss of gain due to this impedance becomes constant. The gain of the amplifier in this region is of course the gain it would have using R_e without a bypass capacitor.

The Low-Frequency 3-db Point Due to C_e

When the coupling capacitor effect is not involved, the frequency at which the gain has dropped 3 db below the midrange value due to C_e is

$$f_1 \cong \frac{1}{2\pi \left[\dfrac{R_g + h_{ie}}{h_{fe}} \right] C_e} \qquad (5\text{–}12)$$

in which R_g stands for the effective source resistance of the signal source connected to the input.

The frequency f_o, at which the gain is 3 db above its final constant low-frequency value, is given by

$$f_o = \frac{1}{2\pi R_e C_e} \qquad (5\text{–}13)$$

and the relative gain is given by

$$\frac{A_{vL}}{A_{vM}} \cong \left[\frac{R_g + h_{ie}}{h_{fe} R_e} \right] \left[\frac{1 + jf/f_o}{1 + jf/f_1} \right] \qquad (5\text{–}14)$$

or

$$\left| \frac{A_{vL}}{A_{vM}} \right| \cong \left[\frac{R_g + h_{ie}}{h_{fe} R_e} \right] \frac{\sqrt{1 + (f/f_o)^2}}{\sqrt{1 + (f/f_1)^2}} \qquad (5\text{–}15)$$

5.9 Analysis of the High-Frequency Response

Figure 5–12 shows the high-frequency equivalent circuit for the output portion of a transistor amplifier. The coupling capacitors are not shown in this equivalent because their effect is negligible in the high-frequency range.

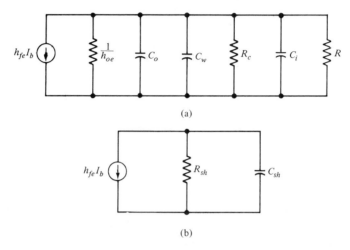

(a)

(b)

FIGURE 5–12
Equivalent circuit for high-frequency range

In part (b) of this figure, all parallel resistances are lumped together and designated R_{sh}, so that $R_{sh} = R_o \parallel R_c \parallel R$. Also all parallel capacitances are lumped together and designated C_{sh}, so that $C_{sh} = C_o + C_w + C_i$. These capacitances were explained earlier in connection with Figure 5–3. C_o represents the transistor's output capacitance; C_i stands for the input capacitance of the next stage, and C_w, the stray wire capacitance.

Again, as in the low-frequency case, the method will be to find an expression for the response relative to the midrange output. In this analysis I_b again is to be assumed constant. The current gain factor h_{fe} will also be assumed constant. The high-frequency effects in the transistor's performance will be represented by its capacitance. (See Chapter 4)

Under these assumptions, the signal voltage developed across the output in the high-frequency range is

$$V_H = h_{fe}I_bZ_{sh} \tag{5–16}$$

in which

$$Z_{sh} = \frac{R_{sh}(-j/\omega C_{sh})}{R_{sh} + (-j1/\omega C_{sh})}$$

while the output at midrange, where the effect of C_{sh} is neglected, is

$$V_M = h_{fe}I_bR_{sh}$$

The *relative response* in the high-frequency region is therefore

$$\frac{A_{vH}}{A_{vM}} = \frac{V_H}{V_M} = \frac{Z_{sh}}{R_{sh}}$$

Thus,

$$\frac{A_{vH}}{A_{vM}} = \frac{-j1/\omega C_{sh}}{R_{sh} - j1/\omega C_{sh}}$$

so that

$$\frac{A_{vH}}{A_{vM}} = \frac{1}{1 + j\omega R_{sh}C_{sh}} \tag{5-17}$$

or

$$\frac{A_{vH}}{A_{vM}} = \frac{1}{\sqrt{1 + (\omega R_{sh}C_{sh})^2}} \tag{5-18}$$

Equation (5–16) above expresses the fact that with a constant current generator ($h_{fe}I_b$), the output voltage is directly proportional to the effective load impedance. Thus, we should expect that as frequency increases, the shunt capacitive reactance part of the load causes a decrease in the output voltage. Equations (5–17) and (5–18) do show this, through the ωRC term in the denominator. These equations also show that as the frequency is lowered, the ωRC term becomes quite small compared to 1, so that $A_{vH}/A_{vM} \to 1$, its midfrequency value.

In order to improve the high-frequency response — that is, to increase the relative response at any given high frequency — it is necessary to decrease the ωRC term. This of course requires using either smaller resistance or smaller capacitance. The same conclusion could have been reached by examination of the circuit, noting that the smaller the value of R_{sh}, the higher the frequency necessary to reduce the reactance of a given amount of C_{sh} to a value low enough to significantly shunt R_{sh}. Similarly, the smaller the value of C_{sh}, the greater is X_C and the higher the frequency necessary to reduce it to a value which is a noticeable shunt across a given R.

The above effects are similar in form to those in the low-frequency case, though opposite in nature, and are illustrated in Figure 5–13 which is a plot of the response for a circuit having $R_{sh} = 10,000$ ohms and $C_{sh} = 500$ pf.

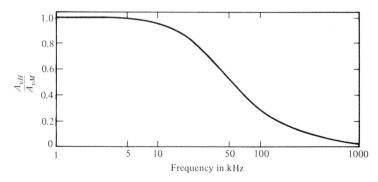

FIGURE 5–13
High-frequency response example (computed from Equation [5–18])

Equations (5–17) and (5–18) can also be transformed into universal response equations as was done in the low-frequency case. The result is

$$\frac{A_{vH}}{A_{vM}} = \frac{1}{1 + jf/f_2} \qquad (5\text{–}19)$$

and

$$\frac{A_{vH}}{A_{vM}} = \frac{1}{\sqrt{1 + (f/f_2)^2}} \qquad (5\text{–}20)$$

in which f_2 is the *upper* 3-db frequency — the point at which the response has fallen 3 db from the midrange response as the signal frequency is increased. As in the low-frequency case, this is the freuqency at which $X = R$; in this case

$$\frac{1}{2\pi f_2 C_{sh}} = R_{sh} \qquad (5\text{–}21)$$

so that

$$f_2 = \frac{1}{2\pi R_{sh} C_{sh}} \qquad (5\text{–}22)$$

Figure 5–14 is a plot of the magnitude of the relative response in the high-frequency range as a function of f/f_2.

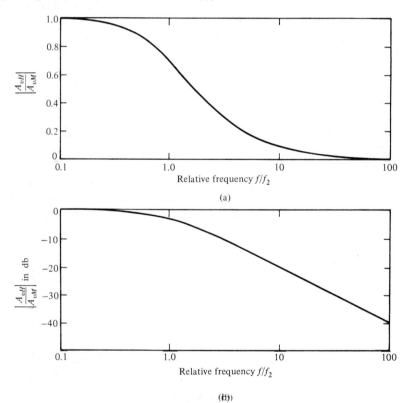

(a)

(b)

FIGURE 5–14
Universal high-frequency response curve

5.10   Bode Plots

The universal response curve permits an approximation which is often found useful. Note that Equation (5–19), when the frequency is fairly high so that f/f_2 is large compared to 1, simplifies to

$$\frac{A_{vH}}{A_{vM}} \cong \frac{1}{j(f/f_2)}$$

or

$$\left|\frac{A_{vH}}{A_{vM}}\right| \cong \frac{1}{f/f_2} = \frac{f_2}{f} \tag{5–23}$$

Expressed in decibels, this is

$$\left|\frac{A_{vH}}{A_{vM}}\right|_{db} \cong 20 \log \left[\frac{1}{f/f_2}\right]$$

$$\left|\frac{A_{vH}}{A_{vM}}\right|_{db} \cong 20 \left[\log 1 - \log (f/f_2)\right]$$

$$\left|\frac{A_{vH}}{A_{vM}}\right|_{db} \cong -20 \log (f/f_2) \tag{5–24}$$

On the other hand, when the frequency is fairly low (i.e., in the midfrequency range) so that f/f_2 is small compared to 1, Equation (5–19) simplifies to

$$\frac{A_v}{A_{vM}} \cong 1$$

or

$$\left|\frac{A_v}{A_{vM}}\right|_{db} \cong 20 \log 1 = 0$$

These two approximations can be graphed, with the high-frequency approximation extending downward from the point where it equals the midfrequency approximation, or zero db. This is illustrated in Figure 5–15, and is known as a *Bode plot*.

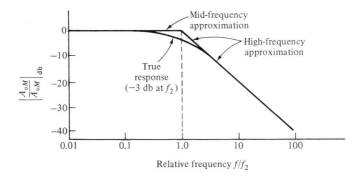

FIGURE 5–15
Bode plot for high-frequency response of single-time-constant circuit

The midrange relative response in the Bode plot is zero db and the high-range response *falls below this* by an amount which is directly proportional to the relative frequency. The point at which the two approximation curves meet is at the relative frequency $f/f_2 = 1$, or in other words the frequency f_2. (At this frequency the high-range approximation has the value $20 \log (f/f_2) = 20 \log 1 = 0$ db, which is the midrange value.)

Analysis of Equation (5–24) shows that the Bode plot falls at a constant rate of 6 db per octave (an octave is a $2:1$ frequency change) and 20 db per decade ($10:1$ frequency change). In addition, the frequency f_2 is the frequency at which the *actual* response is down 3 db, or down to 70.7 percent of midrange response. This very obvious point on the graph serves as a convenient indicator of the band-edge.

The value of the Bode plot lies in the fact that it can be quickly constructed by knowing only the values of resistance and capacitance of the circuit, and it shows immediately the approximate frequency characteristics of the circuit. In fact the knowledge of f_2 and of the 6 db per octave slope often makes a mental picture of the frequency response possible without the actual drawing of the graph.

Construction of the Bode Plot

The Bode plot for a particular circuit may be drawn by first choosing a horizontal line to represent the 0-db midrange response level, and choosing a convenient vertical db scale. Then, $f_2 = 1/2\pi R_{sh}C_{sh}$ should be calculated; the point on the 0-db line at this frequency should be marked, and a horizontal line drawn from this point to the left. Then, a second point should be marked at 6 db below the 0-db level at a frequency twice the value of f_2, and a straight line drawn to join these two points, extending as far down as desired. Figure 5–16 illustrates this. The horizontal scale should be logarithmic, and the vertical scale linear. If desired, a point 20 db below the horizontal line, at $f = 10f_2$, can be used instead of the 6-db point.

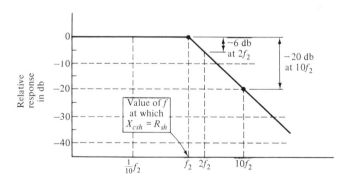

FIGURE 5–16
Construction of a Bode plot

We can now add two more names for the 3-db point to our vocabulary. Because of the graph's appearance the frequency f_2 is often called the *corner frequency* or the *break frequency*.

Accurate Approximation of Actual Response From the Bode Plot

At frequencies well removed from the corner frequency, the 6 db per octave slope of the Bode plot provides a very good approximation of actual response for most practical purposes. For example, at $f = 4f_2$, the error in the voltage ratio is only about 3 percent; the decibel error is roughly 0.25 db out of 12 db. But at frequencies closer to f_2 the error is, of course excessive. In this region, knowledge of the approximate error at only two or three additional points permits sketching in quite an accurate approximation of the actual response, when desired. Table 5–1 lists the approximate amounts by which the actual response falls below the Bode plot values, and Figure 5–17

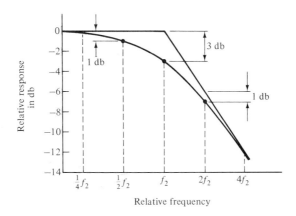

FIGURE 5–17

Sketching in the response near the corner frequency

then illustrates how the curve can be sketched in. Note that beyond $f_2/4$ and $4f_2$, the two plots are practically the same, while within this region only the 1 db difference needs to be remembered — for $f_2/2$ and $2f_2$ — in addition to the basic 3 db at f_2.

TABLE 5–1

Values of f	Approximate error in Bode plot
$f_2/4$	1/4 db
$f_2/2$	1 db
f_2	3 db
$2f_2$	1 db
$4f_2$	1/4 db

Bode plot methods are of course also applicable to the low-frequency response, with Equation (5–9) defining the corner frequency:

$$f_1 = \frac{1}{2\pi C_c(R + R')} \tag{5–9}$$

Figure 5–18 shows a Bode plot of both low-frequency and high-frequency regions.

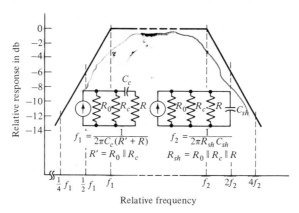

FIGURE 5–18
Complete Bode plot

5.11 h_{fe} High-Frequency Roll-Off

In Chapter 4 we discussed the representation of the transistor's capacitance in terms of the decrease of its short-circuit current gain, h_{fe}, at high frequencies. If you will examine Equation (4–14) for the h_{fe} roll-off, you will see that it is the same as Equation (5–20) if f_{hfe} is replaced by f_2.

Consequently, Figures 5–14 and 5–17 can be used for evaluating the relative short-circuit current gain when comparing transistors with regard to their high-frequency capabilities. The transistor's "beta cutoff" frequency, or f_{hfe}, is simply taken to be the upper 3-db frequency f_2 in Figures 5–14 and 5–17.

5.12 Phase Shift

A study of the low-frequency response Equation (5–6) shows that not only is the *amplitude* of the output affected by the reactance of the coupling capacitor at low frequencies, but the *phase* of the output relative to the input is also affected. The algebra of complex numbers tells us that A_{vL}/A_{vM} from Equation (5–6) has the phase angle whose tangent is $X_C/(R + R')$, or

$$\theta = \tan^{-1} \frac{X_C}{R + R'} \tag{5–25}$$

and the $-j$ in the denominator indicates that A_{vL} *leads* A_{vM}. This may be verified by an examination of the voltage and current relations in Figure 5–6.

Similarly, the high-frequency response Equation (5–17) shows a phase shift such that A_{vH} *lags* A_{vM}. In this case, the phase shift is

$$\theta = \tan^{-1} \frac{\omega R_{sh} C_{sh}}{1}$$

$$\theta = \tan^{-1} \frac{R_{sh}}{X_{sh}} \tag{5–26}$$

In Figure 5–19 the phase shift as a function of frequency is shown for both the low and the high-frequency ranges. Phase shift is not a critical factor in

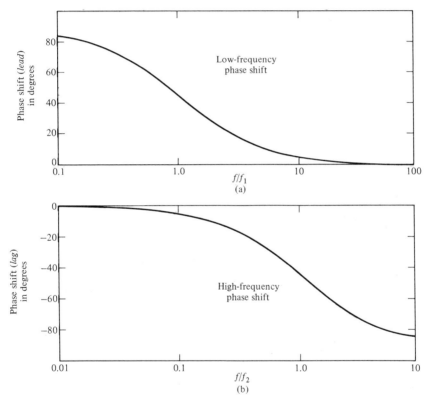

FIGURE 5–19
Phase shift in RC *amplifiers*

audio amplifiers, as the ear does not seem to be sensitive to moderate changes in phase among the frequencies comprising a complex sound. In other applications, however, small changes of phase may be very noticeable.

5.13 Frequency Response Measurement

Since the frequency response of an amplifier is its gain versus frequency characteristic, it may be measured by applying a constant amplitude input signal, varying the frequency of this signal, and measuring the output signal amplitude. Figure 5–20 illustrates the basic test arrangement. Several precautions need to be observed in making such tests. These are listed and briefly discussed in the following material.

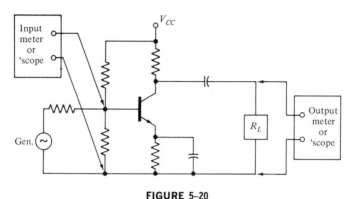

FIGURE 5–20
Frequency response measurement

Constant Amplitude of Test Signal

Many signal generators do not maintain a constant output amplitude over a wide frequency range. Consequently the signal at the input to the amplifier should be monitored during the test, and if its amplitude should change, it should be readjusted to its original amplitude.

Some signal generators are built to maintain a constant output amplitude, within a stated percentage variation. However, the input impedance of an amplifier may vary considerably at very low and very high frequencies. A signal generator having constant output when connected to a constant load, or to a very high impedance load, may not have constant amplitude connected to a low input impedance that is not constant.

Quality of Test Signal

If the test signal frequency is not correct, or the waveform is not a reasonably good sine wave, error in the measurement can result. There is no hard and fast rule for the amount of inaccuracy that may be permitted in the test signal for it depends upon the quality of the equipment being tested and upon the purpose of the test.

For routine testing it may often be sufficient to check the waveform by visual observation on an oscilloscope, to ensure that it shows no visible distortion. However, the ability to detect distortion in the shape of a sine wave varies considerably among individuals. In addition, for some testing purposes the allowable distortion may be so low that more exact methods are required.

Most commercial signal generators are guaranteed to perform within certain specifications listed by the manufacturer. These specifications state the accuracy of the frequency, the maximum distortion, etc. Electronic manufacturers using such equipment in their engineering laboratories, quality control departments, and the like, often have trained personnel to periodically check their test equipment. If not, they have it checked by the equipment manufacturer or by other organizations that specialize in such work, at regular intervals or whenever it is suspected that the equipment may have become defective.

Frequency Response of Meters and Oscilloscopes

Obviously the instruments being used must have frequency response exceeding that of the circuit being tested. Ideally the meter or oscilloscope should be within its specified accuracy over the entire range of test frequencies. Ordinarily this will mean that the measuring instrument's frequency response should be 5 to 10 times better than the frequency range being tested. That is, its high-frequency 3-db point should be 5 to 10 times higher, and its low-frequency 3-db point should be 5 to 10 times lower. Again, there is no hard and fast rule for this; the requirements vary with the quality of the equipment being tested and with the use to which the test data is to be put.

Input Impedance of Meters and Oscilloscopes

In any measurement situation the measuring instrument disturbs the circuit. Consider a meter having a resistance of 10,000 ohms, being used to measure the voltage across one portion of a voltage divider in which the resistances are not very small relative to 10,000 ohms. The parallel combination of the meter and the resistance across which it is connected will be lower than the value of the resistance alone, and the voltage distribution in the voltage divider will change when the meter is connected to it to make the measurement. Consequently the meter, although accurate, will not be recording the correct voltage. In general, then, the input resistance of a meter or oscilloscope should be much greater than the resistance across which it is to be connected.

In addition, when making any high-frequency response measurements, the input capacitance of the meter or oscilloscope should be *low* compared to the shunt capacitance of the circuit being tested. If this requirement is met, the high-frequency response will not be greatly affected by the added capacitance.

The manufacturer's specifications for an oscilloscope or meter that is intended for use over a wide range of frequencies will list the approximate input capacitance of the instrument, so that the user may judge its appropriateness for his particular problem. To do this, he must, of course, know the approximate shunt capacitance of his circuit.

If the circuit shunt capacitance is not known, at least in some preliminary way, this evaluation cannot be made. But a preliminary check of the 3-db point with the intended instrument will permit a calculation of the total shunt capacitance from Equation (5–22):

$$f_2 = \frac{1}{2\pi R_{sh} C_{sh}}$$

(5–22)

If the value of C_{sh} found from this calculation is many times greater than the instrument's capacitance, the instrument will not introduce appreciable error in the frequency response measurement.

If the instrument's capacitance is appreciable in comparison with the circuit capacitance, a different instrument should be chosen, or else a low-capacitance probe should be used if available.

Effect of Source Resistance

In our discussions of frequency response we have considered gain measurements made by applying a constant amplitude signal to the amplifier input, as depicted in Figure 5–20. In at least one instance, however, this method can cause error in the frequency response measurement.

The earlier discussion of the emitter-bypass capacitor's effect on frequency response, for example, showed that the low-frequency 3-db point due to C_e is

$$f_1 \cong \frac{1}{2\pi \left[\dfrac{R_g + h_{ie}}{h_{fe}} \right] C_e}$$

(5–12)

Applying a constant amplitude signal directly at the amplifier's input gives the effect of using a source having $R_g = 0$. A real source, however, is likely to have an output resistance as big as h_{ie}, or greater. Consequently, this test method can cause very great error in the measurement.

To avoid this error, a resistance equal to the actual source resistance may be connected in series with the signal generator, as illustrated in Figure 5–21.

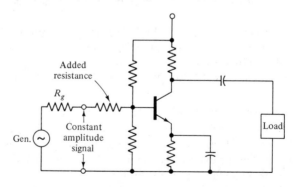

FIGURE 5–21
Adding resistance to simulate the output resistance of the real source

When this is done, it is the signal at the generator terminals which must be monitored and maintained at a constant amplitude, and not the signal at the amplifier input.

PROBLEMS

5–1. What are the 70.7 percent response frequencies in the following two frequency response curves? What is the bandwidth in each case?

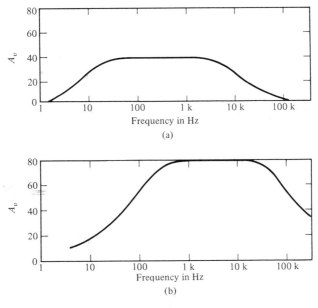

FIGURE P5–1

5–2. The frequency response curve of Problem 5–1(a) is how many decibels below its midrange response at the following frequencies?

(a) 10 Hz

(b) 100 Hz

(c) 100 kHz

5–3. How many db below the midrange response is the curve of Problem 5–1(b) at

(a) 10 Hz

(b) 10 kHz

(c) 100 kHz

5-4. An amplifier's gain is reduced at a certain high frequency by two effects. One of these acts to multiply the gain by the factor 0.6; the other operates on the gain by the factor 0.8. What are the individual effects expressed in db? What is the total effect expressed in db?

5-5. What is the total capacitance shunting the output in each of the following circuits?

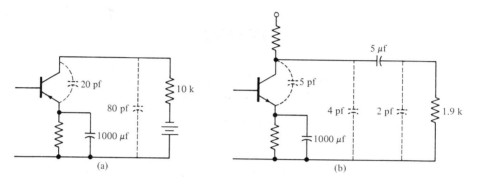

(a)   (b)

FIGURE P5-5

5-6. (a) Draw the equivalent circuit for each of the above cases, showing shunt capacitances.

(b) What is the reactance of the shunt capacitance in (a), at 1000 Hz and 200 kHz?

(c) How does this compare with the value of load resistance?

(d) Roughly how will this affect the voltage gain at 200 kHz (compared to, say, 1000 Hz)?

(e) Roughly how will this affect the current gain from base to 10 kilohm load?

5-7. (a) What is the reactance of the coupling capacitor in Problem 5-5(b) above at 1000 Hz? At 10 Hz?

(b) How does the reactance at 10 Hz compare (roughly) with typical values of input resistance for small-signal transistors?

(c) Considering the 5 μf coupling capacitor and the 1900 ohm load as a voltage divider, how do you think the reactance of the coupling capacitor affects (roughly) the amount of *collector* signal voltage that is delivered to the 1900 ohm load at 10 Hz?

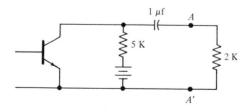

FIGURE P5-8

5–8. Thevenize the following circuit at A-A' on the assumption that the transistor's $R_o \gg 5K$. Assuming that the open-circuit voltage at A-A' is 1 v rms, find the voltage across R at the following frequencies: 15; 50; 100; 500; 1000; and 2000 Hz.

5–9. (a) How should the value of C be altered to provide greater low-frequency output in the above circuit?

(b) How might R be changed to provide more low-frequency output in general?

5–10. Calculate the voltage level *in db* at 50 and 100 Hz relative to the 1000 Hz level for Problem 5–8.

5–11. Find the 3-db frequency (the half-power frequency) for Problem 5–8. Find the 3-db frequency for the same circuit using a 10 μf capacitor.

5–12. Using the universal response curves, find the *relative* response as a ratio and in db, of the circuit of Problem 5–8 at the following frequencies: 2; 4; 6; 10; 20; 40; 80; 1000 Hz.

5–13. Plot the results of Problem 5–12 on semi-log graph paper in a manner similar to that in the text.

5–14. Find the approximate lower 3-db frequency f_1 for the following circuit:

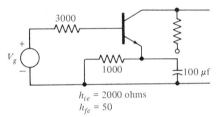

$$h_{ie} = 2000 \text{ ohms}$$
$$h_{fe} = 50$$

FIGURE P5–14

5–15. Find the frequency f_o at which the gain is 3 db above its final constant low-frequency value, for the circuit of Problem 5-14.

5–16. Draw the output portion of the high-frequency equivalent circuit for the following amplifier. Show R_{sh} and C_{sh} as single elements with their effective values indicated.

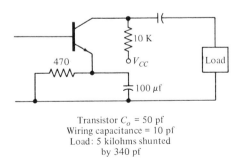

Transistor $C_o = 50$ pf
Wiring capacitance = 10 pf
Load: 5 kilohms shunted
by 340 pf

FIGURE P5–16

5–17. Find the relative response (A_{vH}/A_{vM}) for the above circuit at the following frequencies: 1; 10; 100; 200; 300 kHz.

5–18. (a) What is the upper 3-db frequency for the circuit of Problem 5–16?

(b) If the load capacitance were reduced to 140 pf, what would the improvement in f_2 be?

(c) How could f_2 be improved without reducing the capacitance?

5–19. Use the universal high-frequency response curves to find the *relative* response as a ratio and in db for the circuit of Problem 5–16 at the following frequencies: 1; 10; 50; 150; 250; 500 kHz

5–20. Using semi-log graph paper which has at least 3 cycles, draw the Bode plots fo the following circuits all on one graph. Use a vertical scale range of at least 20 db

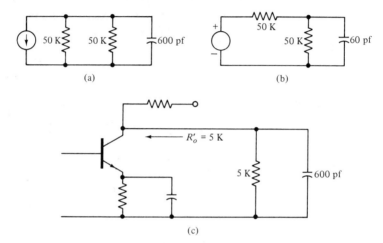

(a)   (b)

(c)

FIGURE P5–20

5–21. Draw the Bode plots for the following circuits.

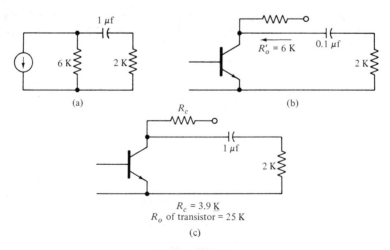

(a)   (b)

$R_c = 3.9$ K
R_o of transistor $= 25$ K

(c)

FIGURE P5–21

5–22. Using the method discussed in the text, draw a good approximation of the actual response on the graphs of Problems 5–20(b) and 5–21(b).

5–23. Draw a complete Bode plot on one graph for the following circuit:

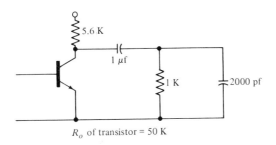

R_o of transistor = 50 K

FIGURE P5–23

5–24. Find the phase of the output relative to the midfrequency phase for the following circuit at the following frequencies: 20; 40; 100; 20,000; 100,000 Hz.

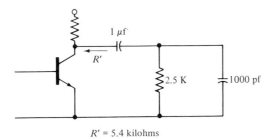

R' = 5.4 kilohms

FIGURE P5–24

CHAPTER 6

Cascaded Amplifiers

6.1 Introduction

The required amplification of a signal is often much greater than can be obtained in a single stage. When this is the case, amplifier stages may be connected so that the output of one stage is fed to the input of another. Such arrangements are called *cascaded* or *multistage amplifiers*.

The total amplification of a cascaded amplifier is the product of the individual stage gains. Consider a signal V_1 applied to a stage having amplification A_1. The output of this stage is then $V_2 = A_1V_1$. If this output is applied to the input of another stage having a gain equal to A_2, the output of this stage is then $V_3 = A_2V_2 = A_2(A_1V_1) = A_2A_1V_1$. Thus the overall gain is

$$A_T = \frac{V_3}{V_1} = \frac{A_2A_1V_1}{V_1} = A_2A_1$$

However, the amount of amplification in an individual stage is greatly dependent upon the effective load impedance. The input impedance of an amplifier stage in a cascaded amplifier is part of the effective load for the preceding stage, and thus may drastically affect the performance of the preceding stage. In some instances amplifier stages capable of quite high voltage and power gain (with high values of load impedance) are operated at relatively low gain because of the low input impedance of the following stage.

The bias network at the input of a stage is in parallel with the input impedance for signal components, and thus is part of the effective load, tending to further reduce the effective load impedance. In addition, such resistance networks constitute current-shunting paths which shunt signal currents away from the next stage input. The signal losses resulting from such effects are often called *interstage losses*.

The frequency response of a cascaded amplifier is usually poorer than that of a single stage. Consider two stages, each having a midrange gain of 50 and each having an upper 3-db frequency of 2.0 MHz, when operated in cascade. The overall two-stage midrange gain is then $(50)(50) = 2500$, and the gain at 2.0 MHz is

$$(0.707 \times 50)(0.707 \times 50) = (1/2)(2500)$$

In other words the gain at 2.0 MHz in the two-stage amplifier is one-half the midrange gain — in contrast with the individual stage performance, which is down only to 70.7 percent of the midrange gain at that frequency.

There are three basic methods of coupling amplifier stages together. One is *RC* coupling, in which a capacitor connects from the output of one stage to the input of the next in order to pass the signal on while blocking the dc bias voltages. Another is transformer coupling, which provides the same two functions but provides in addition an impedance transformation for better matching between the low input impedance of the next stage and the high output impedance of the previous stage. The third is direct coupling, or dc coupling, in which the individual amplifier stage bias conditions are designed so that the two stages may be directly connected together without the necessity for dc isolation. Direct-coupled amplifiers have the advantage of unimpaired low-frequency response because of the absence of capacitors, and consequently form an important segment of amplifier work.

6.2 *RC*-Coupled Amplifiers

Figure 6–1 illustrates a typical two-stage *RC*-coupled amplifier. This example is typical in the sense that the biasing and collector resistances, and the coupling and bypassing, are typical arrangements. The circuit does not, how-

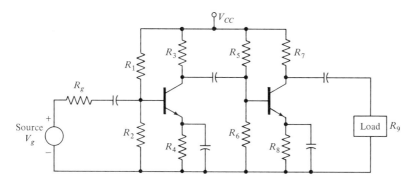

FIGURE 6–1
Typical two-stage RC-coupled amplifier

ever, include feedback which very likely would be used also. Feedback techniques will be examined in a later chapter, but the problems and techniques of cascading can perhaps be most clearly introduced in terms of the basic amplifier circuits without feedback.

Notice in Figure 6–1 that the effective load on the first stage is the *parallel combination* of R_3, R_5, R_6, and the input resistance of the second stage, which might be designated as R_{i2}. *Thus the gain of the first stage cannot be known without knowing the input resistance of the second stage.*

However, recall from Chapter 4 that input resistance depends to some extent upon load resistance, except for those cases where the load and the transistor parameters are such as to permit the approximation $R_i \cong h_{ie}$. *Thus it may be necessary to consider conditions in the output circuit of the second stage before being able to find the gain of the first stage.* Finally, the first stage input resistance, R_{i1}, may be affected by the first stage load, part of which is R_{i2}. Thus it is sometimes necessary to work backward from the final load, computing each stage's R_i.

Once the R_i of each stage has been ascertained, stage-by-stage gain or signal amplitude calculations may be made by working forward from the first stage.

Amplifier Notation

One of the difficult aspects of amplifier analysis for the beginner is often simply the notation. Each of the terms used to describe amplifier characteristics is quite general and may be applied to the amplifier circuit in several different ways. Often the decision as to how to apply the term is up to the individual; certainly it is not the same for all amplifiers. To see this, consider Figure 6–2.

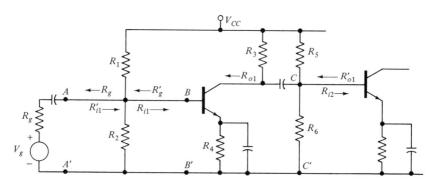

FIGURE 6–2
Cascaded amplifier with input and output resistance designations

This is a repetition of part of Figure 6–1 but with some of the designations which are important in amplifier analysis added to the figure.

Note that R_g designates the source or generator resistance, i.e., the source resistance measured looking back into the points A-A'. However, the effective source resistance for the actual amplifier stage as it is considered in the equivalent circuit performance equations — in calculating R_o of the first stage, for example — is the parallel combination of R_g, R_1, and R_2. This effective source resistance ($R_g \parallel R_1 \parallel R_2$) may be designated by R_g' or some other convenient notation. The important point is that this is the value which must be used in equations containing the term "R_g."

Similarly, R_{i1} (looking into points B-B') is the stage input resistance as given by the equivalent circuit. But for some considerations we need to know the effective input resistance of the stage as a load on the source. This is the parallel combination $R_1 \parallel R_2 \parallel R_i$, and we might wish to designate this as R'_{i1}.

In the output of the first stage, R_{o1} is the output resistance as given by the equivalent circuit equation. But $R'_{o1} = R_{o1} \parallel R_3 \parallel R_5 \parallel R_6$ is the effective source resistance looking back into the points C-C', and *must be the value used for the term R_g in the equation for the second stage output resistance.*

Analysis of a Two-Stage Amplifier

At this point an example illustrating the analysis of a two-stage amplifier would be useful. Consider the circuit shown in Figure 6-3.

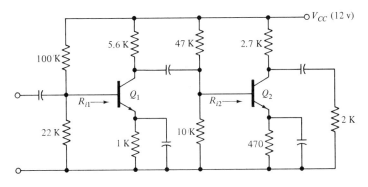

FIGURE 6-3
Two-stage amplifier example

The transistor used for both stages will be the 2N334A, with the first stage biased to operate at a quiescent current of approximately 1 ma and the second stage at about 2 ma.

Reference to the 2N334A data sheet in Appendix A provides h-parameter values for the 1 ma operation. The use of the graph of h-parameter variations with emitter current, and the conversion relations given in Chapter 4, provide the approximate values corresponding to the 2 ma quiescent current. (To review the method of converting, refer to Example 4-2.) The resulting values are:

TABLE 6-1

	Q_1	Q_2	
h_{fe}	38	34	
h_{ie}	1700	800	ohms
h_{oe}	6.0	10.7	μmhos
h_{re}	1.3×10^{-4}	1.12×10^{-4}	
Δ^{he}	52.6×10^{-4}	47.5×10^{-4}	

The first and second stage load and input resistances can be found first:

1. $R_{L2} = 2700 \parallel 2000 \cong 1150$ ohms
2.   This load resistance is so small that h_{ie} is a good approximation for R_i.

$$R_{i2} \cong h_{ie2} \cong 800 \text{ ohms}$$

3. $R_{L1} = 5600 \parallel 47,000 \parallel 10,000 \parallel R_{i2}$

$$R_{L1} \cong \frac{1}{\dfrac{1}{5600} + \dfrac{1}{47,000} + \dfrac{1}{10,000} + \dfrac{1}{800}}$$

$R_{L1} \cong 646$ ohms

4. $R_{i1} \cong h_{ie1} \cong 1700$ ohms

Now, knowing the loads and the input resistances, current gains and voltage gains may be calculated.

5.   Current gain of the first stage:

$$A_{i1} = \frac{h_{fe1}}{1 + h_{oe1} R_{L1}} \cong h_{fe}$$

because the load R_{L1} is so small. Thus,

$$A_{i1} \cong 38$$

However, this is only the current gain from the base lead to the collector lead. In order to evaluate the effect of interstage losses, consider Figure 6–4.

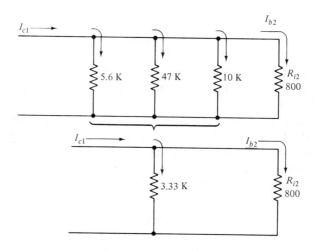

FIGURE 6–4
Effect of shunting resistances on currents

The figure shows that only a part of the collector signal current gets to the input of the second stage (i.e., to the 800 ohm R_{i2}).

The value of the signal current I_{b2} would be, in this circuit,

$$I_{b2} \cong \left[\frac{3330}{3330 + 800} \right](I_{c1}) \cong 0.8 \, I_{c1}$$

and the effective current gain from base to base is actually

$$A'_{i1} = \frac{I_{b2}}{I_{b1}} = \frac{0.8 \, I_{c1}}{I_{b1}} = 0.8 \, A_{i1}$$

$$A'_{i1} \cong (0.8)(38) \cong 30.4$$

6. Voltage gain of the first stage:

$$A_{v1} = A_{i1}\left[\frac{R_{L1}}{R_{i1}} \right]$$

The current gain to be used in this calculation must be the gain from base to collector since R_{L1} is the effective load at the collector. The current gain to the collector lead was found to be h_{fe1}. Thus

$$A_{v1} \cong h_{fe1}\left[\frac{R_{L1}}{R_{i1}} \right]$$

$$A_{v1} \cong 38\left[\frac{646}{1700} \right] \cong 14.4$$

7. Current gain of the second stage:
Again, the effective load (2700 ‖ 2000) is small enough so that the base-to-collector current gain is approximately h_{fe}. Therefore

$$A_{i2} \cong h_{fe2} \cong 34$$

But as before, this current divides between any interstage resistance and the *final* load. In this case the current division results in

$$A'_{i2} = \left[\frac{2700}{2000 + 2700} \right](A_{i2})$$

$$A'_{i2} \cong (0.575)(34) \cong 19.5$$

8. Voltage gain of the second stage:

$$A_{v2} = A_{i2}\left[\frac{R_{L2}}{R_{i2}} \right]$$

$$A_{v2} \cong h_{fe2}\left[\frac{R_{L2}}{R_{i2}} \right] \cong 34\left[\frac{1150}{800} \right]$$

$$A_{v2} \cong 48.9$$

9. The overall voltage gain and current gain can now be found:

$$A_{vT} = A_{v1}A_{v2}$$

$$A_{vT} = (14.4)(48.9) \cong 704$$

$$A_{iT} = A'_{i1}A'_{i2}$$

$$A_{iT} \cong (30.4)(19.5) \cong 593$$

10. In many applications it is the signal power gain which is important. The overall power gain is

$$A_{pT} = A_{p1}A_{p2} = A_{v1}A'_{i1}A_{v2}A'_{i2}$$

Notice the prime marks on the current gain symbols. In the notation we chose to use in the calculations above, this designated base-to-base current gain.

Let us first find the individual stage power gains:

$$A_{p1} = A_{v1}A'_{i1} \cong (14.4)(30.4)$$
$$A_{p1} \cong 438$$

and

$$A_{p2} = A_{v2}A'_{i2}$$
$$A_{p2} \cong (48.9)(19.5)$$
$$A_{p2} \cong 955$$

Then the total power gain is

$$A_{pT} = A_{p1}A_{p2}$$
$$A_{pT} \cong (438)(955) \cong 418,000$$

The total power gain can, of course, also be found as the product of the total current gain and total voltage gain:

$$A_{pT} = A_{vT}A'_{iT}$$
$$A_{pT} \cong (704)(593) \cong 417,000$$

6.3 Transformer-Coupled Amplifiers

In general, cascaded RC-coupled CE stages have low voltage and power gains because of the low values of load resistance presented by the input of each stage to the preceding stage. If the effective load resistance of each stage could be increased, the voltage gain and power gain could be increased. Transformer coupling of the signal between amplifier stages permits more favorable load resistance values. By use of the impedance-changing properties of transformers, the low input resistance of a stage may be reflected as a high load resistance to the previous stage. Thus, transformer coupling may be used to advantage in a number of applications.

Transformers suitable for audio frequency use, however, are bulky, heavy, and expensive, since they must have ample iron cores and many turns of copper wire to achieve the high values of inductance needed to operate properly at low frequencies. Often it is more economical, in terms of cost and size, to use additional RC-coupled transistors to obtain the required overall gain in audio amplifiers. At higher frequencies, however, as in the radio frequency sections of communication equipment, transformer coupling provides definite advantages.

Impedance Transformation with Transformer Coupling

The basic circuit for the transformer-coupled amplifier is shown in Figure 6–5. The impedance transforming properties of the ideal transformer with tight coupling can be expressed as

$$R_1 = \left(\frac{N_1}{N_2}\right)^2 R_2 \qquad\qquad (6\text{–}1)$$

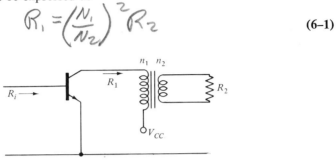

FIGURE 6–5
Basic circuit of the transformer-coupled CE amplifier

This indicates that a low value of load resistance can be "stepped-up" to a more favorable value at the collector of the transistor by using the appropriate turns ratio.

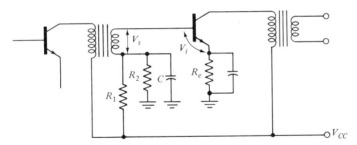

FIGURE 6–6
Biasing arrangement in transformer coupling

Biasing the Transformer-Coupled Amplifier

When transformer coupling is used between stages, the biasing may be handled as shown in Figure 6–6.

This circuit illustrates emitter-resistor stabilizing of the operating point. R_e provides the stabilizing voltage drop, and the voltage divider action of R_1 and R_2 provides the necessary forward-bias just as in RC-coupled stages. However, in RC coupling, the junction of R_1 and R_2 is connected directly to the base, resulting in R_1 and R_2 shunting the signal circuit, while here it is connected to the low potential end of the transformer winding. The dc resistance of the winding is negligible compared to the value of R_1 and R_2, so that the base is effectively connected directly to the divider point as far as the dc conditions are concerned, but the resistors do not shunt the signal circuit. They are, in fact, in series with the signal loop from base to emitter.

The presence of this resistance in series with the base-emitter junction would cause serious loss of signal if the resistance were not bypassed. Thus the capacitor C must be connected from the junction of R_1 and R_2 to ground or common. The effectiveness of the bypassing is determined by how small the resulting parallel impedance $R_1 \parallel R_2 \parallel X_c$ is in comparison to the input resistance of the transistor. X_C will usually be much smaller than $R_1 \parallel R_2$, and R_i will usually be approximately equal to h_{ie}, so that for practical purposes it is the value of X_C relative to h_{ie} that is usually important. If C is chosen large enough so that $X_C \leq h_{ie}/10$ at the signal frequency, the loss will be negligible since

$$V_i/V_s \cong h_{ie}/\sqrt{h_{ie}^2 + X^2}$$

Because R_1 and R_2 do not shunt the signal circuit, they may be made as small as desired. As they are made smaller, of course, they consume more power from the power supply, so that there is a practical limitation on this. However, the task of operating point stabilizing is made easier with lower values of R_1 and R_2. Recall that Chapter 3 showed that for good stability R_e should be large, and $R = R_1 \parallel R_2$ should be small. Of course large R_e requires higher value of supply voltage, while small $R_1 - R_2$ requires greater power supply current capacity. An attempt to achieve a given stability in the case of RC coupling might require an excessively large value of R_e, but with transformer coupling the same result might be achieved by reducing the value of R_1 and R_2.

6.4 Gain Calculations in Transformer Coupling

In order to clarify some of the problems associated with the analysis of transformer-coupled stages, let the transistors from the example of Section 6.2 be used in the circuit of Figure 6–7.

Assume that the output transformer T_3 is designed to transform the final load from 2000 ohms up to 30,000 ohms at the collector of Q_2, and that the interstage transformer T_2 changes the input resistance of the second stage, R_{i2},

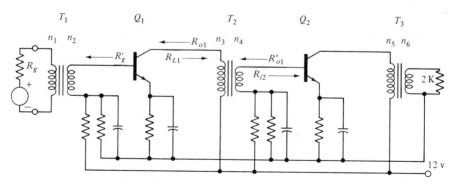

FIGURE 6–7

Two-stage amplifier using transformer coupling

up to 20,000 ohms at the collector of Q_1. Let the transistors be biased to the same operating points, so that the h-parameter values listed in the previous example will still apply. They are repeated here for reference:

TABLE 6–2

	Q_1	Q_2	
h_{fe}	38	34	
h_{ie}	1700	800	ohms
h_{oe}	6.0	10.7	μmhos
h_{re}	1.3×10^{-4}	1.12×10^{-4}	
Δ_{he}	52.6×10^{-4}	47.5×10^{-4}	

Let us find the gains for the first stage. Since the effective collector load for this amplifier is not a low impedance, we can expect that the approximate gain equations may not be accurate enough. We could calculate A_i and then find the voltage gain from the equation

$$A_v = A_i \left[\frac{R_L}{R_i} \right]$$

but this requires calculating R_i which we may not otherwise need for this problem. So it may be more convenient to use Equation (4–5):

$$A_{v1} = \frac{h_{fe1} R_{L1}}{h_{ie1} + \Delta_1{}^h R_{L1}}$$

This will give the voltage gain from base to collector, but the transformer will step it down so that the voltage gain from base to base will be

$$A'_{v1} = A_{v1} \left[\frac{n_4}{n_3} \right]$$

The current gain is similarly affected by the transformer. The current gain equation is

$$A_{i1} = \frac{h_{fe}}{1 + h_{oe} R_L}$$

But this is the current gain from the base to the collector. The gain from the base to the next base is of course this figure modified by the transformer ratio. The transformer ratio is designed to give

$$\frac{R_{L1}}{R_{i2}} = \left[\frac{n_3}{n_4} \right]^2$$

Use of the equation for input resistance from Chapter 4 gives a value of 714 ohms for R_{i2}. (The high value of load impedance warns us we should not assume $R_{i1} \cong h_{ie2}$.) This value for R_{i2} then gives us

$$\left[\frac{n_3}{n_4} \right]^2 = \frac{20,000}{714} \cong 28$$

so that

$$\frac{n_3}{n_4} = \sqrt{28} \cong 5.29$$

The transformer currents are inversely proportional to the turns ratio so that, assuming an ideal transformer (i.e., lossless), we have

$$A'_{i1} = A_{i1}\left[\frac{n_3}{n_4}\right]$$

Note carefully that the turns ratio used for the current gain calculation is the *reciprocal* of that used for the voltage gain calculation.

Now we may calculate the gains:

$$A'_{v1} = \frac{h_{fe1}R_{L1}}{h_{ie1} + \Delta_1{}^h R_{L1}}\left[\frac{n_4}{n_3}\right]$$

$$A'_{v1} \cong \frac{(38)(2 \times 10^4)}{1700 + (52.6 \times 10^{-4})(2 \times 10^4)}\left[\frac{1}{5.29}\right]$$

$$A'_{v1} \cong (421)\left[\frac{1}{5.29}\right] \cong 79.5$$

$$A'_{i1} = \frac{h_{fe1}}{1 + h_{oe1}R_{L1}}\left[\frac{n_3}{n_4}\right]$$

$$A'_{i1} = \frac{38}{1 + (6.0 \times 10^{-6})(2 \times 10^4)}(5.29)$$

$$A'_{i1} = \frac{38}{1.12} \cong (33.9)(5.29) = 179$$

These figures may be compared with the first stage voltage gain and current gain of 14.4 and 30.4 respectively for the *RC*-coupled circuit, using the same transistor, in the example of Section 6.2.

The power gain in the transformer-coupled case is

$$A'_{p1} = A'_{v1}A'_{i1}$$
$$A'_{p1} \cong (79.5)(179)$$
$$A'_{p1} \cong 14{,}200$$

and this may be compared to the figure of 438 for the *RC*-coupled stage.

6.5 Output Resistance Calculations in Transformer Coupling

If the stage output resistance value is needed, account must be taken of the impedance transformations in any coupling transformers. For example, consider the use of Equation (4–6) to find the output resistance of the first stage in Figure 6–7.

$$R_o = \frac{R_g + h_{ie}}{R_g h_{oe} + \Delta^{he}}$$

The R_g in this equation must of course be interpreted as the effective source resistance as seen from the base of Q_1. This must be the resistance designated R'_g in the figure, or the generator R_g multiplied by the impedance transformation ratio $(n_2/n_1)^2$. That is,

$$R'_g = R_g\left[\frac{n_2}{n_1}\right]^2$$

must be used for R_g in Equation (4–6).

Similarly, the resulting R_o value obtained from Equation (4–6) will be the source impedance designated R_{o1} in Figure 6–7, and the source impedance of this stage as it appears at the base of Q_2 will then be

$$R'_{o1} = R_{o1}\left[\frac{n_4}{n_3}\right]^2$$

6.6 The Load Line in Transformer Coupling

In load line analysis the dc load line must be drawn first. This is done in order to locate the operating point, which is, of course, the point defining the dc conditions. The load line representing the ac or signal load is then drawn through this point, since the signal causes the currents and voltages to fluctuate above and below the quiescent point.

In the case of RC-coupled amplifiers the dc load is always greater than the ac load, and the ac load line is therefore always steeper than the dc, as illustrated in Figure 6–8.

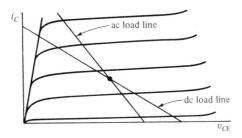

FIGURE 6–8
dc and ac load lines in RC coupling

In transformer coupling, however, the dc load will generally be smaller than the ac load. The dc resistance of a transformer winding, for example, is usually so small compared to the ac impedance of the winding, and the impedance reflected from the load connected to the secondary, that the dc resistance can often be ignored. Figure 6–9 illustrates the several components of the load.

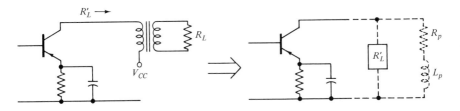

FIGURE 6–9
Components of effective load on transistor in transformer coupling

R_p and L_p represent the resistance and inductance of the primary winding of the transformer. R'_L is the reflected load due to the impedance transformation from the secondary to the primary. Depending upon the type of amplifier, the value of R'_L may range from a few ohms or less to tens of thousands of ohms. The dc resistance R_p of a transformer winding providing such impedances may range from a fraction of an ohm to several hundred ohms — but in any event is usually much smaller than R'_L. Due to the high inductance, the transformer primary *self-impedance* $Z_p = R_p + jX_{Lp}$ is usually many times greater than R'_L in a well designed transformer, except at very low frequencies. As a result, the effective collector load is approximately R'_L. The dc load is of course R_p. Thus the dc and ac load lines for transformer coupling will usually appear as shown in Figure 6–10.

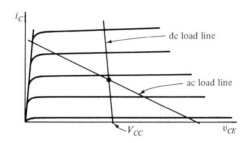

FIGURE 6–10
Load lines in transformer coupling

Notice that the dc load line tends to appear nearly vertical in comparison with the ac load line. *Note also where V_{CC} is indicated on the voltage scale.* The ac load line shows that a large enough signal may very well cause the collector voltage to swing far above the value of V_{CC}. The reason for this lies in the fact that, with a low value of dc resistance, the dc voltage drop in the collector circuit is quite small, so that the quiescent collector voltage is only slightly less than V_{CC}. The ac or signal load impedance due to the transformer action is large enough compared to the dc resistance that the peak signal voltage developed across the winding, when large signals are being handled, may be much greater than the dc voltage drop in the winding. Thus, the maximum upward swing of collector voltage may go much higher than V_{CC}. These voltages are illustrated graphically in Figure 6–11.

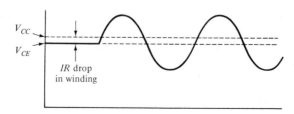

FIGURE 6–11
Signal voltage in ac load exceeding the dc voltage drop

Load Line Example (Transformer Coupling)

As an example of the load line technique in transformer coupling, consider the circuit and collector curves shown in Figure 6–12. Assume that the base current set by the biasing circuitry is 0.6 ma, the dc resistance of the primary

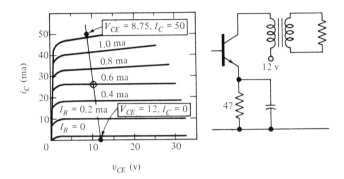

FIGURE 6–12
Circuit and collector curves for load line example

winding is 18 ohms, the effective signal load impedance R'_L is 500 ohms, and the emitter resistor, as shown, is 47 ohms. The total dc resistance in the circuit external to the transistor then is $R_{dc} = 47 + 18 = 65$ ohms.

The dc load line cannot be drawn by the technique used for RC-coupled amplifiers since the intercept with the vertical axis would occur at

$$I_{max} = \frac{V_{CC}}{R_{dc}} = \frac{12}{65}$$

$$I_{max} \cong 185 \text{ ma}$$

which is off the scale. However, the incremental method is appropriate. The dc load line extends from the V_{CC} value on the voltage axis (12 v) upward at a slope determined by $R_{dc} = \Delta V/\Delta I$, in which any convenient increment of current ΔI may be used. A convenient value in this particular case might be 50 ma, since using the maximum value appearing on the graph permits the greatest accuracy in drawing the load line.

Considering dc conditions, when the collector current increases from zero (where the collector voltage must therefore be equal to V_{CC}, or 12 v) to 50 ma, the collector voltage must *decrease* by the amount of the IR drop in R_{dc}. That is, V_{CE} decreases to

$$V_{CE} = V_{CC} - (\Delta I)(R_{dc})$$
$$V_{CE} = 12 - (0.05)(65) = 12 - 3.25$$
$$V_{CE} = 8.75 \text{ v}$$

If the two points $V_{CE} = 12$ v, $I_C = 0$; and $V_{CE} = 8.75$ v, $I_C = 50$ ma are plotted and a line drawn between them, we have the dc load line, as shown in Figure 6–12. This intersects the $I_B = 0.6$ ma (bias) curve at the operating point $V_{CE} \cong 10.3$ v, $I_C \cong 26$ ma.

The ac load line may now be drawn by again choosing a convenient increment of I_C. In this case, the corresponding increment of V_{CE} is found by calculating the voltage change due to the chosen current change in the *ac* load resistance, R'_L. A line is then drawn through the operating point with a slope determined by these two increments. A very convenient value of ΔI_C would be the value of I_C at the operating point. Then

$$\Delta V = (\Delta I_C)(R'_L)$$
$$\Delta V = (0.026)(500) = 13 \text{ v}$$

Thus, from the operating point a straight line is drawn down to a point 26 ma lower and 13 v to the right. That is, the load line extends from the operating point to a point which will be on the voltage axis but 13 v to the right of the operating point. The collector curves with the ac load line added are shown in Figure 6–13.

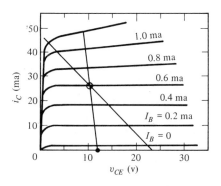

FIGURE 6–13
*Collector curves showing final result: ac load line drawn through
dc operating point*

Since the dc resistance is often quite small (giving a dc load line that is almost vertical), rough calculations, preliminary estimates of performance, and the like are often made by assuming a vertical dc load line. In such cases the dc *collector* voltage is assumed to be approximately V_{CC}, and the operating point is assumed to be at the intersection of the V_{CC} value and the quiescent value of I_B.

6.7 Transducer Gain and Maximum Available Power Gain

The use of impedance transforming methods may permit impedance matching in some applications, with the result that maximum power transfer between circuits is sometimes possible. Impedance matching may occur at the input — in which the stage input impedance is matched to the output impedance of the circuit or transducer acting as the source of signal — and it may occur at the output — in which the load matches the output impedance of the stage. This leads to several ways of describing the performance or the capability of an amplifier. These will be described here briefly.

Transducer Gain

Consider two amplifiers either of which can be used to amplify the signal from a given source. One amplifier has a power gain of 1000 from input terminals to the load connected to the output terminals, but is not well matched to the source at the input. It has an input signal power of 0.5 mw, so that its output power is 0.5 w. The other amplifier has a power gain of only 900 from input terminals to load. However, its input impedance is such that it is matched at the input so that the source is delivering more signal power to it.

When a load resistance matches the source resistance, the power delivered by the source is the maximum that it can deliver, and is often referred to as the *available power* or the *maximum available power*. Suppose that the available power is 0.9 mw in this case. The second amplifier then has an input signal power of 0.9 mw. With the stage gain of 900, the output power is 0.81 w. *Therefore, although the second amplifier has less power gain from input terminals to output terminals, it provides more output.*

The ratio of actual power output to *maximum available* power input for the two cases is:

Case 1. $P_{out}/P_{avail} = 0.5/(0.9)(10^{-3}) \cong 555$

Case 2. $P_{out}/P_{avail} = 0.81/(0.9)(10^{-3}) = 900$

This ratio is known as the *transducer gain*, and as can be seen in the example above, clearly indicates the superiority of one amplifier over another for a particular application even where the terminal-to-terminal gain may not be superior. Comparison of the transducer gains of two amplifiers permits direct comparison of their output signal power when connected to a given source. In the above example, the second amplifier has an output which is $900/555 = 1.62$ times as great as the first amplifier — when both are operated from that particular source. With a different source the results might very well be different, however.

The maximum available power from a given source or transducer may be evaluated by considering the power developed across a load that matches the source resistance (or is the conjugate of the source impedance in the case of sources having reactive components). See Figure 6–14. Now

$$P = I^2 R_L = I^2 R_g$$

but

$$I = \frac{V_g}{R_g + R_L} = \frac{V_g}{2R_g}$$

therefore

$$P = \left[\frac{V_g}{2R_g}\right]^2 R_g$$

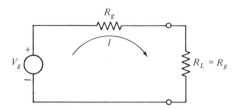

FIGURE 6–14
Basic circuit for evaluating maximum power from a source

so that the maximum available power is

$$P = \frac{V_g^2}{4R_g} \qquad (6\text{–}2)$$

Transducer gain, then, being the ratio of the amplifier's signal power output to the *available power at the input*, is given by

$$TG = \frac{I_{out}^2 R_L}{V_g^2/4R_g} = \frac{4\, I_{out}^2\, R_L R_g}{V_g^2}$$

in which $V_g = I_{in}(R_g + R_i)$ as indicated in Figure 6–15. This gives

$$TG = \frac{4\, I_{out}^2\, R_L R_g}{I_{in}^2(R_g + R_i)^2}$$

$$TG = \frac{4\, A_i^2 R_L R_g}{(R_g + R_i)^2} \qquad (6\text{–}3)$$

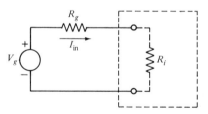

FIGURE 6–15
Amplifier input circuit

Maximum Available Gain (or Maximum Power Gain or Matched Power Gain)

If an amplifier is matched at its input and at its output, its power gain is referred to as the *maximum available gain (MAG)*. Since this condition exists only for source and load resistances that are equal to the amplifier's input and output resistances respectively, it is determined entirely by the transistor parameters. Thus it can serve as a figure of merit describing a transistor's capability. The MAG of transistors can be compared in evaluating them for a particular intended use.

It should be understood, however, that the intended use must be taken into account. Consider two different transistor types being compared for use with a signal source having an output resistance of 1000 ohms. One has an MAG of 38 db, and $R_i = 700$ ohms. The other has MAG = 40 db, and $R_i = 1600$ ohms. If transformer coupling were not feasible (due to cost or size), the type having smaller MAG but more appropriate input resistance might provide more output. The transducer gain (Equation [6–3]) is the correct figure of merit in those cases where there is no possibility of matching at the input.

On the other hand, if matching transformers are to be available — or if there is a choice of transducers so that input matching is possible — decisions should be based upon comparative MAG values along with the transducer sensitivity. (It is possible that the transducer having the lower value of source resistance could provide more signal power input to the amplifier, as Equation [6–2] hints.)

Matched power gain is not usually achieved in practical amplifier circuits, but does serve as a useful figure of merit in some applications. In particular it is often specified by the manufacturer in the case of high-frequency transistors.

6.8   Direct-Coupled or dc Amplifiers

It is often necessary to amplify signals representing very slowly changing quantities. An example of such a signal would be the output of a thermocouple being used to measure the temperature of a component undergoing engineering tests. Phenomena of this type sometimes require time periods of seconds to change value significantly. The dc level of such signals is therefore of fundamental importance, and changes in a signal's amplitude are, for many practical purposes, changes in its dc level. At frequencies approaching dc, capacitors and transformers become impractical as signal-coupling devices. Because of this, amplifiers for such signals are cascaded by connecting them directly together without coupling capacitors or transformers.

Even when signals which are not extremely low frequency are involved, direct-coupled amplifiers are often used because of the great savings in cost (and in size and weight) which are made possible by eliminating the coupling capacitors.

Since direct coupling requires that the collector of one stage be at the same dc potential as the base of the next stage, the design of such amplifiers may be somewhat more difficult than that of ac amplifiers. A more significant problem occurs in the case of the direct-coupled amplifiers used for the slowly-varying type of signals — especially when the signals involved are quite small. This problem arises from the fact that, because the amplifier's signal output is a dc quantity, drift of the operating point (with temperature or age) may be mistaken for signal. There may be an output signal even though the input signal is zero. The design of circuits to minimize such "zero-drift" forms a major aspect of dc amplifier work.

This section will provide a brief introduction to a few of the basic dc amplifier circuits and the techniques most commonly employed for reducing drift.

Some Basic Circuits

Figure 6–16 represents one basic amplifier circuit. The dc potentials are shown only to illustrate the general problem.

Resistors R_{c1}, R_{c2}, and R_{c3} are progressively smaller, while if it were not for the Zener diodes, the emitter resistors R_{e1}, R_{e2}, and R_{e3} would have to be progressively larger, to provide the progressive increase in dc level. (This is

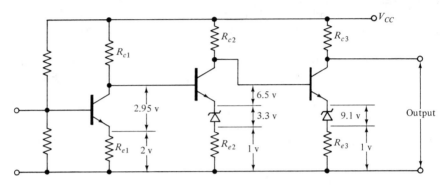

FIGURE 6–16
Direct-connected amplifier circuit illustrating the use of Zener diodes

because each emitter potential must be only a fraction of a volt below its associated base and therefore only a fraction of a volt below the preceding collector.)

Large unbypassed emitter resistors would reduce the amplification excessively. To avoid this, the Zener diodes permit obtaining the necessary increased dc voltage drop with negligible signal voltage drop — since the Zener ac impedance is low. Recall that the Zener characteristic is as shown in Figure 6–17.

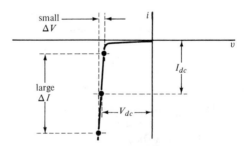

FIGURE 6–17
Zener diode characteristics

Another method using Zener diodes is illustrated in Figure 6–18. Here the combination of large dc voltage drop with small signal-voltage drop permits essentially a dc isolation between each collector and the following base much as the coupling capacitor does in *RC*-coupled stages.

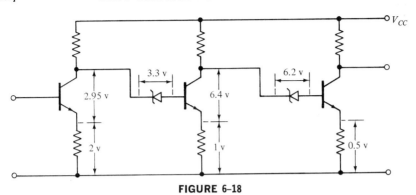

FIGURE 6–18
Another method of applying Zener diodes in direct coupling

6.9 Drift Compensation in dc Amplifiers

The causes of operating point variation in transistor circuits are: temperature effects on the transistor characteristics, supply voltage variation, instability of circuit resistance values, ageing, and unit-to-unit variations among transistors and resistors in the original manufacture.

Unit-to-unit variations and ageing effects can be taken care of by providing circuit adjustment through variable resistance elements. Such adjustments would be needed at the time of original manufacture, when circuit repairs are made, and at certain intervals during the life of the circuit to compensate for ageing. Supply voltages can be made very stable with respect to short-term variations, through well-established techniques of regulated power supply design, and long-term changes can be handled by the type of adjustment mentioned above. Resistances that are highly stable are readily available, and long-term changes in these elements can be taken care of by the same adjustment.

The remaining source of variation is the effect of temperature on the transistor's parameters. This type of change is not easily corrected by manual adjustment since it may occur during amplifier usage and could involve frequent fluctuations. Constant readjustment under such conditions would be impractical and often physically impossible.

Feedback methods such as those considered in Chapter 3 are not suitable for preventing zero-drift in dc amplifiers, since preventing change in quiescent voltages would also prevent the desired dc signal changes. Such methods are applicable only to the maintaining of the dc operating point in ac amplifiers, where bypass capacitors prevent the feedback from affecting the ac conditions. Two general techniques are employed to minimize drift effects in dc amplifiers.

Chopper Amplifiers

One method is to convert the dc signal to ac so that it may be amplified in an ac amplifier which has poor response to the slow drift changes. This method is a form of modulation, or frequency changing, in which the original information is impressed upon a higher frequency "carrier" in order to obtain more favorable operating conditions available at the higher frequency. Such frequency shifting is common in electronics work.

The most popular means of converting a dc signal to ac is by "chopping" it. Figure 6–19 illustrates the basic idea.

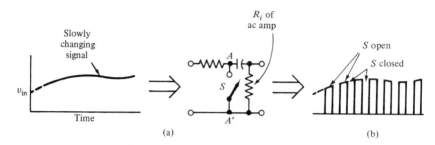

(a)   (b)

FIGURE 6–19
Basic principle of signal chopping

Switch S may be a vibrating relay or an electronic circuit which is capable of producing abrupt alternations from high impedence to very low impedance between A and A'. When the contacts of S are closed, or the impedance from A to A' is very low, the signal is prevented from reaching R_i because the very low impedance from A to A' effectively shorts the signal path. Thus, "chopping" of the original slow-changing signal v_{in} produces pulses as shown at (b), with peak-to-peak amplitudes proportional to the amplitude of the original signal. The rate of chopping in the case of electromechanical choppers is usually between 60 and 400 Hz, but the use of electronic chopping permits higher frequencies.

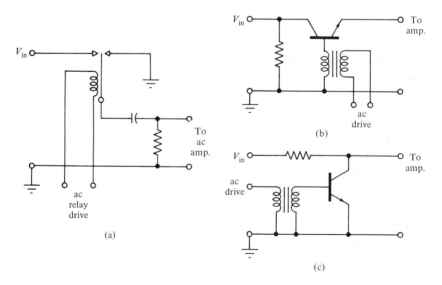

FIGURE 6–20
Basic techniques in signal chopping

Figure 6–20 shows the elementary form of two possible techniques for signal chopping. Part (a) illustrates one form of electromechanical relay chopper. Part (b) shows a transistor in series with the input. A transformer is arranged to provide essentially a square wave drive to the transistor base, so that the transistor is biased alternately on and off. This form is known as a *series transistor chopper*. Part (c) of the figure illustrates a shunt transistor, arranged so that when the transistor is turned on by the ac drive it can conduct heavily, thus acting as a short across the signal path. When turned off by the drive, it becomes an open circuit, thus not interfering with the passage of the signal.

Thermal Stabilizing Methods

Chopper amplifiers can be quite elaborate and can produce very drift-free performance. When simpler circuitry is needed and the drift requirements are not so severe, thermal stabilizing methods may be used. Such methods provide compensation proportional only (essentially) to temperature and therefore do not interfere with signal amplification as would feedback methods.

The basis of thermal stabilizing methods is the use of temperature-sensitive resistance in the bias circuitry. The bias can thus be made to change with temperature in such a way as to match the changes within the transistor. Figure 6–21 shows two ways in which this can be done. In (a) a negative

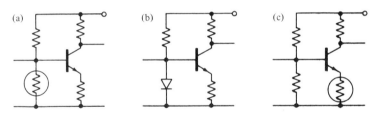

FIGURE 6–21
Use of temperature-sensitive resistors in dc stabilizing

temperature coefficient serves to reduce the amount of forward-bias as the temperature rises, thus helping compensate for the increase in transistor collector current. Sometimes a semiconductor diode may be used as illustrated in (b) in order to take advantage of the similarity in temperature characteristics between the diode and the base-emitter junction.

In (c) a positive temperature coefficient is used, which requires that it be placed in the emitter circuit so that its resistance increase with temperature will produce the same effect — a decrease of forward-bias as the temperature rises.

A fundamental requirement in such stabilizing methods is that the temperature conditions at the transistor and at the temperature-sensitive resistor always be related in the same way. If the two are not in perfect thermal contact, this may not be possible. Therefore the two are usually placed very close together, and often in direct contact. Sometimes they may be encapsulated together so that the high thermal conductivity of the potting material will ensure as nearly as possible their being at the same temperature.

The Differential Amplifier

What might be considered a third technique in dc amplifier drift reduction is the use of the differential or difference amplifier circuit. Figure 6–22 is a simplified version of this amplifier.

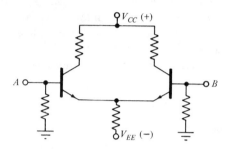

FIGURE 6–22
A simple differential amplifier

The two transistors are of the same type, and to the extent that their characteristics are identical, the signal output of this amplifier is proportional to the *difference* between the input voltages at A and B. This feature is very useful in a number of special applications, but the circuit's basic use in dc amplifiers is as a conventional single-input amplifier. Since the output is proportional to the difference between two inputs, grounding one input (therefore making its signal zero) provides an output which is simply proportional to the signal on the other input.

But even with one input grounded, internal variations in the two transistors act like signals applied to the two inputs. That is, such variations affect the output *only to the extent of the difference between the variations.* Consequently if the two transistors are identical in their temperature characteristics, the output voltage variation resulting from temperature-induced changes in I_{CEO}, h_{FE}, or base-emitter activity, will be zero. For use in low-drift dc amplifiers, therefore, the two transistors would be selected for closely matched temperature characteristics.

PROBLEMS

6–1. The terms shown in the following list either occur in transistor equivalent circuit equations such as those presented in Chapter 4, or are important in general amplifier analysis. Evaluate each of the items in the list *in terms of the resistances shown*. Where the item is a parallel combination of components, it will be sufficient to use the symbol $\|$. For example: $R' = R_1 \| R_2$.

First stage: R_L, R_o, R_g, R_i, and R_i at A-A'.

Second stage: R_L, R_o, R_g, and R_i.

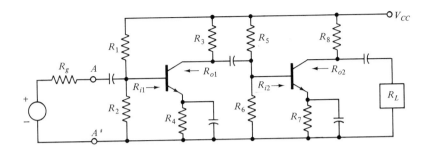

FIGURE P6–1

6–2. Calculate the overall current gain of the amplifier of Problem 6–1 from terminals A-A' to R_L, assuming that the circuit values are as follows:

$R_1 = 50K$	$R_3 = 5K$	$R_{i2} = 2.5K$
$R_2 = 15K$	$R_5 = 68K$	$R_8 = 3.3K$
$R_{i1} = 2K$	$R_6 = 18K$	$R_L = 1.5K$

Base-to-collector current gains:

$T_1 : 100$

$T_2 : 40$

6–3. Calculate the voltage gain from A-A' to R_L for the above circuit.

6–4. Find the indicated impedance transformation ratio, and the indicated impedance, in each of the following cases. (Assume that the transformers are ideal and tight-coupled.)

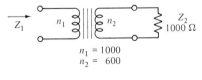

(a)

(b)

(c)

FIGURE P6–4

6–5. What is the effective collector load resistance for each case shown here?

(a)   As in the following circuit:

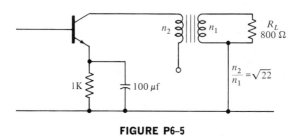

FIGURE P6-5

(b)   Same circuit except $R_L = 1100$ ohms and $n_2/n_1 = 4$.

6–6. Given the following circuit,

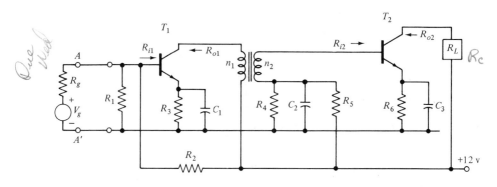

FIGURE P6-6

(a)   Find the current gain from A to R_L. $= 10{,}980$

(b)   Find the voltage gain from A-A' to R_L. $= 5{,}490$

$R_1 = 12K$	$R_{i1} = 1000\ \Omega$
$R_2 = 47K$	$R_{o1} = 20K\ \Omega$
$R_3 = 1.2K$	$R_{i2} = 400\ \Omega$
$R_4 = 3.3K$	$R_{o2} = 8K\ \Omega$
$R_5 = 15K$	$R_L = 500\ \Omega$
$R_6 = 220\ \Omega$	$N_1/N_2 = 3$

The base-to-collector current gains are:

$T_1 : 80$

$T_2 : 50$

6–7. If C_2 were omitted from the above circuit, what would be the effect on circuit performance? Explain.

6–8. Draw the load line for the following circuit.

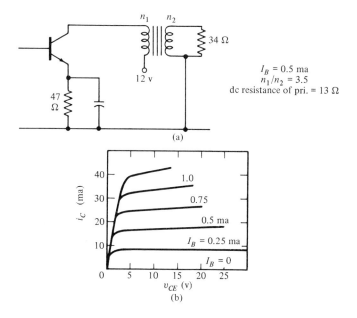

FIGURE P6-8

6-9. Draw the load line for the following circuit on the transistor curves shown here.

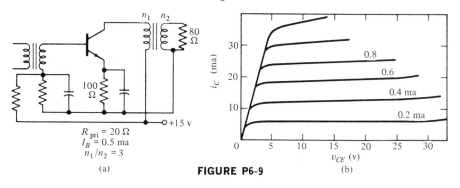

$R_{pri} = 20\ \Omega$
$I_B = 0.5$ ma
$n_1/n_2 = 3$

(a)

FIGURE P6-9

(b)

6-10. Assume the same circuit and same transistor are to be used, but the transformer turns ratio is to be $n_1/n_2 = 4$. Draw the load line on the curves above, and identify it so that it may be distinguished from that of Problem 6-9.

6-11. What is the transducer gain for each of the following cases?

(a) A power gain of 400 from input terminals to load; a maximum available power input of 1 mw; an actual power input of 0.3 mw.

(b) A power gain, terminal-to-terminal, of 200, with actual power input equal to the maximum available power input, 1 mw.

6-12. A transistor amplifier with a 2000 ohm load has a current gain of 300. Its input resistance is 2000 ohms, and its input signal comes from a source with an output resistance of 5000 ohms. What is the transducer gain?

6–13. (a) Why is drift of the operating point considered a more serious problem in some dc amplifiers than in ac amplifiers?

     (b) Why are the bias stabilizing methods of Chapter 3 not generally suitable for correcting such drift?

6–14. (a) Explain why the chopper amplifier provides a solution to the drift problem for dc amplifiers.

     (b) Explain the difference between a series chopper and a shunt chopper.

6–15. (a) Why is a temperature-sensitive resistance often found in the base or emitter circuit of a transistor?

     (b) Why is a semiconductor diode often found in parallel with the base-emitter junction of a transistor?

     (c) Why are the components mentioned in (a) and (b) usually found mounted very close to the transistor?

CHAPTER 7

Power Amplifiers

7.1 Large-Signal Amplifiers

Ultimately, the goal of signal amplification is to operate some device. This may be a loudspeaker, an indicating device such as a cathode-ray tube or meter, or any of a number of electromechanical control devices.

Most of these require signals large enough so that at least the final stage of amplification must be designed to provide the maximum output of which it is capable. This is done in order to avoid the need for an amplifier that is larger or more expensive than necessary. Amplifiers of this type are called large-signal amplifiers. They are distinguished by the fact that the signal swing often extends over as large a part of the amplifying device's useable range as possible in order to obtain as much output as possible. Since the device's nonlinearities are greater near the limits of its operating region, distortion of the signal becomes an important factor, and the design of such amplifiers is usually a compromise between output amplitude and distortion.

Some devices — for example, cathode-ray tubes — require large-signal voltages but negligible power for their operation. Others require appreciable signal power. Amplifiers built to drive the latter type of load are commonly referred to as power amplifiers.

In order to see some of the problems involved in large-signal stages, consider Figure 7–1. This illustrates an amplifier in which the load line and operating point have been chosen so that the possible signal power is the maximum that can be obtained without having the operation go outside the "safe operating region." This region is bounded by the maximum allowable collector current, the maximum allowable collector dissipation, and the collector-emitter breakdown voltage. Note that the transistor's quiescent collector dissipation, or the product of its quiescent collector current and quiescent collector-emitter voltage, is very nearly equal to the maximum collector-dissipation rating as

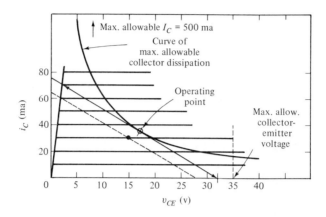

FIGURE 7-1
Example of maximum signal conditions

shown by the curve. The maximum signal power output available in this case would occur when the signal swings the full extent of the load line, as shown by the arrow heads on the load line. The signal power output is

$$P_{\text{out}} = V_{ce}I_c$$

These are rms values, and in terms of peak values it would be

$$P_{\text{out}} = (0.707\ V_{cem})(0.707\ I_{cm})$$
$$\cong [(0.707(15)][(0.707)(0.035)]$$
$$P_{\text{out}} \cong 260 \text{ mw}$$

A signal swing that was any smaller would of course provide less power output since the values of V and I in the above calculation would be smaller.

It should also be noted that locating the load line and operating point further away from the curve of maximum allowable dissipation would result in less signal power output. The dashed load line in Figure 7–1 illustrates this. It gives a maximum possible peak signal current swing of only 30 ma (instead of the 35 above) and a maximum peak voltage swing of only about 13 v, for a power output of about 195 mw.

Several points can now be made, relative to the problem of obtaining high signal power. First, an amplifying device with appropriate dissipation rating must be chosen, and it must be operated near its maximum power rating (or else a larger device with higher power rating, which would probably cost more, would have to be used). Second, it should be operated with as large a signal swing as possible. This usually means that some distortion will be involved since the greater the range of operation, from extremely low currents to very high currents, the more nonlinearity of the transistor characteristics is encountered. (The characteristic curves used in the example above were idealized in order to simplify the example. They show no distortion and no leakage current. In addition to this, much of the transistor's distortion is in the non-linearity of its input characteristic, which was not used in this example.)

Finally, examination of Figure 7–1 reveals that the collector voltage, in swinging downward, must stop at the saturation line, at 2 v in this example. This saturation voltage, $V_{CE\text{ sat}}$, acts to limit the peak-to-peak signal voltage. Lower values of $V_{CE\text{ sat}}$ permit greater signal voltage values. $V_{CE\text{ sat}}$ is usually specified on the transistor data sheet for a stated collector current and base current, or else it is shown by presenting the low voltage portion of the collector curves (sometimes with an expanded scale) so the value of $V_{CE\text{ sat}}$ may be read from the graph. Figure 7–2 illustrates two transistors that are exactly the same except for their values of $V_{CE\text{ sat}}$.

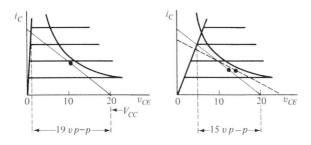

FIGURE 7–2
Effect of $V_{CE\text{ sat}}$

Note that the transistor in part (b), having the larger value of V_{sat}, cannot use as great a value of output signal swing as used in (a), unless it employs a higher value of supply voltage. This would not only increase the transistor dissipation, but also would require a greater dc power input from the power supply. In portable equipment this can be a disadvantage, causing shorter battery life or else requiring larger batteries. In very high power equipment such as radio transmitters or public address systems having outputs in the thousands of watts, both the initial cost of the equipment and the operating costs may be affected sufficiently to be an important factor.

The capability of an amplifier circuit with respect to maximum signal power output for a given dc power input is expressed in terms of its *collector circuit efficiency*, or the ratio of its signal power output to its dc collector power input.

7.2 Amplifier Classes

At this point it becomes necessary to distinguish between certain modes of operation having to do with biasing and current flow in the amplifier. The amplifiers discussed so far have been biased in such a way that collector current flow takes place during the entire signal cycle. This kind of operation is known as Class *A*. It is also possible to obtain useful operation with bias such that the transistor conducts for only a portion of the signal cycle. Such operation has an important advantage in the design of power amplifiers. When the amplifier is biased so that it conducts for one-half of the signal cycle, or 180°, it is called Class B. When biased so that current flows for less than 360° but more than 180°, it is known as Class AB.

A Class C operation, in which the current flow occurs for appreciably less than 180° of the cycle, is used in tuned amplifiers but is not commonly employed for audio amplifiers.

TABLE 7–1

Class	Definition
A	Transistor conducts during entire signal cycle (or 360°)
B	Transistor conducts for essentially one-half of cycle (or 180°)
AB	Transistor conducts for more than 180° but less than 360°
C	Transistor conducts appreciably less than 180°

7.3 Class A Power and Efficiency

DC Power Input

The dc power input to the collector circuit is the product of the collector supply voltage and the average (i.e., dc) collector current:

$$P_{\text{dc}} = V_{CC}I_C \qquad (7\text{–}1)$$

Figure 7–3 shows the circuit measurements which would give these values, and illustrates the quantities graphically.

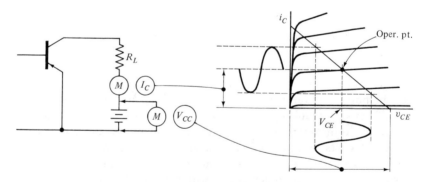

FIGURE 7–3
Collector supply power

Note carefully that it is the *average* collector current, and it is the collector *supply* voltage (and not the average collector-emitter voltage) whose product is the dc input power. In other words, the supply input power involves the *supply* current and the *supply* voltage.

Signal Power Output

The ac or signal power output of the amplifier is the product of the output signal voltage and the output signal current. In terms of rms values this is

$$P_{\text{out}} = V_{ce}I_c \qquad (7\text{–}2)$$

and in terms of peak-to-peak values (which are often convenient quantities to use in load-line work) this would be

$$P_{\text{out}} = [(0.5)(0.707)V_{ce(p-p)}][(0.5)(0.707)I_{c(p-p)}]$$

$$P_{\text{out}} = \frac{V_{ce(p-p)}I_{c(p-p)}}{8} \qquad (7\text{-}3)$$

Collector Circuit Efficiency

The *collector circuit efficiency* is the ratio of the output signal power to the input dc power:

$$\eta = \frac{P_{\text{out}}}{P_{\text{dc}}} \text{ (as a fraction)}$$

or

$$\eta = 100\left[\frac{P_{\text{out}}}{P_{\text{dc}}}\right] \text{ (in percentage)} \qquad (7\text{-}4)$$

Maximum Possible Efficiency

For purposes of comparison among circuits, the theoretical maximum efficiency assuming an ideal transistor ($V_{\text{sat}} = 0$, collector leakage current $= 0$, and no distortion) may be considered. In the resistance-coupled or direct-coupled amplifier, with the load connected directly in the collector circuit as in Figure 7-3 above, the maximum output voltage swing is from V_{CC} to zero with

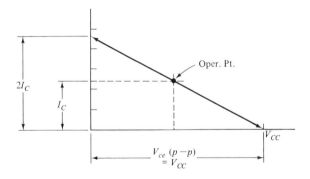

FIGURE 7-4
Idealized maximum output with resistance load connected directly in collector circuit

an ideal transistor. Then $V_{ce(p-p)} = V_{CC}$ and $I_{c(p-p)} = 2I_C$ where I_C is the dc or quiescent collector current. These relations are illustrated in Figure 7-4. Then the power output is

$$P_{\text{out}} = \frac{V_{ce(p-p)}I_{c(p-p)}}{8} = \frac{(V_{CC})(2I_C)}{8}$$

$$P_{\text{out}} = \frac{V_{CC}I_C}{4}$$

and the efficiency is

$$\eta = \frac{P_{\text{out}}}{P_{\text{dc}}} = \frac{V_{CC}I_C/4}{V_{CC}I_C}$$

$$\eta = 0.25 \text{ or } 25 \text{ percent}$$

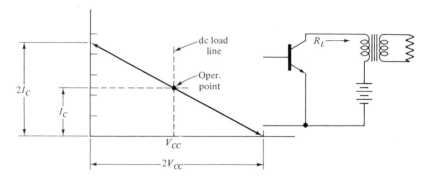

FIGURE 7–5
Idealized maximum output in transformer coupling

In the transformer-coupled amplifier illustrated in Figure 7–5 (in which the dc resistance of the transformer primary is assumed zero as an ideal case), the theoretical maximum efficiency would be twice as great as this, or 50 percent. This is because the maximum possible peak-to-peak signal voltage swing, in the transformer-coupled circuit, is twice the supply voltage. (See Figures 6–10 and 6–11.) This leads to

$$\eta = \frac{P_{\text{out}}}{P_{\text{dc}}}$$

$$\eta = \frac{V_{ce(p-p)}I_{c(p-p)}}{8V_{CC}I_C} = \frac{(2V_{CC})(2I_C)}{8V_{CC}I_C}$$

$$\eta = 0.5 \text{ or } 50 \text{ percent}$$

The reason for the better efficiency in the transformer-coupled case, of course, is the fact that it does not have the dc power loss in the load. The signal power is delivered to the load, but the dc collector current is not.

Note again that in transformer coupling the collector voltage can swing as high as $2V_{CC}$. Consequently V_{CC} must be set *equal to or less than one-half* of the maximum collector-emitter breakdown rating V_{CEO} (or BV_{CEO}).

Ratio of Collector Dissipation to Maximum Signal Output Power

In the resistance-coupled stage the maximum possible power output is

$$P_{\text{out}} = \frac{V_{ce(p-p)}I_{c(p-p)}}{8} = \frac{(V_{CC})(2I_C)}{8}$$

$$P_{\text{out}} = \frac{V_{CC}I_C}{4}$$

while the maximum collector dissipation which the transistor must be capable of handling occurs at times of zero signal, and is

$$P_D = V_{CE}I_C = \left[\frac{V_{CC}}{2}\right](I_C)$$

$$P_D = \tfrac{1}{2} V_{CC}I_C$$

This is based on the assumption that the operating point is set in the middle of the load line for maximum possible signal swing in both directions in the ideal case in which $V_{\text{sat}} = 0$ and $I_{CEO} = 0$, and would be approximately correct for transistors having low values of V_{sat} and I_{CEO}.

The ratio of collector dissipation rating to maximum output signal power then would be, for the Class A resistance-coupled stage,

$$\frac{P_D}{P_{\text{out}}} = \frac{\tfrac{1}{2} V_{CC}I_C}{\tfrac{1}{4} V_{CC}I_C} = 2$$

For the transformer-coupled Class A stage this ratio is the same value. The better efficiency in transformer coupling (50 percent as compared with 25 percent for resistance coupling) is a consequence of the elimination of the dc power loss in the load — because the dc collector current does not flow in the load but only in the transformer primary. For a given power output, this lowers the required power input, but the collector dissipation required for a given power output is the same in both cases.

The unhappy implication of this is that the transistor must have a collector dissipation rating at least twice as great as the desired maximum power output, and since the practical circuit will not be the ideal case — i.e., V_{sat} will not be zero — the dissipation rating in the practical case will need to exceed even this. For example, a Class A stage intended for a maximum output of 5 w would require a transistor having maximum collector dissipation rating somewhat greater than 10 w.

7.4 Introduction to Power Amplifier Design

To illustrate the ideas developed so far — and to introduce some additional considerations — a typical practical problem will be examined: the design of a Class A power output stage to provide a maximum of 2 w to a 4 ohm loudspeaker. As an initial decision, transformer coupling to the loudspeaker will be assumed necessary to provide the optimum load for the transistor. The optimum value of effective load R_L will be investigated at a later point to verify this choice.

Choice of Transistor

The idealized Class A case would require the transistor to have a dissipation rating of twice the required power output. But to allow for the fact that a real transistor will not permit collector voltage and current swings as large as the ideal case, we will make an initial choice of $P_D \cong 2.5$ to 3 times P_{out}.

An available transistor having $P_D = 6$ w is the 2N4234. Note that this 6 w rating applies only if the case is kept at a temperature of 25°C. For this example, we shall assume no temperature problems. In a later section the temperature and power derating problem which must be faced in all practical power amplifier designs will be considered.

Choice of Supply Voltage and Operating Point

Figure 7–6 illustrates the safe operating area of a transistor, and shows two extreme possibilities for the location of load line and operating point. The load line should not enter the region above the $P_{D(max)}$ curve, and should not

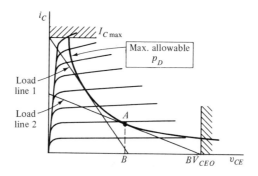

FIGURE 7–6
Transistor safe operating area

carry the operation beyond the maximum allowable current or voltage ratings. Of the two load lines shown, the higher impedance (number 2) is often preferred because it more nearly matches the transistor output impedance. Operation with this load line places the quiescent point at A, and with transformer coupling this fixes the supply voltage V_{CC} at B, or one-half the maximum collector voltage rating. Then the collector voltage peaks will not exceed the rating under maximum signal conditions.

If operation without an output transformer was necessary, a load line tending toward the position of number 1 in Figure 7–6 would be investigated. That is, the operating point would involve high current and low voltage, for low impedance.

In this example we shall assume that a high collector load impedance is preferred, and shall proceed on the basis of a quiescent point at A. Actual values of $V_{CE\,sat}$, I_{CEO}, and dc voltage drop in the transformer primary may change the figures somewhat, but an initial choice may be made on the above basis, to be modified if necessary after examination of the actual operating conditions with the chosen transistor.

In the case of the 2N4234 which we have made our initial choice, the data sheet reveals a maximum V_{CEO} rating of 40 v. Thus V_{CC} may be made 20 v as an initial choice.

If we had perfect bias stability and no component variations, the load line should just touch the $P_{D(\max)}$ curve at the operating point, as at A in Figure 7-6. This gives

$$P_D = V_{CC}I_C$$

$$I_C = \frac{P_D}{V_{CC}} = \frac{6}{20}$$

$$I_C = 300 \text{ ma}$$

In the practical case a lower value would be chosen, in order to provide a margin of safety for expected operating point shifts due to temperature and unit-to-unit variations. Let us choose 250 ma to meet this requirement. Thus the operating point will be

$$V_{CC} = 20 \text{ v}$$

$$I_C = 250 \text{ ma}$$

Load Impedance

The above choices have now determined for us what we must use as an effective collector load resistance. That is, since the chosen operating point permits maximum signal swings of

$$V_{cem} \cong 40 - 20 = 20 \text{ v}$$

and

$$I_{cm} \cong 250 \text{ ma}$$

the load resistance then must be

$$R_L = \frac{V_{cem}}{I_{cm}} = \frac{20}{0.25} = 80 \text{ ohms}$$

The output transformer will be chosen or designed to transform the 4 ohms of the speaker to 80 ohms at the collector of the transistor.

Adjustment of Operating Values

We now have a set of values based on initial design choices or estimates. At this point we can check the transistor specifications to modify some of the above figures as necessary to make them fit the "real" transistor as opposed to the ideal case.

The 2N4234 data sheet provides curves of V_{CE} in the saturation region. These show that $V_{CE \text{ sat}}$ is roughly 0.4 v just before saturating heavily, at $I_C = 500$ ma. Since driving the input hard enough to go well into saturation causes excessive distortion, it might be best to count on going no lower than 0.5 v. The signal voltage swing will then be 0.5 v less than originally planned. Other factors that will either reduce the collector voltage swing or else will require supply voltage larger than the 20 v figure assumed so far, are the dc voltage drops in the transformer winding and in the emitter resistor.

In this simple example we shall make no attempt to choose a transformer or design the bias circuit, but shall assume that about 2.5 v are lost in these resistances at the quiescent current of 250 ma. Thus the dc load line puts the operating point at $20 - 2.5 = 17.5$ v, if the supply voltage is kept at 20.

With the operating point at 17.5 v and $V_{CE\ \text{sat}}$ equal to 0.5 v, the maximum voltage swing becomes 17 v, and the peak voltage reached by the collector becomes $17.5 + 17 = 34.5$. Figure 7–7 shows the ac load line drawn from $V_{CE\ \text{sat}}$ at 500 ma to 34.5 v at zero ma. The load resistance now has become

$$R_L = \frac{V_{cm}}{I_{cm}} = \frac{17}{0.25} = 68 \text{ ohms}$$

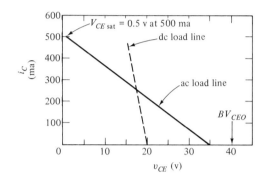

FIGURE 7–7
Final operating conditions of class A design example

Note that the various reductions have resulted in the peak collector voltage being well below the maximum allowable value of 40 v.

Final Power Calculations

The maximum power output under the final conditions above would be

$$P_{\text{out}} \cong \frac{V_{ce(p\text{-}p)} I_{c(p\text{-}p)}}{8}$$

$$P_{\text{out}} \cong \frac{(34)(0.5)}{8} \cong 2.2 \text{ w}$$

and the maximum collector dissipation would be

$$P_D = V_{CE} I_C$$
$$P_D \cong (17.5)(0.25) = 4.38 \text{ w}$$

7.5 Class *B* Amplifiers

The low efficiency of the circuits discussed above can be a serious short-coming in systems handling large amounts of power. Large radio transmitters and public address systems handle signals in the range of kilowatts. If the operating efficiency of such equipment is low, the operating costs will be high. The initial cost of the equipment will also be high, as a consequence of the need for more expensive, higher-power components.

A large part of the power loss in amplifiers is in the collector dissipation.

(In transformer-coupling, this is the *only* loss for the idealized case.) Therefore a significant improvement in efficiency could be achieved if the collector dissipation could be substantially reduced.

Since power is the product of current and voltage, the power dissipated at the collector must be proportional to the collector voltage and the collector current. Consequently, if it were possible to restrict the collector current flow to only the time during the cycle when the collector voltage was passing through its lower peak, the collector dissipation should be significantly lowered. This may be done by biasing the amplifier at "cutoff" — making it nonconducting for zero-signal conditions. With a sine wave input, the transistor then will conduct only during one-half of the time of the input signal — during that portion of the cycle when the signal carries the operation above cutoff. During the other half of the cycle it will be in the cutoff or nonconducting region. This fits the definition of Class *B* operation introduced in Section 7.2.

Figure 7–8 shows the waveform for such operation (for a sine wave signal)

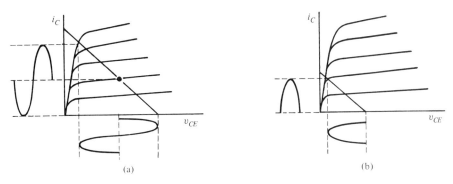

FIGURE 7–8
Class A and Class B, for one cycle of the signal

in comparison with Class *A*. In part (a) the Class *A* operation reveals the collector current flowing during the entire cycle of collector voltage. In part (b), Class *B* operation is shown; the current flows only during the lower half of the collector voltage cycle, and is cut off the remainder of the time.

A Practical Class *B* Resistance-Coupled Circuit

For most purposes, of course, this would be an unacceptable distortion of the signal. However, two such amplifier circuits may be operated together in such a way as to produce a normal undistorted waveform. Figures 7–9 and 7–10 show how this may be done. In the simplest arrangement two identical amplifiers, *each biased at cutoff*, are fed the same signal except that the input to one of the amplifiers is 180° out of phase with the other. Since the two amplifiers are identical, the current flow and output voltage waveform is the same polarity for both. But as a consequence of the 180° phase inversion of the input signals, the identical output half-sine waves *occur during alternate halves of the input signal.*

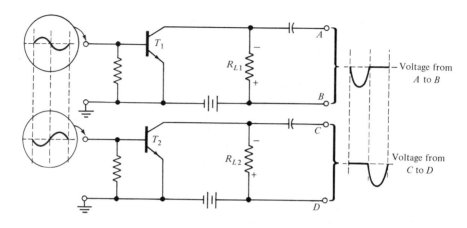

FIGURE 7-9
Basic mechanism of push-pull operation

Note that both half-sine waves in Figure 7–9 are of the same polarity. However, if the output signal of one of the two amplifiers could be inverted, the two
half-sine waves would then form the desired normal waveform. This may be
done by reversing the output terminals of one of the amplifiers, so that the
total output is taken from A to B to D to C, as illustrated in Figure 7–10. In
part (a) the two circuits are connected together (B to D) so that the output is
from A to C. In parts (b) and (c) the individual waveforms and their resultant,
when taken this way, are illustrated. In part (d) the two separate power supplies
are combined into a single supply, and the two amplifiers' common return lines
are combined into one. Note that the input signal waveforms shown in both

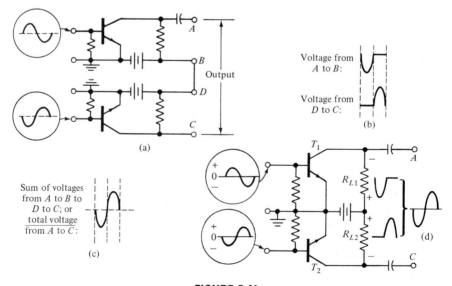

FIGURE 7-10
Individual and composite waveforms in push-pull

parts (a) and (d) are the signal voltages at the indicated input terminals with respect to ground or common (the terminal between the two input terminals). Although one of the circuits is shown "upside down," the signal polarities are correct, not upside down.

As indicated in this figure, the total output between terminals A and C will be formed by the half-sine wave due to the current in R_{L1} during the first 180° of the cycle (while transistor T_2 is nonconducting) followed by the half-sine wave due to current through R_{L2} during the second 180° of the cycle (while transistor T_1 is nonconducting). The combination of the two amplifiers is considered to be one push-pull amplifier. *Each half operates as shown originally in Figure 7–8(b), with current flowing only while the collector voltage is low.*

If we were to use the same transistors and bias them as shown in Figure 7–8(b), the total signal power output would be approximately the same as in part (a) of the figure, but the collector dissipation would be much less. This decrease of collector dissipation, however, permits moving the bias to a point that will accommodate a much larger signal output. Analysis in the next section will show that the output available from such a two-transistor Class B arrangement is much more than that which the same two transistors could provide when operated Class A.

The Transformer-Coupled Class B Circuit

When transformer coupling is used in the push-pull circuit, an arrangement basically as shown in Figure 7–11 can be employed.

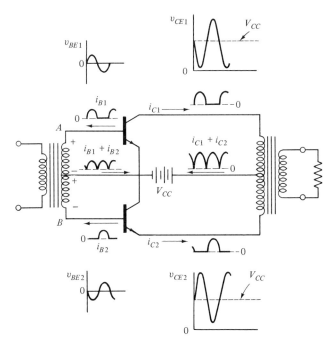

FIGURE 7–11
Transformer-coupled push-pull circuit

The center-tapped input transformer provides the necessary phase-inversion at the input. Since one end of a transformer winding is opposite in potential from the other end at every instant throughout the voltage cycle, the waveform of the voltage from end A to the center-tap must be 180° out of phase with the waveform of the voltage from B to the center-tap. Note the polarity markings at the secondary of the input transformer, indicating the polarity along the winding at one particular instant during the cycle. The transformer is actually serving here to change the ground "reference" from one end of the circuit to the center point, to make the circuit "balanced" to ground.

The voltage waveforms shown at the primary of the output transformer in the figure show a full voltage cycle for each half-winding rather than just the half-cycle across each half of the output as in the resistance-loaded circuit of Figure 7–10. The reason for this is that in the transformer the voltage swing downward from V_{CC} toward zero in the conducting half-winding causes a voltage swing upward by the same amount in the nonconducting half-winding, by normal transformer action. Thus when the conducting transistor's collector voltage swings nearly to zero, the nonconducting transistor's collector swings upward to nearly 2 V_{CC}.

The transformer coupling at the output permits changing the ground reference back to the "single-ended" form if desired. It also permits impedance transforming in case the final load is not the optimum value.

Biasing Conditions for Class B

Since each half of the Class B pair must be nonconducting for approximately half of the cycle, each transistor must be biased at (or near) cutoff. In the simplest case this means that no bias voltage should be used. Examination of the circuit of Figure 7–10(d) shows that the base is connected directly to the emitter through a resistance. There is no power supply connection to the base or emitter circuit. Similarly, in Figure 7–11 the base is connected to the emitter through the transformer secondary winding without connection to any power supply. However, in most practical circuits a small amount of forward-bias is used, to minimize distortion which occurs in operation near cutoff. This will be discussed in Section 7.1.

7.6 Class B Power and Efficiency

In Class A, the dc value of the supply current was simply the quiescent collector current, so that the dc power input was calculated as $P_{dc} = V_{CC}I_C$. But in Class B the quiescent collector current is essentially zero, so that the supply current is essentially zero when there is no signal, and rises only with signal. The supply current is composed of the collector currents from the two transistors, each of which, during a sine wave signal, consists of approximately half-sine wave pulses as shown in Figure 7–12.

The average or dc value of the supply current for Class B therefore is

$$I_{dc} = \frac{2I_{cm}}{\pi} \cong 0.636\, I_{cm} \qquad (7\text{–}5)$$

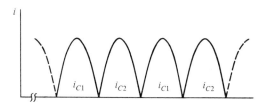

FIGURE 7–12
Waveform of the supply current in Class B *push-pull operation*

in which I_{cm} is the peak value of the collector current during the signal cycle. The dc input power is then

$$P_{\text{dc}} = V_{CC}I_{\text{dc}} = \frac{2V_{CC}I_{cm}}{\pi}$$

$$P_{\text{dc}} \cong 0.636\, V_{CC}I_{cm} \tag{7–6}$$

The signal output power is, by Equation (7–3),

$$P_{\text{out}} = \frac{V_{ce(p\text{-}p)}I_{c(p\text{-}p)}}{8} \tag{7–3}$$

in which $I_{c(p\text{-}p)}$ is a peak-to-peak value arrived at in the following way. Since half-cycles of current occur in alternate succession in the two primary half-windings and each produces output in the secondary, the effect is the same as though a full cycle of current (having a peak-to-peak value twice that of the single transistor's *peak* value) were flowing. Thus, the output signal power is carried by an equivalent peak-to-peak collector current equal to twice the peak value of one transistor's current.

Since the effect at the output is that of a current wave whose two halves are the alternate half-cycles from each transistor, flowing in opposite directions in the transformer primary, and a voltage wave which carries each collector from V_{CC} downward by the amount I_cR_L and upward by the same amount, "composite" output characteristics are often used to show the operation graphically. This is done by arranging the transistors' collector characteristics "back-to-back" as shown in Figure 7–13.

From the input and output power expressions developed above, the efficiency is

$$\eta = \frac{V_{ce(p\text{-}p)}I_{c(p\text{-}p)}\pi}{16V_{CC}I_{cm}} (100) \text{ percent} \tag{7–7}$$

Using the ideal case to evaluate the maximum possible efficiency, the maximum possible peak-to-peak output voltage swing would be $2\,V_{CC}$, leading to

$$\eta = \frac{\pi}{4}(100) \text{ percent} \cong 78 \text{ percent} \tag{7–8}$$

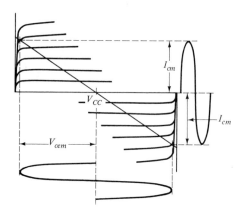

FIGURE 7–13

*Output characteristics placed "back-to-back" for graphical analysis
in push-pull operation*

7.7 Ratio of Collector Dissipation to Maximum Signal Power Output in Class *B* Operation

Class *B* efficiency is evidently an improvement over Class *A* efficiency. But the real advantage of Class *B* over Class *A* in the matter of power is more fully revealed by considering the required transistor dissipation ratings relative to the power output.

In Section 7.3 we showed that the required collector dissipation rating for Class *A* operation had to be at least twice the signal output power. We will show here that Class *B* involves a total collector dissipation that is only one-fifth of the Class *A* dissipation. Thus Class *B* requires a dissipation rating for each of the two transistors that is only one-tenth that required for the Class *A* transistor.

The ratio of $P_{D(\text{max})}$ to $P_{\text{out(max)}}$ for Class *B* operation may be arrived at in the following way. The maximum possible power output for the two transistors is, from Equation (7–3),

$$P_{\text{out(max)}} = \frac{(2V_{CC})\left[\dfrac{2V_{CC}}{R_L}\right]}{8}$$

$$P_{\text{out(max)}} = \frac{V_{CC}^2}{2R_L} \tag{7–9}$$

Maximum collector dissipation may be found by starting from the fact that the dissipation with transformer coupling must equal the input dc power minus the signal power output, or

$$P_D = P_{\text{dc}} - P_{\text{out}} \tag{7–10}$$

since there is assumed to be no power loss in the transformer winding in the ideal case. If this equation is written with P_{dc} and P_{out} expressed in terms of the signal current amplitude, it may then be analyzed to determine what current amplitude produces the greatest collector dissipation.

For this purpose, then, P_{dc} may be written

$$P_{dc} = V_{CC}I_C = (V_{CC})\left[\frac{2\,I_{cm}}{\pi}\right] \tag{7-11}$$

as the total dc power input to the two transistors in the push-pull circuit. Similarly, the output power for the two transistors may be expressed

$$P_{out} = I_c^2 R_L$$

which, converting I_c from rms to peak, gives

$$P_{out} = 0.5\,I_{cm}^2 R_L$$

so that finally

$$P_D = \frac{2V_{CC}I_{cm}}{\pi} - \frac{I_{cm}^2 R_L}{2} \tag{7-12}$$

This equation may be differentiated with respect to I_c to show that maximum P_D occurs when the signal has the amplitude

$$I_{cm} = \frac{2V_{CC}}{\pi R_L} \tag{7-13}$$

This value of collector signal current substituted in Equation (7–12) then results in

$$P_{D(max)} = \frac{(2V_{CC})(2V_{CC})}{(\pi)(\pi R_L)} - \frac{(2V_{CC})^2 R_L}{(\pi R_L)^2(2)}$$

$$P_{D(max)} = \frac{4V_{CC}^2}{\pi^2 R_L} - \frac{2V_{CC}^2}{\pi^2 R_L}$$

$$P_{D(max)} = \frac{2V_{CC}^2}{\pi^2 R_L} \tag{7-14}$$

and this is for the two transistors.

It should be noted that this maximum dissipation does not occur at maximum power output, but instead at an intermediate level — at which the peak collector current is only $(2/\pi)$ times the maximum possible value of V_{CC}/R_L (for the ideal case).

The ratio of $P_{D(max)}$ to $P_{out(max)}$ may now be obtained from Equations (7–9) and (7–14):

$$\frac{P_{D(max)}}{P_{out(max)}} = \frac{2V_{CC}^2/\pi^2 R_L}{V_{CC}^2/2R_L} = \frac{4}{\pi^2}$$

$$\frac{P_{D(max)}}{P_{out(max)}} \simeq 0.405 \tag{7-15}$$

Since the Class A transistor must have a power rating equal to 200 percent of maximum P_{out}, this 40 percent represents only one-fifth the Class A requirement. Consequently, each of the two transistors in Class B needs a power rating only one-tenth the Class *A* requirement, as pointed out at the beginning of this section. For example, in building an amplifier for a maximum output of 50 w, Class *A* design would require a transistor having at least a 100-w rating. But Class *B* design would permit using two 10-w transistors.

In spite of this very great advantage of Class *B* over Class *A*, Class *A* will be found in many low to medium power applications. The additional component and labor cost associated with the more complex circuit of the push-pull arrangement will often make it more expensive in spite of its use of lower power transistors. In addition, the Class *B* circuit tends to produce more distortion. At higher power levels, the savings in power supply cost and operating cost resulting from the higher efficiency, added to the savings due to the use of smaller transistors, may make the Class *B* more desirable. In addition, the lack of transistors having great enough power rating makes the Class *B* circuit mandatory in some very high power applications.

7.8 Class A Push-Pull

It is possible to operate Class *A* push-pull by employing the same general type of circuit as the Class *B* push-pull but biasing both transistors at normal Class *A* operating points. When this is done, the circuit conditions are as indicated in Figure 7–14.

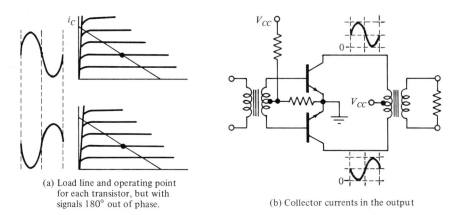

(a) Load line and operating point
for each transistor, but with
signals 180° out of phase.

(b) Collector currents in the output

FIGURE 7–14
Class A *push-pull operation*

Both halves of the output transformer primary winding are carrying current at all times, instead of only one-half at a time as in Class *B*. The effect of these currents on the output is additive. This may be seen by noting that the two currents are in opposite directions in the winding. This difference in direction through the winding cancels the 180° phase difference of the collector currents. Another way of putting this is that since the two currents are in opposite directions in the primary, their effect in the output is proportional to their *difference*.

Figure 7–15 shows what happens when the difference between two equal but out-of-phase currents is taken.

The importance of Class A push-pull operation is that it offers significantly lower distortion than either the Class B push-pull or the single-ended Class A.

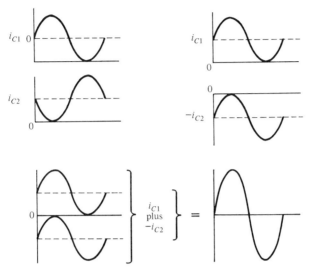

FIGURE 7–15
Current addition in push-pull Class A

The essential reason for this reduced distortion is that the simultaneous out-of-phase operation of the two transistors causes some of the distortion components to be cancelled out. This cancellation does not take place in Class B since the two transistors are not on at the same time in the latter mode of operation.

Thus, where additional power output is desired and distortion is critical, the Class A push-pull amplifier may offer advantages. However, the efficiency is no better than that of the single-ended amplifier; the two transistors simply permit twice the power output. Distortion effects in amplifier circuits will be considered in Section 7.11.

7.9   Additional Advantages of Push-Pull Amplifiers

Smaller Transformer in Class A Push-Pull

An additional advantage inherent in Class A push-pull is that the output coupling transformer may be built with less iron and therefore be smaller and less expensive. The reason for this is that the quiescent collector currents of the two transistors flow in opposite directions in the two halves of the primary. Thus the dc fluxes produced by the two currents are oppositely directed and to the extent that the transistors (and the windings) are matched, there will be cancellation of the dc flux in the iron core. The peak value of flux during signal will consequently be smaller in amplitude and the cross-section area of iron needed to avoid saturation effects will be less.

Hum Cancellation in Push-Pull Operation

Another practical advantage in the push-pull circuit (Class A or Class B) is its general insensitivity to hum (ripple) in the power supply. The supply voltage is applied to the two transistors in parallel even though the signal is applied push-pull. Note, for example, that the polarity of V_{CC} is the same for both bases in Figure 7–14(b) (as well as for both collectors). Thus ripple currents, produced by the power supply's ripple voltage, will be in phase rather than 180° out of phase like the signal. Consequently, at the output where the signals become effectively in-phase, the ripple currents will by the same action be made out of phase and will cancel.

A benefit resulting from this feature is that in low-cost equipment the voltage for high-power output stages can often be taken from an unfiltered or only lightly filtered point in the power supply, with the filtered output supplying the other, lower-current stages. This permits the use of smaller, lower-cost filter components.

Hum cancellation in push-pull operation occurs only for hum arising in the push-pull stage, of course. Hum that arrives with the signal, from an earlier, single-ended stage, will be amplified along with the signal.

7.10 Output Transformer Turns Ratio for Push-Pull Circuits

The required turns ratio in the output transformer must be calculated on a different basis for Class A push-pull and Class B push-pull. In the Class A case where R_L is the required collector load resistance for each transistor, and the notation is as indicated in Figure 7–16, the relationship is perhaps most easily

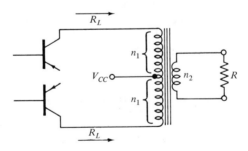

FIGURE 7–16
Output transformer relations in push-pull

expressed in terms of the collector-to-collector impedance, $2R_L$. The reason that the total load, $2R_L$, must be considered at one time is that with current flowing in both halves of the primary, mutual inductance between the two halves prevents them from being independent of each other. Thus it is easiest to consider the whole winding ($2n_1$ and $2R_L$):

$$\frac{(2R_L)}{R} = \left[\frac{2n_1}{n_2}\right]^2$$

resulting in

$$R_L = 2\left[\frac{n_1}{n_2}\right]^2 R \qquad \text{(7–16)}$$

In the Class B circuit, current is flowing in only half of the winding at one time, and each half is therefore isolated from the other. Each half may be considered separately. Since each half must provide the load R_L, we will have

$$\frac{R_L}{R} = \left[\frac{n_1}{n_2}\right]^2$$

$$R_L = \left[\frac{n_1}{n_2}\right]^2 R \qquad \text{(7–17)}$$

7.11 Distortion

Distortion in transistor amplifiers may be considered in terms of the non-linearity of the input and the output characteristics. Recognition of the nature of these nonlinearities and the effect on them of the associated amplifier circuitry will help in understanding practical aspects of amplifier design and operation.

The Input Characteristic

Figure 7–17 illustrates the general nature of the input characteristic of a transistor in the CE connection. Although some curvature exists throughout the range, it is most extreme at the very low currents. Note that the current wave resulting from an applied sine wave of v_{BE} shows a greater compression of the negative peak in part (a) of the figure than it does in part (b), because the signal is biased to a higher part of the curve in (b) — and also because the signal in (b) is smaller.

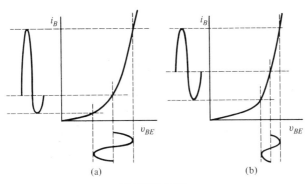

(a)   (b)

FIGURE 7–17
CE *input characteristic*

Effect of Source Resistance on the Input Nonlinearity

The transistor input circuit may be viewed as in Figure 7–18(a), in which the source resistance of the transducer or amplifier supplying the input signal is marked R_s, and the transistor's nonlinear input resistance is R_i. If the source

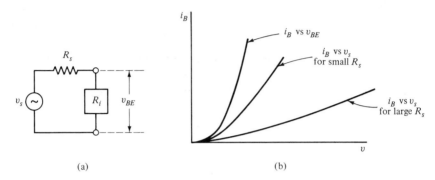

(a)   (b)

FIGURE 7–18
Effect of source resistance on the input nonlinearity

resistance is small, the total resistance in series with the source voltage v_s is predominantly the nonlinear R_i, and the resulting current flow — that is, the transistor input current — will not be linearly related to the signal v_s. It will be distorted. Thus a voltage source — a source with low output resistance —may produce considerable distortion of the input (base) signal current, especially if driven hard as in Figure 7–17(a).

But if R_s is large, the total circuit resistance will be more linear. Thus a current source, or one having a high source resistance, will produce less distortion of the input current wave. Figure 7–18(b) illustrates the effect of linear source resistance on the input current-voltage characteristic.

Variation of h_{FE}

In general, h_{FE} tends to be low at very low values of collector current, rises at moderate currents, and begins to decrease again at higher currents. For

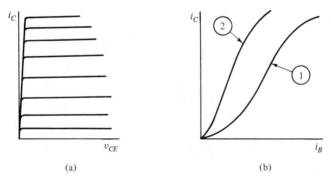

(a)   (b)

FIGURE 7–19
Compression in the output at very low and very high currents

equal increments of base current this means compression at both extremes, as shown in Figure 7–19(a). This figure exaggerates the effect so that it may be readily visible.

The Transfer Characteristic

Part (b) of Figure 7–19 shows transfer curves, i_C versus i_B, exhibiting this general characteristic. In many transistors the compression at the lower currents is much less significant than at the higher currents, so that most of the compression of the current waveform will occur in the upper peak, as in curve number 2.

The effects of both the input characteristic and the h_{FE} characteristic may be combined in a single transfer curve, i_C versus v_{BE}, illustrated in Figure 7–20.

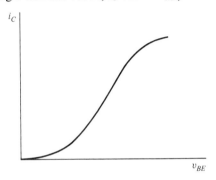

FIGURE 7–20
Transfer curve, i_C versus v_{BE}

When this curve is made for a transistor *in an operating circuit*, so that it includes the effect of the load, it is called a *dynamic transfer curve*. If the curve includes the effect of the source resistance in the input circuit, it will be a complete dynamic transfer curve of i_C versus v_s, and can be used for distortion analysis.

Power amplifiers designed for maximum power output generate sufficient distortion so that negative feedback is often employed to reduce the distortion. Although this also reduces the gain, necessitating an increase in the number of stages prior to the power stage, it may still provide advantage over the alternative. The alternative involves using transistors with much higher current ratings so that the signal current swings will not use as large a portion of the operating region, and thus will generate less distortion; or using more transistors in push-pull or in parallel to achieve the same "over-rating."

Introductory Ideas of Harmonic Analysis

Later, in Section 7.13, we will describe methods for quantitatively analyzing the amount of distortion produced by an amplifier. At this point a brief introduction to the ideas of harmonic analysis of a waveform will aid in an understanding of some of the distortion mechanism, especially in push-pull operation.

Mathematical methods for analyzing nonlinear effects show that when a sine wave is distorted, additional sine wave components are created. The frequencies of these "distortion" components are exact multiples of the frequency of the original wave. That is, if f represents the frequency of the original, then the distorted wave may contain components at frequencies $2f$, $3f$, $4f$, and so on.

The original frequency is often called the *fundamental frequency*, while the multiples $2f$, $3f$, etc., are termed *harmonics*. $2f$ is the second harmonic, $3f$ is the third harmonic, and so on.

The harmonic content of a wave may be measured by the use of filters adjusted to respond only to a narrow band of frequencies. When a complex waveform is applied to the input of such a filter and the filter is tuned to, for example, the third harmonic, the output will be principally at the frequency of that harmonic. In other words, the output will essentially be a sine wave of that frequency. The amplitude of the output will then be a measure of the amount of "third harmonic" content in the wave.

Commercial equipment is available which uses such techniques for measuring distortion. In most cases the lower harmonics are the greatest in amplitude, and consequently distortion measurement and analysis often involve only the second and third harmonics.

Two simple examples can be used to illustrate the role of harmonic components in distortion analysis. Figure 7–21 depicts a sinusoidal signal v_s applied to two circuits having nonlinear characteristics. The output current in each case can be graphically plotted from the given transfer curve. In (a) the operat-

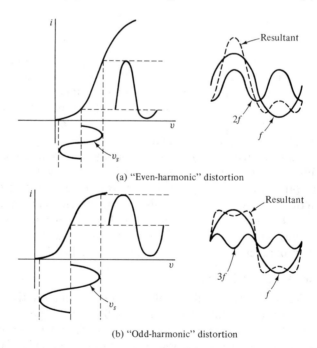

(a) "Even-harmonic" distortion

(b) "Odd-harmonic" distortion

FIGURE 7–21
Even-harmonic and odd-harmonic distortion

ing point and signal amplitude are such as to involve the curvature only at one end of the characteristic. This results in compression of the lower portion of the current wave. In (b) both ends of the characteristic are involved, so that compression of the wave occurs at both peaks.

In each case a figure is included which illustrates how the sum of a sine wave and a smaller amplitude harmonic tends to show the same effect. In (a) the second harmonic is required to produce the blunting of just one peak. In (b) it is the third harmonic, because both peaks are blunted. In both cases, adding more harmonics [$4f$ and $6f$ in (a); $5f$ and $7f$ in (b)] would make the resultant more closely approach the actual distorted wave.

The type of distortion illustrated in (a), in which only one peak is compressed, is often called even-harmonic distortion, because only the even-multiple frequencies exist in the harmonic analysis. That shown in (b) is termed odd-harmonic distortion.

7.12 Distortion in Push-Pull Amplifiers

The push-pull Class A amplifier has the unique characteristic of inherently tending to cancel even-harmonic distortion.

This feature is the result of the fact that the two transistors are operating 180° out of phase, so that the signal is carrying one transistor through the upper part of its characteristic while the other is swinging through the lower part of its characteristic. Even-harmonic distortion, as illustrated in Figure 7–22(a), imposes distortion of essentially opposite nature on the two halves of

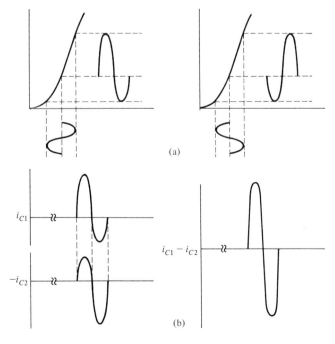

FIGURE 7–22
Distortion reduction in Class A push-pull

a wave (stretching one half and compressing the other). Therefore, the two out-of-phase waves tend to cancel this distortion when they are combined in the output, because the compression in one wave is occurring at the same time as the stretching is occurring in the other wave. Part (b) of the figure shows this effect in the output. Remember that the effective output current in the collector-to-collector circuit is the difference between i_{C1} and i_{C2}, as shown in Section 7.8.

Harmonic analysis shows this reduction of even-harmonic distortion more

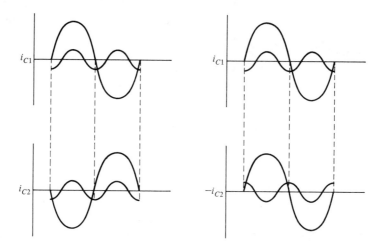

FIGURE 7–23
Effect of phase of even-harmonic components in the output of the push-pull circuit

clearly. Using the graphical approach employed in Figure 7–21, and again showing only the second harmonic for clarity, the result is as shown in Figure 7–23. When i_{C2} is subtracted from i_{C1}, as in the output of the push-pull circuit,

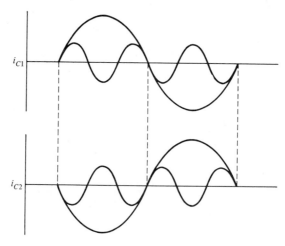

FIGURE 7–24
Phase of odd-harmonics in the push-pull circuit

the *harmonics* shown in this figure will cancel, while the fundamentals add as illustrated originally in Figure 7–15. This cancellation will occur for all even harmonics but not for the odd harmonics. Figure 7–24 illustrates why this is so. The phase of odd harmonics is such that they are additive in just the same way that the fundamentals are.

The cancellation of even harmonics is an important improvement in performance for Class *A* push-pull as compared with the single-ended amplifier. However, this improvement exists only to the extent that the two transistors are matched in their characteristics. If the transistors are not matched, the cancellation will not be complete.

Cross-Over Distortion in Class *B*

The distortion due to the curvature of the lower end of the transfer characteristic is eliminated in push-pull Class *A*, but not in Class *B*. Figure 7–25 illustrates the result.

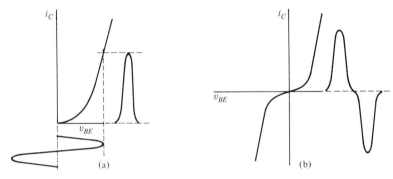

FIGURE 7–25
Cross-over distortion

Part (a) depicts the waveform of current in either of the two transistors. Notice that the lower portion of the collector current half-sine wave is distorted. Part (b) shows the resulting complete cycle of output current. (This method of presentation, by placing two copies of the transfer curve "back-to-back" in this way, is often employed to show the composite effect in push-pull.)

This distortion may be greatly reduced by forward-biasing the two transistors to a point such that both units are conducting at the same time in the most distorted portion of the transfer curve. Since the output is proportional to the difference between the two collector currents, the two curvatures tend to cancel each other. Figure 7–26 illustrates this. The principle being utilized in this, of course, is the same as that which distinguishes Class *A* operation: the cancellation of even harmonics. Since this method of operation has the two transistors conducting more than one-half cycle each, it is sometimes called Class *AB*.

7.13 Distortion Analysis

It is possible to make detailed analyses of the expected distortion for different transistors and circuit arrangements, in order to arrive at optimum designs.

The methods are tedious when performed without computers, so that many engineers depend instead upon initial estimates based on an examination of the transistor curves and on their experience. Adjustments are then made on operating circuits to optimize the performance.

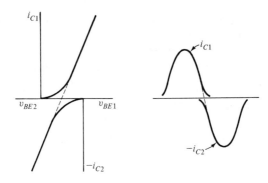

FIGURE 7–26
Biasing to reduce cross-over distortion

Where appropriate facilities are available, however, prediction of distortion and other performance may be made readily enough to permit major decisions concerning transistor types and circuit types — decisions that might not be as feasible by empirical methods. Even where the advantages of high-speed computation are not involved, the relationships that permit the analytical expression of distortion are useful in providing insight into these phenomena.

The dynamic transfer characteristic of i_C versus v_s is, in general, a curve which does not follow any simple law. In the operating region such a curve can be represented by the power series

$$i_C = a_1 v_s + a_2 v_s{}^2 + a_3 v_s{}^3 + \cdots \tag{7-18}$$

The values of the coefficients a_1, a_2, a_3, etc., depend upon the shape of the curve, and can be determined by making certain measurements on the curve.

If the input signal v_s is a sinusoidal voltage it can be expressed as

$$v_s = V \cos \omega t \tag{7-19}$$

This may be substituted in Equation (7–8) to give

$$i_C = a_1 V \cos \omega t + a_2 V^2 \cos^2 \omega t + a_3 V^3 \cos^3 \omega t + \cdots \tag{7-20}$$

Then by the use of trigonometric identities such as

$$\cos^2 \omega t = \tfrac{1}{2}(\cos 2 \omega t + 1)$$
$$\cos^3 \omega t = \tfrac{1}{4}(\cos 3 \omega t + \cos \omega t)$$

and by including a term I_Q to account for the quiescent current resulting from normal bias, the following may be obtained:

$$i_C = I_Q + A_0 + A_1 \cos \omega t + A_2 \cos 2\omega t + A_3 \cos 3 \omega t + \cdots \tag{7-21}$$

The various terms in this series expression for the collector current indicate that when the input voltage is a sine wave, the nonlinear characteristic results in the production of sinusoidal components at various frequencies, plus a dc term (A_o).

The dc term either adds to or subtracts from the quiescent current I_Q, depending upon the nature of the distortion. (A familiar example of dc component produced by distortion is the dc produced in the output of a power supply rectifier. Rectification is an example of deliberate distortion.)

The term $A_1 \cos \omega t$ indicates a component at the same frequency as the input; the $\cos 2 \omega t$ indicates a component at twice the frequency ($2 \omega t = (2)(2\pi f)(t) = (2\pi)(2f)(t) = 2\pi f' t$ in which the frequency f' is twice the input frequency f), and so on.

If the transfer characteristic were a perfectly straight line (no nonlinearity), Equation (7–8) above would simply be

$$i_C = a_1 v_s$$

which is a linear, or straight-line equation (involving variables only to the first power). The most common electrical example of this of course is the transfer function involving a simple resistor:

$$i = a_1 v = \frac{v}{R}$$

In this case a_1 has the value $1/R$. In other words, the squared, cubed, and higher power terms represent the curvature in the characteristic. Since these are the terms which led (by the trigonometric identities) to the A_0, $A_2 \cos 2 \omega t$, $A_3 \cos 3 \omega t$, etc., terms in Equation (7–21), a perfectly linear transfer curve should result in all the constants being zero except I_Q and A_1 in Equation (7–21). Examples involving the calculation of the coefficients in this equation will be considered later.

Predicting Distortion by Calculations Made on the Transfer Curve

The method of calculating the distortion that a particular transfer function will produce consists of calculating the amplitudes of the components, by means of measurements on the transfer curve. If the amplitude of the dc component, the fundamental, and three harmonics are to be obtained, the values of the five coefficients A_0, A_1, A_2, A_3, and A_4 must be found from the equation

$$i_C = I_Q + A_0 + A_1 \cos \omega t + A_2 \cos 2\omega t$$
$$+ A_3 \cos 3\omega t + A_4 \cos 4\omega t \qquad (7\text{–}22)$$

This equation consists of the first five terms of the series represented in Equation (7–21) and is probably an accurate enough expression of distortion for most work.

These coefficients can be evaluated by using five known values of i_C at five known instants of time (ωt). This permits writing five equations in five unknowns, which then can be solved simultaneously. Figure 7–27 illustrates the method of obtaining the five instantaneous values of i_C.

Note that this method utilizes the values of current at the quiescent point, at i_{max}, i_{min}, and at two intermediate points. These two intermediate points are

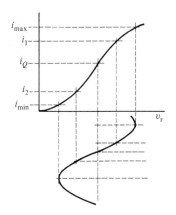

FIGURE 7–27
Values of i_C used in distortion analysis

almost as simple to locate as the above three. They are conveniently chosen to be the current values produced when the input signal v is at one-half its positive peak value and one-half its negative peak value.

Thus, the current values needed are those produced by the signal voltage values summarized in Table 7–2, and are easily found graphically as shown in Figure 7–27 above.

TABLE 7–2

Signal voltage value	Collector current symbol
v_{peak}	i_{max}
$\frac{1}{2}v_{peak}$	i_1
0	i_Q
$-\frac{1}{2}v_{peak}$	i_2
$-v_{peak}$	i_{min}

For these points, the simultaneous solution of the five equations gives the following evaluations for the five coefficients:

$$A_0 = \frac{1}{6}(I_{max} + 2I_1 + 2I_2 + I_{min}) - I_Q$$

$$A_1 = \frac{1}{3}(I_{max} + I_1 - I_2 - I_{min})$$

$$A_2 = \frac{1}{4}(I_{max} - 2I_Q + I_{min}) \qquad\qquad \textbf{(7–23)}$$

$$A_3 = \frac{1}{6}(I_{max} - 2I_1 + 2I_2 - I_{min})$$

$$A_4 = \frac{1}{12}(I_{max} - 4I_1 + 6I_Q - 4I_2 + I_{min})$$

The distortion is commonly expressed in terms of the amplitude of each component as a percentage of the fundamental amplitude. That is,

$$\left[\frac{A_2}{A_1}\right](100) \text{ is the percentage of 2nd harmonic}$$

$$\left[\frac{A_3}{A_1}\right](100) \text{ is the percentage of 3rd harmonic}$$

and so on. The total distortion is

$$D = \sqrt{\left[\frac{A_2}{A_1}\right]^2 + \left[\frac{A_3}{A_1}\right]^2 + \left[\frac{A_4}{A_1}\right]^2 + - - - -} \qquad (7\text{–}24)$$

and may be expressed in percentage by multiplying by 100.

Example of Distortion Calculation

A certain transistor circuit has a dynamic transfer characteristic as shown in Figure 7–28. If this transistor is biased and operated so that the input voltage swings from a quiescent value of 0.7 v down to a minimum of 0.3 and up to a

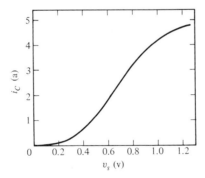

FIGURE 7–28
Dynamic transfer curve

TABLE 7–3

Voltage		Current	
at positive peak:	1.1 v	I_{max}	= 4.5 amps
at 0.5 peak:	0.9 v	I_1	= 3.75
at zero signal:	0.7 v	I_Q	= 2.5
at −0.5 peak:	0.5 v	I_2	= 1.2
at neg. peak:	0.3 v	I_{min}	= 0.3

maximum of 1.1 v, the resulting collector current values to be used in the distortion calculations of Equation (7–23) are found in Table 7–3. The resulting distortion calculations using Equation (7–23) are:

$$A_0 \cong \frac{1}{6}[4.5 + (2)(3.75) + (2)(1.2) + 0.3] - 2.5$$

$$A_0 \cong -0.05 \text{ amp}$$

$$A_1 \cong \frac{1}{3}[4.5 + 3.75 - 1.2 - 0.3]$$

$$A_1 \cong 2.25 \text{ amps}$$

$$A_2 \cong \frac{1}{4}[4.5 - (2)(2.5) + 0.3]$$

$$A_2 \cong -0.05 \text{ amp}$$

$$A_3 \cong \frac{1}{6}[4.5 - (2)(3.75) + (2)(1.2) - 0.3]$$

$$A_3 \cong -0.15 \text{ amp}$$

$$A_4 \cong \frac{1}{12}[4.5 - (4)(3.75) + (6)(2.5) - (4)(1.2) + 0.3]$$

$$A_4 \cong 0$$

These coefficients are current amplitudes, as indicated by Equation (7–21). Since the A_2 and A_3 terms are negative, they are 180° out of phase with the harmonics assumed in the equation.

The A_0 value indicates that the dc collector current is decreased 0.05 amp by the rectifying action of the amplifier nonlinearity. The A_1 value indicates the peak value of the fundamental. The A_2 value shows a second harmonic of 0.05 amp peak, and A_3 reveals a third harmonic of 0.15 amp peak value.

In percentages, the second harmonic is

$$\left[\frac{A_2}{A_1}\right](100) = \left[\frac{0.05}{2.25}\right](100) = 2.22 \text{ percent}$$

and the third harmonic is

$$\left[\frac{A_3}{A_1}\right](100) = \left[\frac{0.15}{2.25}\right](100) = 6.66 \text{ percent}$$

while the fourth harmonic is approximately zero. The total distortion is

$$D \cong (100)\sqrt{\left[\frac{A_2}{A_1}\right]^2 + \left[\frac{A_3}{A_1}\right]^2 + \left[\frac{A_4}{A_1}\right]^2}$$

$$\cong (100)\sqrt{(0.0222)^2 + (0.0666)^2 + 0}$$

$$D \cong 7 \text{ percent}$$

Similar calculations made for a larger peak-to-peak swing would show greater distortion, while for a smaller signal the distortion would be less.

7.14 Heat Dissipation and Power Derating

The major power dissipation in the transistor is at the collector-base junction. This is because the collector-to-base voltage is much greater than the base-emitter voltage, while the currents through the two junctions are almost the same. The collector dissipation, therefore, is typically much greater than the base-emitter dissipation. As a consequence, many transistors are rated, with respect to power handling ability, on the basis of their maximum allowable collector power dissipation.

This power is dissipated in the junction as heat, which causes a temperature rise above the temperature of the air or other medium in which the transistor is located. The amount of temperature rise depends upon the amount of power being dissipated and upon the ability of the transistor to conduct the heat away. The ability of the transistor to conduct away heat depends on the *thermal conductivity* or *thermal resistance* of the conducting path from the junction to the surrounding air, and on the temperature of the surrounding air (the *ambient temperature*). Heat radiating structures, with fins or with large-area surfaces, are available to improve the transfer of heat from the transistor to the surrounding air. Such structures are known as heat sinks. Special mounting materials to improve the conduction of heat from the transistor to the chassis upon which it is mounted may also be used.

The materials used in the construction of the transistor determine the maximum temperature at which the junction can be permitted to operate. The maximum allowable operating temperature for germanium transistors is generally 85° to 110°C, while for silicon units it will be 175° to 200°C.

Since the temperature varies with the power dissipation, the heat conducting conditions, and the ambient temperature, the dissipation rating of transistors is usually specified for a given case temperature, or ambient temperature, or both. For example, a dissipation rating might read: "Total device dissipation (at 25°C case temperature) — 6 w." It might also list the dissipation rating at an *ambient* temperature of 25°C as 1 w. In the latter situation, it is assumed that no heat sink is used, so that the case of the transistor will be considerably hotter than 25°, and this is why the rating is lowered from 6 w to 1 w.

Derating Transistors

In either case, if in actual operation the temperature of the specified element (case or ambient air) is expected to be higher than the specified temperature, the transistor must be *derated*. The transistor of the above example might have deratings as follows.

1.   With respect to the 6 w rating for a case temperature of 25°C, the specification might require a derating of 34 mw per degree C (mw/°C).

Thus, if permitted to operate under conditions which caused the case to rise to 65°C, or 40° above the specified 25°, the power rating would have to be reduced to 6: $(40)(0.034) = 6 - 1.36 \cong 4.6$ w. Under these conditions the maximum allowable dissipation would be only about 4.6 w instead of 6 w.

2.   With respect to the 1-w rating at an ambient temperature of 25°C, the same transistor might have a derating of 5.7 mw/°C.

Thus, for example, if operated in an ambient of 60°C, or 35° above the specified temperature, the maximum allowable dissipation would be $1 - (35)(5.7 \times 10^{-3}) = 1 - 0.1995 \cong 0.8$ w.

Derating such as this is designed to prevent the transistor junction from exceeding a certain maximum temperature. The derating will reduce the allowable dissipation to zero when the external temperature equals the maximum allowable temperature of the junction.

Thermal Resistance

The relationship which expresses the temperature rise per watt of power dissipation is called the *thermal resistance*, defined by

$$\theta = \frac{\Delta T}{P} \tag{7–25}$$

The thermal resistance from junction to case is then

$$\theta_{JC} = \frac{T_J - T_C}{P} \tag{7–26}$$

in which T_J is the maximum allowable junction temperature, T_C is the case temperature, and θ_{JC} is the thermal resistance from junction to case.

In case (1) above, where the derating was 34 mw/°C, the maximum allowable junction temperature was 200°C. The thermal resistance from junction to case for this transistor was 29.4 *degrees per watt*. Thus, if the case is held at a temperature of 25°C, we have

$$\theta_{JC} = \frac{T_J - T_C}{P} \tag{7–26}$$

So that

$$P = \frac{T_J - T_C}{\theta_{JC}} = \frac{200 - 25}{29.4}$$

$$P \cong 6 \text{ w}$$

and this is the maximum allowable power, as given in the specification.

But if the case were operated at 65°C as in the example given previously,

$$P = \frac{T_J - T_C}{\theta_{JC}}$$

$$P = \frac{200 - 65}{29.4} = \frac{135}{29.4}$$

$$P \cong 4.6 \text{ w}$$

which is the derated figure obtained in example 1.

Where ambient temperature is specified, the thermal resistance from junction to ambient, θ_{JA}, can be used.

$$\theta_{JA} = \frac{T_J - T_A}{P} \tag{7–27}$$

In case (2) above, θ_{JA} would have been 175° per watt. Thus 1 w of dissipation would give a temperature rise of 175° above the ambient of 25°, for a junction temperature of 200°C, the limit.

The ambient of 60° used in the example would lead to

$$P = \frac{T_J - T_A}{\theta_{JA}}$$

$$P = \frac{200 - 60}{175} = \frac{140}{175}$$

$$P = 0.8 \text{ w}$$

as before. In choosing mounting materials and heat sinks for a power amplifier, thermal resistances specified by the transistor manufacturer and the heat sink manufacturer, and as determined by engineering tests for various mounting methods and materials if necessary, may be used to determine the total thermal resistance.

Thus, since

$$\theta = \frac{\Delta T}{P} = \frac{T_J - T_A}{P}$$

we have

$$\theta_{\text{TOTAL}} = \frac{(T_J - T_C) + (T_C - T_{\text{SINK}}) + (T_{\text{SINK}} - T_A)}{P}$$

$$\theta_{\text{TOTAL}} = \frac{T_J - T_C}{P} + \frac{T_C - T_{\text{SINK}}}{P} + \frac{T_{\text{SINK}} - T_A}{P}$$

So that

$$\theta_{\text{TOTAL}} = \theta_{JC} + \theta_{CS} + \theta_{SA} \qquad (7\text{--}28)$$

Heat Sinks

The ability to conduct heat from a transistor to the surrounding air or other cooling medium depends upon the amount of surface area in contact with the cooling medium, and on the rate of flow of the cooling medium past the heat dissipating surfaces. In order to increase the surface area, power transistors are often built with large flanges having large flat surfaces which can be mounted directly upon metal chassis in order to provide good contact. The metal chassis (as well as the portion of the transistor flange exposed to the air) serves as a heat sink, to absorb heat generated by the transistor, and pass it on to the air.

Separate structures to be used as heat sinks by attaching to the transistor are built in a great variety of sizes and shapes. Again the primary purpose is to provide large surface area exposed to the cooling medium. This is very commonly done by providing fins protruding from a main body which is in contact with the case of the transistor. Air is commonly used as the cooling medium for small and medium power transistors, with natural circulation, or "convection cooling." For medium to high power units, forced air cooling is often used. In these cases, the equipment in which the transistors are used may be equipped with a blower which forces air over the surfaces and thus increases the rate of flow compared to that with just convection cooling.

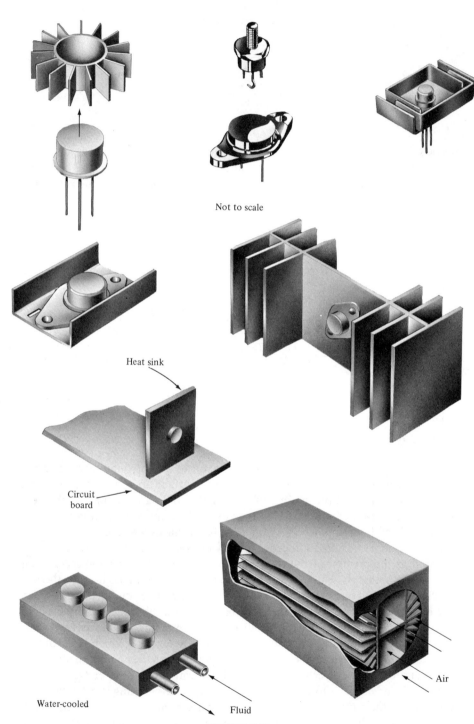

Not to scale

Heat sink

Circuit
board

Water-cooled

Fluid

Air

FIGURE 7–29
Various heat sink types

For very high power transistors, some heat sinks are avilable in the form of enclosures with fins and provision for mounting the transistors inside, so that air from a blower may be forced through the enclosure over the fins. In this way the cooling air from the blower may be confined to the units needing the greatest cooling, and a high rate of flow obtained over these units.

Water cooling is also available, where great amounts of heat must be dissipated, and the space available for the equipment makes it mandatory to accomplish the greatest amount of cooling in the smallest possible space. In this type of cooling, water is forced through piping or tubing by a pump, and the transistor is mounted in or on a compartment or container to which the tubing is connected.

Figure 7–29 illustrates the form and mounting technique for a number of common types of convection cooled heat sinks, a forced-air cooled type and a simple water-cooled type.

7.15   Biasing Push-Pull Stages

Biasing circuits for push-pull amplifiers utilize all the methods introduced previously. This includes thermal stabilizing techniques such as the use of semiconductor diodes and temperature-sensitive resistors discussed in Chapter 6. However, applying these methods so as to obtain the operating benefits offered by push-pull circuits requires an understanding of the effects of these circuits on the bias currents and voltages in addition to an understanding of the effect of the operating point on the circuit's operation.

Class A Biasing

Several common biasing circuit arrangements are summarized in Figure 7–30, which shows how they would be applied to Class A push-pull stages.

In (a), a conventional resistance divider applies forward-bias to the bases of the push-pull pair by means of the connection to the center-tap of the input transformer. The use of separate unbypassed emitter-resistors permits signal negative feedback in addition to the usual dc stabilizing. If negative feedback were not wanted, bypass capacitors would be required. The use of a common resistor, as in (b), provides only dc stabilizing. There is no signal feedback in (b) because the two emitter current signal components are 180° out of phase in the resistor and therefore cancel each other. Because of this cancellation, emitter bypassing is not necessary.

The circuit of (a), although requiring an additional resistor, provides better dc stability and better balance. The individual resistors R_e provide individual dc stabilizing to the two transistors. If one tends to drift more than the other, the stabilizing affects only that unit, and thus tends to restore balance. In the circuit of (b), lack of a match in the drift characteristics causes the current of both transistors to be affected. The one that has risen more receives the additional compensation it needs, but unfortunately the other one receives this amount also. This tends to maintain the unbalance.

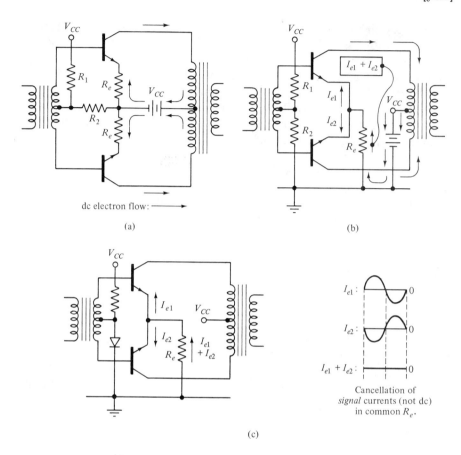

FIGURE 7–30

Some class A *push-pull biasing arrangements*

Class B Biasing

Although the Class *B* push-pull circuits illustrated so far have been biased at zero base current, the practical circuit usually employs some forward-bias to minimize crossover distortion and is thus really Class *AB*. This was discussed in Section 7.12.

The general form of the bias circuits for Class *B* push-pull operation is as shown in Figure 7–31. These circuits are of the same general form as the Class *A* circuits shown in Figure 7–30. However, where the Class *A* circuit might use bypass capacitors across the separate emitter-resistors if desired, the Class *B* circuit should not, because the voltage on the capacitor would be proportional to the signal amplitude. The bias consequently would not remain at the correct value.

The amount of forward-bias for crossover distortion reduction will vary with transistor types. Reference to Figure 7–26 shows that it should be sufficient to permit the straighter portions of the two transfer curves to "line up"

with each other. This indicates that the base-emitter voltage should be roughly
in the vicinity of the "knee" of the curve. The point indicated by the dashed
line in the figure is sometimes called the *extended cutoff*. In the case of german-

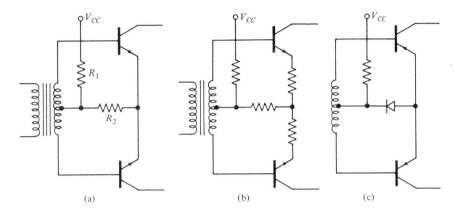

FIGURE 7–31
Class B *push-pull forward-bias to reduce crossover distortion*

ium transistors this will be in the vicinity of a few tenths of a volt, while for
silicon transistors it would probably lie in the range of 0.6 to 0.8 v. However,
the upper part of the curve is not actually straight, so that the decision as to
the portion to be "lined up" is not necessarily clear-cut. In practice it would
probably be done by making an initial estimate from the transistor's $i_B - v_{BE}$
curve, and making final adjustments on the operating circuit during the early
testing.

It is important that the amount of forward-bias used be no greater than
necessary since such biasing tends to reduce the efficiency by departing from
Class *B* conditions.

7.16 Phase Splitters

Although the center-tapped transformer is a convenient source of the two
equal out-of-phase signals required to drive a push-pull system, it has a number
of disadvantages. Transformers are expensive, bulky, and heavy, and this
makes them inappropriate for a number of applications. In addition, wide frequency response is difficult to attain with transformers. As a result, a number
of other methods have been used. Generally, such circuits are called *phase-
splitters* or *phase-inverters*.

The Split Load Circuit

One of the simplest sources of drive for push-pull circuits utilizes equal load
resistors in the emitter and the collector leads, as shown in Figure 7–32.

The load in the emitter circuit of the drive transistor develops a signal
voltage in phase with the input (due to the *IR* drop across R_1, which is in

phase with I_e and therefore in phase with V_{be}) while the collector voltage is of course 180° out of phase with V_{be}. If R_1 and R_2 are the same size, the two signal voltage outputs at terminals A and B will be approximately equal in amplitude

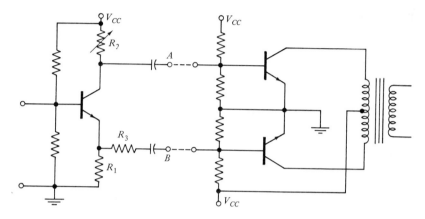

FIGURE 7–32
Split-load driver

because the emitter signal current differs from the collector signal current only by the usually small base signal current. One of the two resistors can be made adjustable to provide for any necessary balance adjustment.

One disadvantage of this circuit is the fact that its source resistances, looking back into the circuit from terminals A and B, are not equal. This can cause an imbalance in the inputs to the push-pull stage. A correction for this is the addition of a resistance (R_3 in Figure 7–32) in the emitter output, which is the output having the smaller source resistance.

Another disadvantage of this circuit is that the voltage gain of the phase-splitter is slightly less than 1. The reason for this will be developed in a later chapter.

The Differential Amplifier as a Phase-Splitter

Figure 7–33 presents a differential or difference amplifier used as a source of drive for a push-pull system. Although the operation of this type of amplifier will not be examined in detail here, it can be noted that the outputs at the two collectors are 180° out of phase with each other.

The difference amplifier has the advantage (compared with the split load circuit) of having equal R_o values at the two outputs. Additionally, when used in direct-coupling, it offers good thermal compensation against drift of operating point.

Several more complex circuits for phase-splitting are available but will not be presented here. One other arrangement that is very popular utilizes complementary-symmetry, or a *PNP-NPN* matched pair for the push-pull circuit. This permits a single input signal to be used, since opposite effects are produced by a given input signal polarity in *PNP* and *NPN* transistors. However, since these circuits require changes in the push-pull circuitry, they will be examined in the next section.

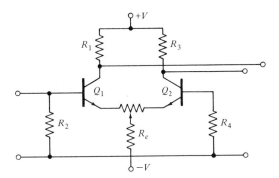

FIGURE 7-33
The differential amplifier as a push-pull driver

7.17 Single-Ended or Series-Output Push-Pull Circuits

A push-pull circuit which permits elimination of the output transformer is shown in Figure 7–34.

In part (a), the basic circuit configuration is shown without biasing and other details. Notice that in this arrangement two power supplies are required, and the emitters are not connected together or to a common ground as in the

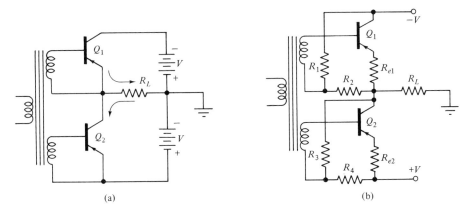

(a)   (b)

FIGURE 7-34
Direct-connected series output push-pull

circuits examined previously. The current (electron-flow) arrows indicate that under no-signal conditions the currents of the two transistors are in opposite directions in the load and therefore cancel. Thus direct-coupling (no coupling capacitor) is possible without dc current in the load. This is an advantage when the load is a loudspeaker voice coil for it leaves the voice coil in its normal rest position.

Under signal conditions, when the current from transistor Q_1, flowing to the right in the load as shown, is increasing, the current from Q_2, flowing in the opposite direction, will be decreasing since the two input signals are 180° out of phase. Thus there will be a net flow to the right. When the signal reverses at the inputs, the Q_1 current will be decreasing; the Q_2 current will be increasing, and the net flow will be to the left. The load current, in other words, is the *difference* between the two transistor currents just as in the case of the effective output current in the push-pull circuits considered previously. As a result of the combination of opposite direction and opposite phase, the net result is that the absolute value of the total *signal component* is the sum of the absolute values of the two transistor signal components — just as previously.

Part (b) of Figure 7–34 shows a complete circuit for this arrangement. Note that the driver transformer cannot be a simple center-tapped type, but instead must have separate secondary windings because the emitters of the two transistors must be at different dc potentials.

The bias circuitry is conventional, with forward-bias applied to the bases by the voltage dividers $R_1 - R_2$ and $R_3 - R_4$, and dc stabilizing contributed by the emitter resistors. The circuit arrangement may seem confusing at first glance, with some doubt as to where the bias dividers should be connected. Perhaps the easiest way to view this circuit is as two separate *CE* amplifiers sharing the same load R_L, with the load and supply voltage positions reversed from their conventional positions, in one of the circuits, and with the ground connection at an unfamiliar point in the circuits. In each case the bias divider is connected from the collector to the base (through the secondary winding) to the end of the emitter resistor away from the emitter, as in amplifier stages studied previously.

Tracing around the circuit loop of each transistor "stage" will show that individually the circuit action is the same as the conventional *CE* stages already studied, in spite of the fact that some of the parts have been moved about.

Another commonly used single-ended push-pull circuit is illustrated in Figure 7–35. This arrangement needs only one power supply instead of the two supplies of Figure 7–34, but does require a coupling capacitor. With low

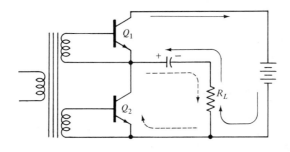

FIGURE 7–35
Capacitively-coupled series-output

impedance loads such as loudspeaker voice coils, the coupling capacitor must be quite large if adequate low-frequency response is to be obtained. Typical values are in the range of 1000 to 2000 μf.

The circuit action may be understood by considering the electron flow in the Q_1 loop (solid arrows) and noting that this current charges the capacitor with the polarity indicated. The effective supply voltage for Q_2 is this capacitor voltage. The signal action is then similar to that of Figure 7–34.

Complementary Symmetry

The above series-output push-pull circuits require the usual phase-inverted inputs. By the use of an *NPN* and *PNP* unit for the push-pull pair, input signals of the same phase may be employed. Such *NPN-PNP* combinations are called *complementary pairs,* and the circuit arrangement is known as *complementary symmetry.* Figure 7–36 illustrates the circuit principle.

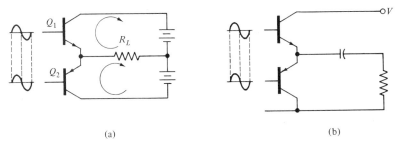

(a)   (b)

FIGURE 7–36
Complementary symmetry

While Q_1 is being turned on, Q_2 is being turned off by the same polarity of input signal, and there will be current flow to the left in R_L. During the next half-cycle of input, Q_1 will be turning off while Q_2 will be turning on.

Figure 7–37 shows a circuit diagram illustrating a practical driver circuit

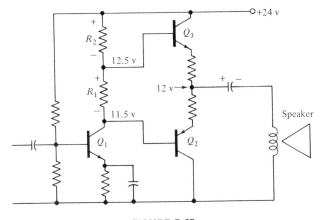

FIGURE 7–37
Practical complementary symmetry power amplifier

and biasing arrangement for a complementary symmetry power amplifier. The signal voltage fluctuations at the collector of Q_1 serve as input to Q_2 and Q_3. The principal load resistance for Q_1 is R_2, while R_1 is a small resistance to provide forward-bias to Q_2 and Q_3 to eliminate crossover distortion.

PROBLEMS

7-1. The output signal voltage and current of an amplifier are 5 v rms and 200 ma rms. What is the power output?

7-2. The output signal voltage and current of an amplifier are 10 v peak-to-peak and 5 amp peak-to-peak. What is the power output?

7-3. Calculate the output signal power, P_{out}, for the following cases, assuming the signal amplitude is as indicated by the arrowheads on the load lines.

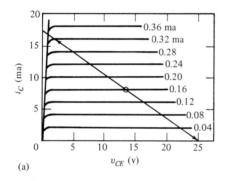
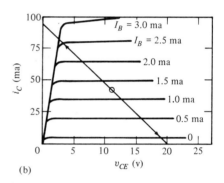

FIGURE P7-3

7-4. Draw load lines and locate the operating points on the following collector characteristics so as to permit the maximum possible output power, without going beyond the maximum allowable i_C, v_{CE}, P_D. (*Hint:* You will have to plot the P_{Dmax} line.)

   (a) The transistor whose collector curves are shown here has the following ratings: max $I_C = 100$ ma, $BV_{CEO} = 40$ v, and $P_{Dmax} = 400$ mw.

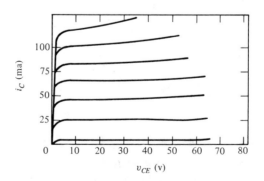

FIGURE P7-4(a)

(b) This transistor has the following ratings: max I_C = 500 ma, BV_{CEO} = 60 v, and P_{Dmax} = 2w.

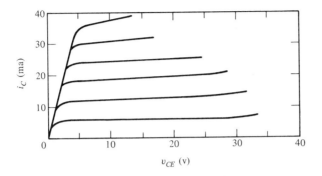

FIGURE P7-4(b)

7-5. Assume that the load lines in 7-3 above are the ac load lines for two power amplifiers, that the value of V_{CC} in each case is 30 v, and that the operating points are as indicated.

(a) Find the dc power input from the collector supply in each case.

(b) Find the collector efficiency in each case.

7-6. Assume that the circuit of Problem 7-3(a) above is transformer-coupled, and that the total resistance of the transformer primary plus the emitter resistor is 187 ohms.

(a) What is the value of V_{CC}? (*Hint:* Review Section 6.6 if necessary.)

(b) What is the dc input power?

(c) What is the collector efficiency?

7-7. In the ideal case, what is the ratio of the required transistor dissipation rating to the maximum possible power output, for Class A?

7-8. In order to obtain a signal power output of 10 w with a Class A amplifier, which of the following transistors would you choose?

Transistor	P_D Rating
A	5 w
B	10 w
C	30 w

7-9. Draw a Class B push-pull amplifier circuit with transformer-coupled input and output. Show typical signal voltage waveforms at the primary of the input transformer and at each transistor input. Show the correct phase relations between these waveforms. Show the collector current waveforms and the voltage waveforms across each transistor output and across the transformer secondary. Show proper phase relations to all other waveforms.

7-10. Express the average (i.e., dc) value of push-pull Class B collector supply current in terms of the peak value of collector signal current. Draw a neat sketch of the collector supply current.

7–11. The load line shown here represents the operation of each transistor of a push-pull Class *B* pair. The extent of the signal swing is indicated by the arrowhead on the load line.

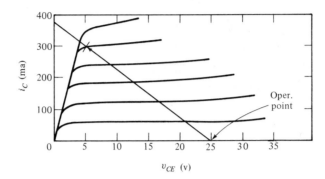

FIGURE P7–11

(a) What is the *peak* value of the collector current pulse, in each transistor?

(b) What is the dc collector *supply* current?

(c) What is the effective peak-to-peak output (collector) current for the entire circuit (as used in Equation [7–3])?

(d) What is the effective peak-to-peak collector voltage?

(e) What is the signal power output?

(f) What is the dc input power?

(g) What is the efficiency?

7–12. Answer the same questions as in Problem 7–11 for the following load line and signal.

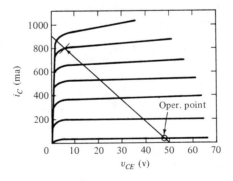

FIGURE P7–12

7–13. A Class *B* push-pull power amplifier is to be built to provide a maximum of 50 w of signal power to a 4 ohm load. Which of the following transistor types would be considered most suitable?

Transistor:	(a)	(b)	(c)
Max. allow. P_C:	15 w	100 w	25 w

7–14. Draw the circuit diagram of a simple Class A push-pull amplifier transformer-coupled at input and output. Show the bias circuitry. Show the input voltage and current waveforms for each transistor, with the proper phase relations. Show the collector current and collector voltage waveforms for each transistor, and the voltage waveform at the transformer secondary.

7–15. What are two likely reasons for the use of a Class A push-pull instead of a Class A single-ended amplifier, regardless of coupling method?

7–16. What is the advantage of Class A push-pull over Class B, regardless of coupling method?

7–17. What is the advantage of Class B push-pull over Class A regardless of coupling method?

7–18. What advantage does Class A push-pull offer, compared to single-ended Class A or to Class B, with regard to the output transformer?

7–19. A Class A push-pull amplifier has an output transformer with a turns ratio, between the entire primary and the secondary, of 6 to 1. If the load connected to the secondary is 8 ohms, what load does the transformer provide for each transistor collector?

7–20. A Class A push-pull amplifier is to be built. The output transformer must provide a load of 50 ohms for each collector. The load to be connected to the secondary is 4 ohms. What turns ratio is required?

7–21. If the circuit of Problem 7–19 above were a Class B amplifier, what would the load be for each collector?

7–22. If the circuit of Problem 7–20 above were a Class B amplifier, what turns ratio would be required?

7–23. Discuss the effect of the typical i_B/v_{BE} characteristic on waveform distortion.

7–24. Discuss the effect of signal source resistance on distortion in the input of a transistor amplifier.

7–25. Discuss the collector characteristic of a typical transistor with regard to distortion. Draw a curve of h_{FE} for the typical transistor. Draw a curve i_C versus i_B for this typical transistor.

7–26. Draw a typical dynamic transfer characteristic incorporating the general characteristics mentioned in 7–23 and 7–25 above.

7–27. Explain the term "even-harmonic distortion." Explain "odd-harmonic distortion." Show representative waveforms for each type.

7–28. What kind of distortion does Class A push-pull operation tend to eliminate?

7–29. Explain why Class A push-pull operation reduces distortion. Use waveform diagrams to illustrate your explanation.

7–30. Explain what cross-over distortion is, and how it may be minimized.

7–31. Use the five-point method to calculate the distortion in the collector current when the following transfer characteristic is used, with an input signal voltage biased at 0.4 v, and having a peak value of 0.3 v. Assume single-ended Class *A* operation.

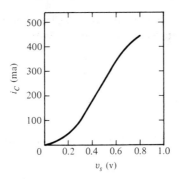

FIGURE P7–31

7–32. What would the distortion be for the above conditions *but using Class A push-pull*?

7–33. Compute the percentage of second harmonic distortion for the transfer curve shown here, on the assumption that the transistor is biased at a base-emitter voltage of 0.7 v, and the input signal is a sine wave having a peak value of 0.5 v.

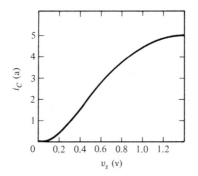

FIGURE P7–33

7–34. The 2N2987 has a dissipation rating of 1 w at 25°C ambient temperature. The data sheet specifies that it should be derated at the rate of 5.7 mw/°C. What is the maximum allowable dissipation if operated in an ambient temperature of 85°C?

7–35. The same transistor has a rating of 15 w at a case temperature of 100°C, with a derating of 150 mw/°C. What is the maximum allowable dissipation if operated such that the case temperature rises to 140°C?

7–36. What is the maximum allowable dissipation of the 2N4874 if operated so that its case temperature is 130°C?

7-37. What is the maximum allowable dissipation of the 2N4874 if operated in an ambient temperature of 100°C?

7-38. The 2N1529 (a germanium transistor) has a P_D rating of 106 w at a case temperature of 25°C, a maximum allowable junction temperature of 110°C, and a thermal resistance, junction to case (θ_{JC}) of 0.8°C/w. What is the maximum allowable dissipation if operated at a *case* temperature of 70°C?

7-39. The 2N3766 (a silicon transistor) has a dissipation rating of 20 w at a case temperature of 25°C, a thermal resistance, θ_{JC}, of 7.5°C/w and a maximum allowable junction temperature of 175°C. What is its maximum allowable dissipation if operated so that its case temperature is 90°C?

7-40. (a) Draw the Thevenin equivalent circuit for the bias circuit illustrated in Figure 7-31(a), as it appears at the junction of R_1 and R_2. (*Hint:* If necessary review the brief discussion of the bias divider in Chapter 3 in connection with Figures 3-7 and 3-8.)

   (b) If $R_1 = 100$ ohms, $R_2 = 4.7$ ohms, and $V_{CC} = 15$ v, what is the *open-circuit* dc voltage of the bias network? (That is, the voltage at the junction of R_1 and R_2 when there is no dc base current flow.)

   (c) If the dc base current of each transistor is 10 ma, what value of dc base-emitter voltage will the bias circuit provide?

7-41. A pair of germanium transistors is to be operated Class *A* push-pull using the bias arrangement of Figure 7-30(a). The quiescent collector current is to be 0.95 amp per transistor; the base current is 50 ma. The emitter resistors are to be 1.0 ohm each. Assuming that the required dc base-emitter voltage is 0.5 v, what voltage will be required at the junction of R_1 and R_2?

7-42. A pair of silicon transistors are to be used in a Class *A* push-pull amplifier using the bias arrangement of Figure 7-30(b).

$$I_C = 1.5 \text{ amp per transistor}$$
$$I_B = 60 \text{ ma}$$
$$V_{BE} = 0.9 \text{ v}$$
$$R_e = 0.25 \text{ ohm}$$

What voltage will be required at the junction of R_1 and R_2?

7-43. A germanium transistor is to be used in a push-pull Class *B* amplifier with $V_{CC} = 30$ v and is to be forward-biased at $V_{BE} = 0.25$ v to minimize crossover distortion. The base current at this voltage is 10 ma. Using the bias circuit of Figure 7-31(a), with an effective value of approximately 20 ohms for the parallel resistance of the bias divider, what should the values of R_1 and R_2 be?

7-44. Draw the circuit of the split-load phase inverter, including waveforms at input and both outputs, showing the correct phase relationships between all the waveforms.

7-45. (a) Draw a complete circuit diagram of a direct-coupled series-output push-pull amplifier stage. Include the necessary circuitry for forward-biasing (as for crossover distortion in Class *B* or normal forward-biasing in Class *A*).

(b) Show Class *A* waveform diagrams with proper phase relationships at both inputs and at the load.

(c) Show Class *B* waveform diagrams in the same way.

7–46. Repeat Problem 7–45 for the capacitively-coupled series-output push-pull circuit.

7–47. Draw the circuit of a capacitively-coupled complementary symmetry push-pull stage complete with driver stage and the necessary biasing and bias stabilizing components.

CHAPTER 8

Feedback Amplifiers

8.1 Introduction

Feedback is the introduction of a small portion of the output of an amplifier back into the input so that the operation of the amplifier is influenced by the condition of its output signal. When the technique known as *negative feedback* is used, the result is to reduce the input signal by the amount of output signal fed back.

A number of beneficial effects can be obtained using this technique. For example, unwanted variations in an amplifier's gain, such as occur due to thermal changes in transistors, can be minimized. Should the amplifier output signal amplitude increase due to such changes, the result is an increase in the fed back signal. This causes a reduction in the amplifier's input signal amplitude, and thus serves to counteract the increase caused by the thermal effects.

Applications of this gain-stabilizing feature of negative feedback are almost without limit. A prominent example is in test equipment such as oscilloscopes, electronic voltmeters, and the like. The amplifiers in such equipment are used to raise the level of small signals to amplitudes great enough to operate indicators or recorders. Variations in gain resulting from inherent variations in the characteristics of amplifying devices such as transistors would destroy the accuracy of these measurements. By using negative feedback, very stable amplification can be achieved and thus highly accurate measurements made.

8.2 Feedback Amplifier Principles

Some insight into the characteristics of feedback amplifiers may be gained by considering a block diagram illustrating one type. In Figure 8–1(a) an amplifier without feedback is shown. The voltage gain of this amplifier is

$$A_v = \frac{V_o}{V_i} = \frac{V_o}{V_g}$$

In part (b) of Figure 8–1, an arrangement is illustrated which applies a portion of the output of an amplifier back to the input, in series with the source V_g. The portion which is fed back can be expressed as βV_o where β is defined as the

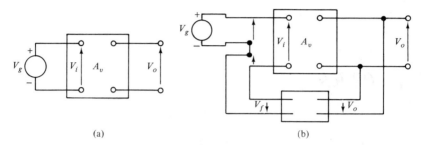

(a)   (b)

FIGURE 8–1
General principles of feedback

ratio of the feedback voltage to the output voltage, or the fractional portion which is fed back. That is,

$$\beta = \frac{V_f}{V_o} \tag{8–1}$$

so that
$$V_f = \beta V_o$$

The voltage V_i now appearing at the amplifier input terminals may be expressed as the sum of the feedback voltage V_f and the source voltage V_g:

$$V_i = V_g + V_f = V_g + \beta V_o \tag{8–2}$$

But V_i is amplified by the gain A_v so that

$$V_o = A_v V_i = A_v(V_g + \beta V_o)$$

giving
$$V_o - A_v \beta V_o = A_v V_g$$
$$V_o(1 - A_v \beta) = A_v V_g$$

and finally
$$\frac{V_o}{V_g} = \frac{A_v}{1 - A_v \beta}$$

Now the ratio of V_o to the source signal V_g may be recognized as the "gain" of this circuit from the signal source to the amplifier output. This is different from the gain V_o/V_i because of the feedback signal V_f appearing in the input, in series between V_g and V_i. If V_f were not there, V_g and V_i would be the same, and the gain V_o/V_g would be identical with V_o/V_i, as it was in the circuit shown in part (a) of the figure. The gain V_o/V_g is called the gain with feedback and may be designated here as A_v'. That is, for Figure 8–1(b),

$$A_v' = \frac{V_o}{V_g}$$

so that we have

$$A_v' = \frac{A_v}{1 - A_v \beta} \tag{8–3}$$

This equation tells us that the gain with feedback depends upon the *gain without feedback* (the gain of the original amplifier directly from its input to the output) and upon the *feedback factor β*.

Equation (8–3) is very important in providing an understanding of the effects of feedback. It reveals three special cases depending upon the polarity and magnitude of the term $Aβ$:

1. If the product $Aβ$ is positive and smaller than one, the A' is greater than A. Thus, the effect of the feedback in such a case is to increase the effective gain of the amplifier. This is caused by a feedback such that the voltage fed back to the input is in phase (or at least has a component which is in phase) with V_g and therefore serves to increase the voltage V_i. This is known as *positive feedback*.

2. If $Aβ$ is positive and its value approaches one, then $(1 - Aβ) \to 0$, and A' increases without limit. In the practical manifestation of this, any chance fluctuation at the input is amplified by the amplifier, to cause such a large feedback that the input fluctuation is thereby increased and amplified again, causing even more feedback. Since chance fluctuations are always present, in the form of noise and the like, a circuit having this much positive feedback would provide an output without having an input signal. This is called an *oscillator*.

3. If $Aβ$ is negative, then $(1 - Aβ) > 1$, and $A' < A$. The effective gain of the amplifier has been reduced by feedback. This is the result of a feedback voltage which is out of phase with V_g, so that $V_i < V_g$. Because the feedback opposes the input signal, this is called *negative feedback*. It is this type of feedback which provides the advantages mentioned in Section 8.1.

At this point an observation is in order concerning Equation (8–2) above. This equation expressed the total input to the amplifier as $V_g + V_f$, because Figure 8–1(b) and the accompanying discussion were being used to show the general case in which the feedback might be either positive or negative. For the case of negative feedback, of course, V_f is out of phase with V_g so that the two signals would have opposite signs when actual values are substituted. In other words, in negative feedback $|V_i|$ is the *difference* between $|V_g|$ and $|V_f|$. (Some writers set the block diagram up for the negative feedback case rather than the general case, and let the total input V_i then equal $V_g - V_f$.) V_i is sometimes referred to as the *difference signal* or *error signal*.

It should be noted also that not only is $|V_i|$ the difference between $|V_g|$ and $|V_f|$, but V_f will always be smaller than V_g — it cannot equal or exceed it. To see this, consider what would happen if you started with a given V_g and A_v, and tried to increase V_f from an initial value that was smaller than V_g. This might be done, for example, by varying the value of $β$. As V_f got larger, $V_i = (V_g - V_f)$ would get smaller. For V_f to become equal to V_g, V_i would have to become zero. But this would then mean that $V_o = (AV_i)$ would be zero and consequently $V_f = (βV_o)$ would be zero. But this would be impossible because then it could not be approaching V_g in amplitude. Since $V_g > V_f$, it is evident that V_i must always have the polarity of V_g.

As an example of the effects of negative feedback, consider a *CE* amplifier having a gain without feedback of 100, and using negative feedback such that 9 percent of the output is fed back to the input, out of phase with the source signal V_g. Since the *CE* amplifier output is 180° out of phase with its input, it is automatically the correct polarity to provide negative feedback. Thus in the Equation (8–3), A_v will be given the value of -100 to account for the amplifier's phase inversion, and β will be $+0.09$, since the feedback circuit will not produce any additional phase inversion. The gain with feedback is computed as follows:

$$A'_v = \frac{A_v}{1 - A_v\beta} \qquad\qquad (8\text{–}3)$$

$$A'_v = \frac{-100}{1 - (-100)(0.09)} = \frac{-100}{1 + 9}$$

$$A'_v \cong -10$$

Negative feedback is distinguished by the fact that the denominator in Equation (8–3) is greater than one, so that the gain with feedback is always less than the gain without feedback.

Loop Gain

The gain with feedback is often called the *closed-loop gain* while the gain without feedback is called the *open-loop gain*. These terms come from the fact that the amplifier and the feedback circuit form a "loop" from the input of the amplifier to its output, and then back by way of the feedback circuit to the input again. When this loop is "opened" by disconnecting the feedback from the input, the amplifier's gain is A, the "open-loop" gain. When the loop is "closed" by connecting the feedback, the gain decreases to A', the "closed-loop" gain.

A similar term encountered in feedback work is "loop gain" used to refer to the product $A\beta$. This is the gain the signal experiences from the input to the amplifier output (A) *and then back through the feedback circuit* (β) to the input again. Note how this differs from the terms open-loop gain and closed-loop gain, which refer to the gain of the *amplifier only*. Therefore, loop gain is $A\beta$, open-loop gain is gain without feedback, A, and closed-loop gain is gain with feedback, $A' = A/(1 - A\beta)$.

Gain Stabilizing Through Negative Feedback

Suppose that the amplifier of the above example suffered a 50 percent increase in its open-loop gain due to the effects of temperature rise upon the transistor's characteristics. The closed-loop gain would then become:

$$A' = \frac{A}{1 - A\beta}$$

$$A' = \frac{-150}{1 - (-150)(0.09)} = \frac{-150}{1 + 13.5}$$

$$A' \cong -10.34$$

The gain *with* feedback increased only about 3.4 percent even though the amplifying device's characteristics changed so much that the gain without feedback increased by 50 percent.

This conclusion is somewhat oversimplified, and the case merits more careful examination. For example, since feedback reduces the gain, additional stages are needed with feedback, and any comparison should take this into account. In the example above, two stages would be required to equal the gain of 100 available from one stage without feedback. Consequently, if the open-loop gain of each stage changes by 50 percent, the closed-loop gain would be $(10.34)(10.34) \cong 107$ for a 7 percent increase rather than just a 3.4 percent increase.

This is still quite an improvement over amplifiers without feedback, but a different arrangement permits much better results with the same number of stages. Instead of feedback in each stage, one feedback from the output of the second stage to the input of the first is employed, as illustrated in Figure 8–2.

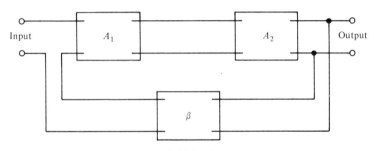

FIGURE 8–2
Feedback over two stages

(*Note:* Circuit methods of obtaining negative feedback will be developed in the remainder of the chapter. Feedback incorrectly applied — especially when involving two stages — can cause oscillations as described in case 2 of Equation (8–3) above.)

With $A_1 = A_2 = 100$ as in the example above, and $\beta = 0.01$, the result is

$$A' = \frac{A}{1 - A\beta}$$

in which $A = A_1 A_2 = (100)(100) = 10^4$.
Thus

$$A' = \frac{10^4}{1 + (10^4)(10^{-2})}$$
$$A' \cong 99$$

and when the individual open-loop gains increase by 50 percent as before, the result is

$$A' = \frac{(150)(150)}{1 + (150)(150)(10^{-2})}$$
$$A' \cong 99.5$$

With this arrangement, a 125 percent increase in gain without feedback caused only about one-half of 1 percent increase of gain with feedback.

Gain of a Negative Feedback Amplifier When Aβ is Quite Large

In the final example above, the term $A\beta$ in the feedback equation had the value

$$A\beta = (10^4)(10^{-2}) = 100$$

in contrast with the example just before it where $A\beta = (100)(0.09) = 9$. Analysis of Equation (8–3) indicates that when $A\beta \gg 1$,

$$A' = \frac{A}{1 - A\beta} \cong \frac{A}{-A\beta}$$

$$A' \cong -\frac{1}{\beta} \qquad\qquad (8\text{–}4)$$

That is, when $A\beta$ is very large, the feedback amplifier tends to be independent of the characteristics of the amplifying device, and the gain is determined almost entirely by the feedback fraction β. This is borne out in the above example. $\beta = 0.01$, and $A' \cong 1/\beta \cong 100$, and changed only 0.5 percent when A changed 125 percent. If the feedback fraction is determined by resistors — as, for example, a voltage divider across the output, proportioned to feed a certain fraction of the output (βV_o) to the input — then the gain can be very stable, since resistors are highly stable components.

8.3 Circuit Arrangements

The circuits in Figure 8–3 are simple versions of several amplifier circuits using negative feedback. In order to show the feedback more clearly, some of the bias circuitry has been omitted. The following material will explain the basic workings of these circuits.

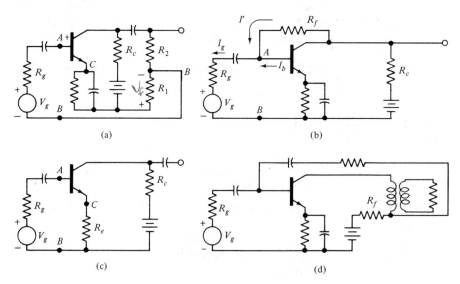

FIGURE 8–3
Single-stage feedback circuits

Figure 8–3(a): Voltage Feedback, Series Input

This is the kind of arrangement on which the block diagram analysis of the preceding section was based. In this particular version, there is a resistive voltage divider across the output, so that the voltage across one element of this divider is a "sample" of the output voltage. By connecting one end of the signal source to a point such as B, this sample of the output voltage is applied in series with the input. That is, the total input to the amplifier is the sum of the signal voltages in the input loop, or from A to B to C, and thus includes the fraction of the output voltage appearing across resistor R_1. In this circuit, since the CE amplifier inverts the signal, this fed-back voltage is out of phase with the applied signal V_g. This may be verified by noting the signal polarities in the figure. With the input signal V_g having the polarity indicated, the input at the base will be of the same polarity, as discussed in Section 8.2. The output signal polarity will then be opposite this, since this is a CE amplifier. The portion of the output signal across R_1 will therefore have the polarity shown.

Now if we trace around the series input loop starting at point A, going through V_g and R_1 to C, we find that the signal voltage polarities for this direction of travel are $+$ to $-$ across V_g and $-$ to $+$ across R_1. Thus the feedback voltage is indeed out of phase with the source voltage.

This is called voltage feedback because it "samples" or "senses" the output voltage. Its effect is to stabilize the output voltage, and it does it by controlling the input voltage. For example, if some change takes place in the amplifier circuit or in the device characteristics such as to increase the output voltage, there will be an increase in the feedback voltage. Since this is out of phase with the input signal, there will be a decrease of the effective input voltage at the base (even though V_g is constant). The overall result then is that the output increase is less than it would have been without feedback.

If the voltage gain of the amplifier is defined as the voltage gain from the terminals *A-B* to the output, then we can say that the output voltage is stabilized by control of the voltage gain. The voltage gain from terminals *A-B* to the output is given by Equation (8–3):

$$A'_v = \frac{A_v}{1 - A_v\beta} \tag{8–3}$$

and the stabilizing effect was illustrated in Section 8.2.

The current gain is unaffected by the feedback, except to the extent that a resistance such as $R_1 + R_2$, in parallel with the output, would affect current gain in any event. Not all the feedback arrangements provide the same kind of control, as examination of the other circuits of Figure 8–3 will show.

Figure 8–3(b): Voltage Feedback, Shunt Input

This circuit also provides voltage feedback. The resistor R_f and the effective circuit resistance between points A and B form a voltage divider across the output. A portion of the output is applied *in shunt with the input,* rather than in series with the input as in part (a).

Because of the shunt input connection, this circuit is analyzed in terms of the feedback current that flows into the base, rather than the feedback voltage. R_f forms a path for current to flow from the output to the input, out of phase with the base current that constitutes the normal input signal without feedback. Thus, should an increase occur in the output voltage, the amount of feedback *current* to the base increases, tending to reduce the input current. This then reduces the output current, and thus tends to minimize the increase of output voltage.

It should be noted carefully that although it is the output voltage which is being sampled and controlled, the control in this case is accomplished by adjustment of the input current. If the amplifier's current gain is defined as the gain from the generator terminals to the output, or I_o/I_g, then we can say that the output voltage is regulated *by control of the current gain*. The equation for the current gain with feedback is

$$A'_i = \frac{A_i}{1 - A_i\beta} \tag{8-5}$$

in which A_i is the current gain without feedback.

The voltage gain is unaffected by the feedback, except to the extent that a resistance such as R_f, in parallel with the output, would affect voltage gain in any event.

Figure 8–3(c): Current Feedback, Series Input

The term "current feedback" is used to indicate that the feedback samples or senses the output current; in other words the feedback is *proportional to the output current*. In the circuit illustrated here the collector signal current flowing in R_e causes a signal voltage in series with the input. The total input is the signal voltage from A to B to C. Any collector current variations cause signal voltage variations in the input loop, and stabilizing action follows as before.

Current feedback tends to stabilize *output current. It does not stabilize output voltage unless changes in output voltage are caused by changes in output current.* For example, an increase in the value of R_L would tend to cause an increase in A_v and V_o, but since this would not cause an increase in the output signal current flowing in R_e, there would be no increase in the feedback voltage and no stabilizing effect. However, an increase of h_{fe}, which without feedback would cause an increase in output current, and an increase in the output voltage due to the increase of I_oR_L, would in this circuit be accompanied by an increase in the signal voltage across R_e. Thus there would be a stabilizing effect due to feedback. Note here that since the feedback connection to the input is in series with the input, *the regulating of the output current is by control of the voltage gain.* While the circuit of Figure 8–3(a) controlled the output *voltage* by controlling voltage gain, this circuit controls output *current* by controlling voltage gain. The voltage gain equation is, of course, Equation (8–3):

$$A'_v = \frac{A_v}{1 - A_v\beta} \tag{8-3}$$

The current gain is unaffected by the feedback except to the extent that the presence of the resistance R_e in series with R_c would affect current gain even if R_e were not in the input loop, causing feedback.

Figure 8–3(d): Current Feedback, Shunt Input

This circuit represents another possible current feedback arrangement. In this circuit R_f is a small resistance, and the IR_f drop is proportional to the output current flowing in the transformer primary winding. The feedback connection is in shunt at the input. This circuit regulates output current, and does it by control of the current gain.

Summary

In this section we have considered four possible feedback arrangements:

(A) Voltage feedback in series with the input, which *stabilizes output voltage by controlling voltage gain*

(B) Voltage feedback in shunt with the input, which *stabilizes output voltage by controlling current gain*

(C) Current feedback in series with the input, which *stabilizes output current by controlling voltage gain*

(D) Current feedback in shunt with the input, which *stabilizes output current by controlling current gain*

8.4 The Feedback Ratio, β

The analysis of Section 8.2 was based upon voltage feedback in series with the input. A similar analysis can be made for the other possible configurations, and the resulting equations showing the relationship between open- and closed-loop gain have the same general form. In some cases the gain affected is the current gain rather than the voltage gain, and so the feedback ratio β may be I_f/I_o rather than V_f/V_o, but the form of the equation in each case would be

$$A' = \frac{A}{1 - A\beta}$$

Thus the two factors, gain without feedback and feedback ratio, are of fundamental importance. As pointed out earlier, in many applications $A\beta$ is made very large in order to have very stable gain, and the gain is then

$$A' = -\frac{1}{\beta} \tag{8–4}$$

In such cases the gain without feedback is important only in the sense that it should be very high to make Equation (8–4) valid, and accurate quantitative knowledge of it is not required. β, on the other hand, must be known accurately even in these cases.

In order to see how β may be evaluated, several of the circuits discussed above are repeated in Figure 8–4. In the circuit of part (a), the feedback voltage is the voltage across resistor R_1.

Thus
$$V_f = \left(\frac{R_1}{R_1 + R_2}\right)V_o$$

so that
$$\beta = \frac{R_1}{R_1 + R_2} \tag{8–6}$$

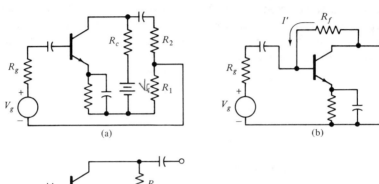

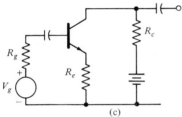

FIGURE 8–4
Single-stage feedback circuits

In the circuit of (b) it is the feedback current that is of interest. This current flows from the collector through R_f and then through the parallel combination of R_g and the transistor signal input resistance R_i. Consequently

$$I' = \frac{-V_c}{R_f + \dfrac{R_g R_i}{R_g + R_i}}$$

Usually R_f is much larger than $R_g \parallel R_i$, so that

$$I' \cong \frac{-V_c}{R_f}$$

This current divides up between the source resistance R_g and the transistor's signal input resistance R_i. The current effective as feedback current is that portion of I' which flows into the transistor. Designating this as I_f, we have

$$I_f = \left(\frac{R_g}{R_i + R_g}\right)I'$$

So that
$$I_f = -\left(\frac{V_c}{R_f}\right)\left(\frac{R_g}{R_i + R_g}\right)$$

Now
$$I_o = \frac{V_c}{R_L}$$

where R_L is the effective resistance of the total load on the amplifier. Then

$$\beta = \frac{I_f}{I_o} = -\left(\frac{V_c}{R_f}\right)\left(\frac{R_g}{R_i + R_g}\right)\left(\frac{R_L}{V_c}\right)$$

$$\beta = -\left(\frac{R_L}{R_f}\right)\left(\frac{R_g}{R_i + R_g}\right) \qquad\qquad (8\text{--}7)$$

When the source resistance is quite large compared to R_i, this equation simplifies to

$$\beta = -\frac{R_L}{R_f} \qquad\qquad (8\text{--}8)$$

In part (c) the feedback ratio is the ratio of the signal voltage across R_e to that across R_c (or R_L in the more general case). Thus

$$\beta = \frac{I_e R_e}{I_o R_L}$$

But $I_e \cong I_c = I_o$, so that

$$\beta \cong \frac{R_e}{R_L} \qquad\qquad (8\text{--}9)$$

8.5   Input and Output Impedance Effects

The changes brought about in the output and input portions of an amplifier circuit by the addition of feedback cause the output and input impedances to be quite different from those of the amplifier without feedback.

Input Resistance

Input circuit effects are illustrated in Figure 8–5. In the case of feedback in series with the input as shown in part (a) of this figure, the feedback voltage cancels part of the generator voltage. The small remaining signal voltage at

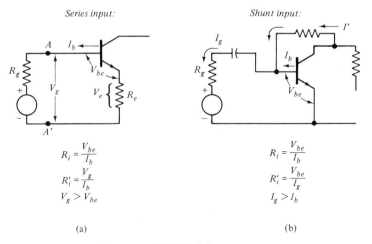

(a)   (b)

FIGURE 8–5
Input impedance effects with feedback

the input terminals of the transistor produces less input signal current than if the full generator voltage had been applied to the transistor. Thus the input circuit *at terminals A-A'* acts like a higher impedance than without feedback.

With feedback in shunt with the input, shown in part (b), the generator current flow is larger than actually flows in the base lead (because the feedback current is cancelling part of the base current). Thus the circuit acts like a smaller impedance than without feedback: a generator voltage equal to V_{be} is accompanied by a generator current greater than I_b. Figure 8–5 summarizes these relationships, and Equations (8–10) and (8–11) give the input resistance with feedback for each type. Input resistance with feedback in series with input:

$$R_i' = R_i(1 - A_v\beta) \qquad (8–10)$$

Input resistance with feedback in shunt with input:

$$R_i' = \frac{R_i}{1 - A_i\beta} \qquad (8–11)$$

Example 8–1

An amplifier using an unbypassed emitter resistor, as in Figures 8–4(c) and 8–5(a), has the following values:

$$h_{fe} = 150$$
$$h_{ie} = 3000 \text{ ohms}$$
$$R_L = 2500 \text{ ohms}$$
$$R_e = 390 \text{ ohms}$$

Input resistance without feedback is approximately equal to h_{ie}. Therefore $R_i = 3000$ ohms. The feedback factor is

$$\beta \cong \frac{R_e}{R_L} \qquad (8–9)$$

$$\beta \cong \frac{390}{2500} = 0.156$$

The voltage gain without feedback is

$$A_v \cong -h_{fe}\frac{R_L}{h_{ie}}$$

$$A_v \cong -(150)\left(\frac{2500}{3000}\right) \cong -125$$

Now using Equation (8–10) we obtain for the input resistance with feedback:

$$R_i' = R_i(1 - A_v\beta) \qquad (8–10)$$
$$R_i' \cong (3000)[1 - (-125)(0.156)]$$
$$R_i' \cong (3000)(20.5) = 61,500 \text{ ohms}$$

Results such as this show quite clearly that if high input resistance is needed in an amplifier, this type of feedback could be employed to obtain it.

Example 8–2

The same transistor is to be used with shunt feedback as in Figures 8–4(b) and 8–5(b). The pertinent values are:

$$R_g = 5000 \text{ ohms}$$
$$R_L = 2500 \text{ ohms}$$
$$R_f = 50 \text{ kilohms}$$

In this case Equation (8–11) applies. The current gain without feedback is

$$A_i \cong h_{fe} = 150$$

The feedback factor is

$$\beta = -\left(\frac{R_L}{R_f}\right)\left(\frac{R_g}{R_i + R_g}\right) \tag{8–7}$$

$$\beta = -\left(\frac{2500}{50,000}\right)\left(\frac{5000}{3000 + 5000}\right)$$

$$\beta \cong -0.0312$$

This then gives

$$R_i' = \frac{R_i}{1 - A_i\beta} \tag{8–11}$$

$$R_i' \cong \frac{3000}{1 - (150)(-0.0312)}$$

$$R_i' \cong \frac{3000}{5.68} \cong 528 \text{ ohms}$$

Output Resistance

The output impedance of feedback amplifiers is also a function of the type of circuit. Voltage feedback tends to stabilize the output voltage; that is, it makes it more constant in spite of load current changes. This is the effect that would accompany a decrease of internal impedance, where less internal voltage drop means less change of output voltage with changes of load current. Thus voltage feedback amplifiers have lower output impedance than the same amplifiers without feedback; they tend to behave more like constant voltage (i.e. zero resistance) sources.

By contrast, with current feedback the current is more constant than without feedback, and the circuit therefore acts more like a constant current source, or one having a high source impedance.

In order to show the magnitude of the effect of feedback upon output resistance, and also to show the practical factors that must be considered in evaluating this effect, the equation for output resistance with voltage feedback will be considered. This is

$$R_o' = \frac{R_o}{1 - A\beta} \tag{8–12}$$

in which A is A_i if the feedback is shunt connected at the input, and A_v if series connected.

R_o in this equation is the output resistance of the circuit without feedback, and should include the effect that any components required by the feedback arrangement would have while connected to the circuit but with the feedback disconnected. Similarly, the gain without feedback, A, should include the effect that the feedback circuitry would have on the gain with the feedback disconnected.

In order to clarify this, consider Figure 8–6. This illustrates a *CE* amplifier using voltage feedback with series input. The voltage divider $R_1 - R_2$ provides the feedback, and is of course also providing the forward-bias for the tran-

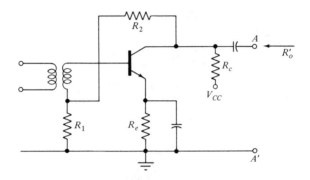

FIGURE 8–6
Voltage feedback circuit for output resistance example

sistor. DC bias stability is being provided by $R_1 - R_2$ and by R_e. If negative signal feedback were not desired, R_1 would have a bypass capacitor across it. Thus bias would still be provided but without the signal feedback.

The problem is to evaluate the output resistance of this circuit as "seen by" a load which might be connected to terminals A-A'. The series combination of R_1 and R_2 would be shunting the output even if the input transformer winding were not connected to the junction of the two resistors but instead were connected to ground. Thus the presence of R_1 and R_2 would affect the source resistance without feedback, R_o, as measured at terminals A-A'. R_1 and R_2 would also affect the gain without feedback since the total effective load on the amplifier would be $R_c \parallel (R_1 + R_2)$.

Thus R_o in Equation (8–12) would be

$$R_o \cong R_c \parallel (R_1 + R_2)$$

and A_v would be

$$A_v = \frac{h_{fe}[R_c \parallel (R_1 + R_2)]}{h_{ie}}$$

using the approximations developed in Chapter 4.

Example 8–3

The transistor of the previous example will be used in the circuit of Figure 8–6. The pertinent values are

$$h_{fe} = 150$$
$$h_{ie} = 3000 \text{ ohms}$$
$$R_c = 5600 \text{ ohms}$$
$$R_1 = 2700 \text{ ohms}$$
$$R_2 = 56 \text{ kilohms}$$

The effective load on the amplifier is

$$R_L = R_c \parallel (R_1 + R_2)$$
$$R_L = \frac{(5600)(56 + 2.7)(10^3)}{(5.6 + 56 + 2.7)(10^3)}$$
$$R_L = \frac{(5600)(58.7)}{64.3}$$
$$R_L \cong 5120 \text{ ohms}$$

This is also the approximate value of the output resistance without feedback, assuming that $1/h_{oe}$ for this transistor is much higher. This results in a voltage gain of

$$A_v \cong -h_{fe}\left(\frac{R_L}{R_i}\right)$$
$$A_v \cong -(150)\left(\frac{5120}{3000}\right)$$
$$A_v \cong -256$$

The feedback factor is

$$\beta = \frac{R_1}{R_1 + R_2}$$
$$\beta = \frac{(2.7)(10^3)}{(58.7)(10^3)}$$
$$\beta \cong 0.046$$

Using these values in Equation (8–12) then gives

$$R_o' = \frac{R_o}{1 - A\beta} \qquad\qquad \text{(8–12)} \;\checkmark$$
$$R_o' \cong \frac{5120}{1 - (-256)(0.046)} \cong \frac{5120}{12.8}$$
$$R_o' \cong 400 \text{ ohms}$$

Table 8–1 summarizes the general nature of the impedance effects in feedback amplifiers and includes terminology which can serve as a memory aid.

TABLE 8–1

Effect of Feedback Upon Circuit Impedances

*Type of Connection at Input or Output	Effect Upon Corresponding Input or Output Impedance
Shunt	Lower
Series	Raise

*Voltage feedback is obtained from elements connected in shunt with the output; current feedback is obtained from elements in series with the output. Note that at both the output and input, the shunt connection lowers the impedance, while the series connection raises the impedance.

8.6 The CE Amplifier with Unbypassed Emitter Resistor

The current feedback circuit shown originally in Figure 8–3(c) is very frequently encountered. In this section we will develop an expression for its input resistance in terms of circuit component and transistor parameter values, and we will also examine a simple practical example.

The circuit, with bias components and load, is shown in Figure 8–7. Since

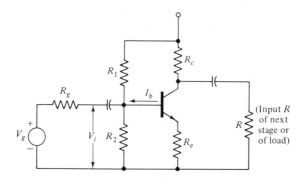

FIGURE 8–7
Current feedback, series input

R_1 and R_2 effectively shunt the input, the effect of these bias resistors must be included in any consideration of the input resistance of the stage as a load on the signal source. However, this effect will be considered separately in order to be able to show clearly the feedback effects. Initially the generator current will be considered to be equal to the base signal current I_b. The voltage V_i is the effective stage input signal, and is the sum of the base-emitter voltage and the voltage across R_e:

$$V_i = V_{be} + I_e R_e$$

But

$$I_e = I_c + I_b = A_i I_b + I_b$$

or

$$I_e = (A_i + 1)I_b$$

so that

$$V_i = V_{be} + (A_i + 1)I_b R_e$$

The input resistance with feedback, R'_i, is

$$R'_i = \frac{V_i}{I_b}$$

Therefore

$$R'_i = \frac{V_{be} + (A_i + 1)I_b R_e}{I_b}$$

or

$$R'_i = \frac{V_{be}}{I_b} + (A_i + 1)R_e$$

Now V_{be}/I_b is the input signal resistance without feedback, or R_i.

Thus

$$R'_i = R_i + (A_i + 1)R_e \qquad (8\text{–}13)$$

A useful approximation when A_i is large compared with 1, is

$$R'_i \cong R_i + A_i R_e \qquad (8\text{–}14)$$

and in the quite common case where $A_i \cong h_{fe}$, and $R_i \cong h_{ie}$, a further approximation that is very convenient is

$$R'_i \cong h_{ie} + h_{fe}R_e \qquad (8\text{–}15)$$

Now when the effect of this circuit as a load on the source is being considered, the bias network $R_1 - R_2$ must be included. Where this type of feedback is being used for the purpose of obtaining high input resistance, the effect of R_1 and R_2 may well prove to be a serious limitation.

The following example will help to illustrate the use of the above relationships.

Example of Current Feedback by Use of Unbypassed Emitter Resistor

A 2N334A transistor is to be used in the circuit of Figure 8–8. The quiescent emitter current is to be approximately 1 ma, so that the h-parameters will be

$$h_{fe} = 38$$
$$h_{ie} = 1700 \text{ ohms}$$
$$h_{oe} = 6.0 \times 10^{-6} \text{ mhos}$$
$$h_{re} = 1.3 \times 10^{-4}$$

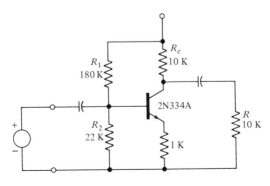

FIGURE 8–8
Circuit for feedback example

Since R_c and R are each 10,000 ohms, the effective load, R_L, will be 5000 ohms. The approximate performance equations for gain and input resistance without feedback can be used here. Thus

$$A_v \cong \frac{h_{fe}R_L}{h_{ie}}$$

$$A_v \cong \frac{(38)(5000)}{1700} \cong -112$$

$$A_i \cong h_{fe} = 38$$

$$R_i \cong h_{ie} = 1700 \text{ ohms}$$

The feedback ratio is

$$\beta \cong \frac{R_e}{R_L}$$

$$\beta \cong \frac{1000}{5000} = 0.2$$

The voltage gain with feedback then is

$$A_v' = \frac{A_v}{1 - A_v\beta} \tag{8-3}$$

$$A_v' \cong \frac{-112}{1 - (-112)(0.2)} = -\frac{112}{1 + 22.4}$$

$$A_v' \cong 4.8$$

The input resistance with feedback (not including the effect of the bias divider) is

$$R_i' \cong h_{ie} + h_{fe}R_e \tag{8-15}$$

$$R_i' \cong 1700 + (38)(1000)$$

$$R_i' \cong 39,700 \text{ ohms}$$

For certain applications, high input resistance is a great advantage. For example, the input amplifier of an oscilloscope or electronic voltmeter usually must present a high input impedance to avoid unduly loading down the circuit being tested. In such instances, circuits using the above technique — usually arranged to provide much higher impedances — have been employed. However, in such circuits special steps must be taken to minimize the shunting effect of the bias divider. The following calculations show how drastic this shunting effect can be if not eliminated. The effective input resistance of this stage presented as a load on the generator is

$$R = \frac{1}{\dfrac{1}{R_1} + \dfrac{1}{R_2} + \dfrac{1}{R_i'}}$$

$$R \cong \frac{1}{\dfrac{1}{180 \times 10^3} + \dfrac{1}{22 \times 10^3} + \dfrac{1}{39.7 \times 10^3}}$$

$$R \cong 13.1 \text{ kilohms}$$

Thus the bias circuitry in this case reduced the effective input resistance of the stage from approximately 40 kilohms to about 13 kilohms.

In order to see the advantage of negative feedback in minimizing the effects of the great variations in transistor parameters, consider the change in voltage gain that would occur in this amplifier with a change in h_{fe} from its typical value of 38 to its maximum value of 90. This is what could happen when one transistor is replaced with another in the repair of equipment, for example.

Without feedback the voltage gain would increase from 112 to

$$A_v = \frac{h_{fe}R_L}{h_{ie}}$$

$$A_v = \frac{(90)(5000)}{1700} \cong 264$$

This is an increase of

$$\frac{264 - 112}{112}(100) \cong 136\%$$

This would be a rather drastic change, for a parameter variation that does not represent a defect, but merely a manufacturing limit. But with the feedback used in this case the change would be from

$$A'_v = \frac{A_v}{1 - A_v\beta} \cong \frac{-112}{1 - (-112)(0.2)} \cong -4.8$$

to

$$A'_v = \frac{-264}{1 - (-264)(0.2)} \cong \frac{-264}{1 + 53} \cong -4.9$$

for about a 2 percent increase.

Relationship Between Bias Stabilization and Signal Feedback in the Emitter Resistor Feedback Circuit

This circuit is the same as that often used for bias stabilization except for the omission of the bypass capacitor. But the emitter resistor value needed for the desired bias stability might give more signal feedback and therefore lower gain than desired. When this is the case, arrangements such as Figure 8–9 may be used.

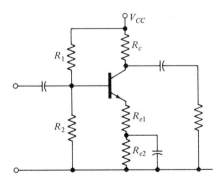

FIGURE 8–9
Combination of bias stabilization and signal feedback

In this arrangement the total resistance $R_{e1} + R_{e2}$ is determined by the dc stability requirement in accordance with the methods of Chapter 3, while R_{e1} is determined by the signal feedback requirements. The feedback ratio would of course be

$$\beta = \frac{V_f}{V_o} = \frac{I_e R_{e1}}{I_o R_L} \cong \frac{R_{e1}}{R_L}$$

Whatever the decision concerning the relative importance of the two effects, the final dc design — or choice of values for R_1 and R_2 relative to R_e and the desired quiescent collector current — can be performed by the methods discussed in Chapter 3.

8.7 Effect of Emitter Bypassing at Low Frequencies

Section 8.6 revealed that an impedance in the emitter circuit of a *CE* amplifier increases the input impedance. Equation (8–13) can be written in more general terms as

$$Z_i' = Z_i + (A_i + 1)Z_e \tag{8–16}$$

This equation can be used to evaluate the input impedance of an amplifier using emitter bypassing, in the very low-frequency range where C_e ceases being a perfect bypass across R_e. The impedance Z_e in Equation (8–16) would be the parallel combination of C_e and R_e. It is apparent that as the frequency is lowered, the rising input impedance due to this effect will decrease the input current, and that it will increase the load impedance presented to the source and consequently increase the voltage gain of the source.

In addition, "emitter compensation" is often used to improve the high-frequency response of some amplifiers. This is done by using emitter bypassing designed so that the bypassing is effective only at relatively high frequencies, rather than down to very low frequencies as in conventional use of the bypass capacitor. Thus the response due to the emitter bypassing (see Figure 5–11) is a rising response in the high-frequency region, and the frequency range in which this rise occurs can be made to be that in which the high-frequency roll-off due to shunt capacitances occurs. As a result, a level response through this portion of the high-frequency region is achieved.

In the region below the rise, the amplifier's gain is that of a feedback amplifier using an unbypassed emitter resistor as in Figure 8–7 or 8–8. The basic low-frequency gain of this kind of amplifier may be found by using Equation (8–3). In other words, the voltage gain in the lower plateau of Figure 5–11 is given by

$$A_v' = \frac{A_v}{1 - A_v \beta} \tag{8–3}$$

in which $\beta = R_e/R_L$.

8.8 The CE Amplifier with Collector Feedback

Another frequently encountered circuit is shown in Figure 8–10. This is the voltage feedback circuit shown originally in Figure 8–3(b). Since the feedback

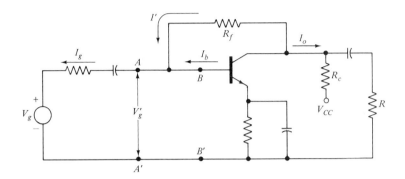

FIGURE 8–10
Voltage feedback, shunt input

connection is in shunt at the input, it will be the current gain which will be affected. The current gain equation therefore is

$$A'_i = \frac{A_i}{1 - A_i\beta} \tag{8-5}$$

in which $\beta = -R_L/R_f$ and A_i is positive.

The shunt input connection of the feedback tells us the input resistance will be lower than without feedback. The input resistance is given by Equation (8–11):

$$R'_i = \frac{R_i}{1 - A_i\beta} \tag{8-11}$$

Example of Collector Feedback

The 2N334A will be used again. The circuit will be as shown in Figure 8–11. As before, the quiescent emitter current is 1 ma, so the *h*-parameter values

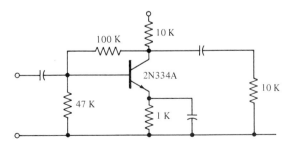

FIGURE 8–11
Example of collector feedback

will be the same as in the previous example. The input resistance and current gain without feedback are:

$$R_i \cong h_{ie} = 1700 \text{ ohms}$$
$$A_i \cong h_{fe} = 38$$

The 47 kilohm resistor from base to common is large enough relative to the base input signal resistance of 1700 ohms, so that its effect can be ignored for routine practical calculations. The current gain with feedback is

$$A_i = \frac{A_i}{1 - A_i \beta} \cong \frac{A_i}{1 - A_i \left(-\dfrac{R_L}{R_f} \right)}$$

$$A_i \cong \frac{38}{1 - (38) \left(-\dfrac{5000}{100,000} \right)} \cong \frac{38}{1 + 1.9}$$

$$A_i \cong 13.1$$

The input resistance presented to the generator is

$$R_i' = \frac{R_i}{1 - A_i \beta} \cong \frac{h_{ie}}{1 + h_{fe}(R_L/R_f)}$$

$$R_i' \cong \frac{1700}{1 + (38)(0.05)} \cong \frac{1700}{2.9}$$

$$R_i' \cong 586 \text{ ohms}$$

It is interesting to note that this circuit is obtaining its bias point stability from both emitter resistor feedback and collector feedback, while the signal feedback is only from the collector — and is therefore voltage feedback only.

8.9 Feedback Over More Than One Stage

Recall the example, in Section 8.2, showing that feedback over two stages seemed to result in better gain stability, for the same overall gain with feedback, than from two stages each employing feedback. In general this is true, and as a result, typical practical applications of feedback will very commonly involve feedback over more than one stage. (Note that the phrase "feedback over two stages" is being used here in a very general way. It should not be assumed from this that just any two-stage feedback is permissible. For example, feedback from a collector to a base over two *CE* stages would not be negative feedback, since the collector signal of any stage would be in phase with the base signal of the preceding stage when *CE* amplifiers are used.)

The general principles developed in this chapter will apply to multistage feedback amplifiers; that is, with regard to gain with feedback, input and output impedance, and the like. In applying feedback equations in which the term $A\beta$ appears, the gain without feedback, A_v or A_i, will be the total effective gain of whatever number of stages over which the feedback is applied, and the feedback ratio β must be evaluated for the same overall feedback.

In order to illustrate the application of these principles to such circuits in general, an example of feedback over two stages will be examined here. The circuit is shown in Figure 8–12. By virtue of the voltage divider formed by R_{10}

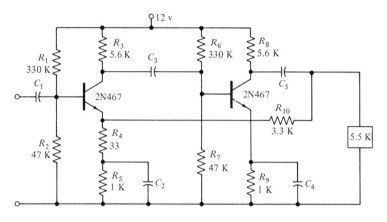

FIGURE 8–12
Negative feedback over two stages

and R_4, a portion of the signal voltage at the second stage collector is being applied to the input (base-emitter loop) of the first stage. Since this is shunt, or voltage feedback, we can expect the output impedance to be lowered. Since it is connected in series with the input we should expect the input impedance to be raised.

Since the feedback is in series at the input, the voltage gain will be affected. The equation for the overall gain will be

$$A'_v = \frac{A_v}{1 - A_v\beta} \tag{8-3}$$

In this equation A_v is the "gain without feedback" — or, more accurately, the open-loop gain. This was calculated by assuming R_{10} to be disconnected from R_4 and connected instead to ground or common, in order to eliminate the feedback from the second stage to the first. This leaves negative feedback in the first stage, due to the unbypassed R_4. Thus A_v as used above still includes some feedback.

The 2N467 transistor has the following characteristics at $V_{ce} = 6v$, $I_E = 1$ ma:

$$h_{fe} = 180 \text{ TYP}$$

$$h_{ie} = 5500 \text{ TYP}$$

The following procedure illustrates how to obtain the performance of this circuit:

1. Effective load for second stage: $R_{L2} = 5600 \parallel 3300 \parallel 5500 = 1510$

2. In view of the low load impedance, the approximation equations may be used. Thus the input impedance of the second stage is:

$$R_{i2} \cong h_{ie} = 5500 \text{ ohms}$$

3. The gain of the second stage is:

$$A_{v2} \cong \frac{h_{fe}R_L}{h_{ie}} = \frac{(180)(1510)}{5500}$$

$$A_{v2} \cong 49$$

4. The effective load on the first stage:

$$R_{L1} = 5600 \parallel 330{,}000 \parallel 47{,}000 \parallel 5500$$

$$R_{L1} \cong 2600 \text{ ohms}$$

5. The gain of the first stage (*without feedback*):

$$A_{v1} \cong \frac{h_{fe}R_{L1}}{h_{ie}} = \frac{(180)(2600)}{5500}$$

$$A_{v1} \cong 85$$

6. The gain of the first stage *with the feedback* due to the unbypassed 33 ohms:

$$A'_{v1} = \frac{A_{v1}}{1 - A_{v1}\beta_1}$$

in which

$$\beta_1 = \frac{R_4}{R_{L1}} = \frac{33}{2600} \cong 0.0127$$

$$A'_{v1} = \frac{-85}{1 - (-85)(0.0127)} \cong 41$$

7. Overall gain of both stages without the feedback due to R_{10}:

$$A_{vT} = A'_{v1}A_{v2} = (41)(49) \cong 2000$$

8. Overall gain with the feedback due to R_{10}:

$$A'_{vT} = \frac{A_{vT}}{1 - A_{vT}\beta_2}$$

in which

$$A_{vT} \cong 2000$$

$$\beta_2 = \frac{R_4}{R_{10} + R_4} \cong \frac{R_4}{R_{10}} = \frac{33}{3300} = 0.01$$

so that

$$A'_{vT} \cong \frac{2000}{1 + (2000)(0.01)} = \frac{2000}{21}$$

$$A'_{vT} \cong 95$$

9. Input impedance of first stage with its local feedback only:

$$R'_i = R_i(1 - A_{v1}\beta_1)$$

$$R'_i \cong (5500)(2.08) \cong 11{,}400 \text{ ohms}$$

10. Input impedance with overall feedback:

$$R_i'' \cong R_i'(1 - A_{vT}\beta_2)$$
$$R_i'' \cong (11,400)(21) \cong 240,000 \text{ ohms}$$

8.10 "Bootstrapping" for High Input Resistance

The high input impedance obtained above will be nullified by the shunting effect of the bias resistor R_2, which is only 47 kilohms. If a high input impedance is desired, an arrangement such as shown in Figure 8–13 can be used.

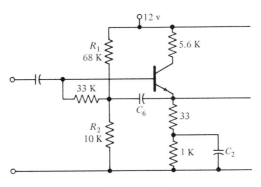

FIGURE 8–13
Bootstrapping

Capacitor C_6 serves to effectively connect the 33-kilohm resistor to the emitter for signal frequencies, so that the signal voltage across this resistor is now the small base-emitter voltage instead of the larger input signal. Thus the signal current drawn by this resistor is much smaller than with the connection of Figure 8–12. The dc bias conditions are maintained approximately as they were, however. This arrangement effectively places the 33-kilohm resistor in parallel with the transistor's input resistance ($\cong h_{ie}$), so that the effective input resistance may then be calculated as follows:

$$R_i \cong 33,000 \parallel h_{ie} \cong 4720 \text{ ohms}$$
$$R_i' = R_i(1 - A_{v1}\beta_1) \cong (4720)(2.08)$$
$$R_i' \cong 9800 \text{ ohms}$$
$$R_i'' = R_i'(1 - A_{vT}\beta_2) \cong (9800)(21)$$
$$R_i'' \cong 206,000 \text{ ohms}$$

The input resistance is maintained at quite a high level in spite of the bias circuitry shunting the input.

8.11 Frequency Response with Feedback

Since negative feedback reduces the effect of parameter and circuit variations, it is logical to expect that variations of gain due to signal frequency changes would be reduced. To see this, assume the solid line in Figure

8–14 is the frequency response of an amplifier without feedback. The midrange voltage gain of this amplifier is 100; its half-power point is 10,000 Hz. Thus, its gain is down 3 db, to approximately 71, and it has a phase angle of $-45°$ at 10 kHz. At 100,000 Hz it is down 20 db, or to one-tenth its midrange value, and its phase angle is roughly $-84°$.

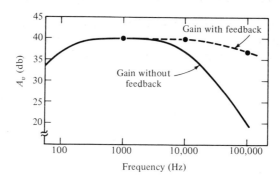

FIGURE 8–14

Effect of feedback upon frequency response of an amplifier

A feedback amplifier with open-loop gain of 10^3 and $A\beta = -9$ would have midrange gain of the same value:

$$A'_M = \frac{A_M}{1 - A_M\beta}$$

$$A'_M = \frac{1000}{1 + 9} \cong 100$$

If this amplifier's open-loop frequency response were the same as the amplifier above, its gain at 10,000 Hz would be:

$$A' = \frac{(10^3)(0.707)\underline{/-45°}}{1 + (9)(0.707)\underline{/-45°}} \cong 99.5\underline{/-6°}$$

and at 100,000 Hz it would be:

$$A' = \frac{(10^3)(0.1)\underline{/-84.3°}}{1 + (9)(0.1)\underline{/-84.3°}} \cong 71\underline{/-45°}$$

These points are plotted in Figure 8–14.

In the above example it was assumed that β was unaffected by the frequency changes. In the practical case this may often not be true unless special precautions are taken. In some cases β may be purposely made to change with frequency in order to provide a particular frequency characteristic for the gain with feedback.

It is useful to know the amount of effect of negative feedback on the frequency response in the simple case of constant β. From Chapter 5 we have

$$\frac{A_H}{A_M} = \frac{1}{1 + j(f/f_2)} \qquad \textbf{(5–19)}$$

or

$$A_H = \frac{A_M}{1 + j(f/f_2)}$$

while the example above reminds us that the gain with feedback at any frequency is related to the gain without feedback at the same frequency according to Equation (8–3) so that we may write

$$A'_H = \frac{A_H}{1 - A_H\beta} \tag{8-17}$$

Consequently

$$A'_H = \frac{A_M/(1 + jf/f_2)}{1 - A_M\beta/(1 + jf/f_2)}$$

$$A'_H = \frac{A_M}{1 - A_M\beta + jf/f_2} \tag{8-18}$$

So when $\qquad f/f_2 = 1 - A_M\beta$

or $\qquad\qquad f = f_2(1 - A_M\beta)$

the gain is down 3 db from its midrange value of $A_M/(1 - A_M\beta)$. Therefore we can define the half-power point with feedback:

$$f'_2 = f_2(1 - A_M\beta) \tag{8-19}$$

Equation (8–19) tells us that the half-power frequency of the feedback amplifier of the above example is

$$f'_2 = f_2(1 - A_M\beta)$$
$$f'_2 = (10^4)(1 + 9) = 100 \text{ kHz}$$

and this checks with the previous calculation for the gain at this frequency, which showed it to be down to about 71 from its midrange value of 100.

Equation (8–18) of course also shows this:

$$A_{100\text{kHz}} = \frac{A_M}{1 - A_M\beta + j(f/f_2)} = \frac{1000}{1 + 9 + j(10^5/10^4)}$$

$$= \frac{1000}{10 + j10}$$

$$A_{100\text{kHz}} \cong 71\underline{/-45°}$$

8.12 Distortion in Feedback Amplifiers

If the gain of an amplifier were perfectly constant during the entire signal excursion, there would be no distortion produced by the amplifier. The amplitude of the output would be a constant multiple of the amplitude of the input, and thus the waveform of the output would be the same as the waveform of the input. The nonlinearity, or curvature in the characteristics of an amplifying device, is simply the manifestation of a change in a parameter value which causes a change in the gain of the amplifier. Anything that tends to make the gain of the amplifier more constant, serves to reduce the distortion generated in the amplifier.

One of the simplest examples of distortion is "clipping" or "compression" of the signal. Figure 8–15 illustrates this, showing a typical waveform in the output of an amplifier which is being over-driven. The dashed line indicates the form the signal should have if there were no distortion, for a sine wave input.

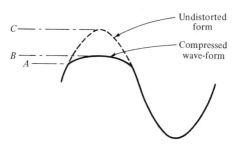

FIGURE 8–15
Compression of a sine wave

In this simplified example the compressed portion of the waveform (from A to B) is only about one-fourth the amplitude that it should be, as indicated by the dashed portion (from A to C). In other words the gain of the amplifier was apparently reduced, during this part of the signal, to only one-fourth the value it had during the rest of the cycle. If this were the characteristic of the amplifier without feedback, the application of feedback could be used to hold the gain more nearly constant during the entire cycle, so that the output would show much less distortion.

The effect of negative feedback upon distortion may be analyzed by using the methods of Section 8.2, but adding a term for a "distortion voltage" in the output. See Figure 8–16.

Since distortion is usually a function of signal amplitude — and also since

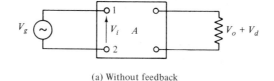

(a) Without feedback

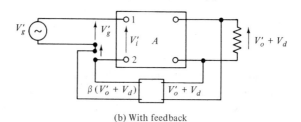

(b) With feedback

FIGURE 8–16
Terms for distortion analysis

for the purpose of this analysis we are using distortion voltage rather than percentage — comparison of distortion with and without feedback should be made on the basis of outputs which are equal except for the distortion components. Then, since both amplifiers are identical from terminals 1-2 to the output, they each will add the same distortion component V_d to the signal as it passes from input to output.

Note carefully that V_d in part (b) of the above figure does not express the *total* distortion voltage. Since $V'_o = AV'_i$, part of V'_o is amplified fed-back distortion $(A\beta V_d)$. The following development will evaluate the total distortion.

Now

$$V'_i = V'_g + \beta V'_o + \beta V_d$$

so

$$V'_o = A_v V'_i = A_v V'_g + A_v \beta V'_o + A_v \beta V_d$$

and

$$V'_o = \frac{A_v V'_g}{1 - A_v\beta} + \frac{A_v \beta V_d}{1 - A_v\beta}$$

Thus the total output with feedback is

$$V'_o + V_d = \frac{A_v V'_g}{1 - A_v\beta} + \frac{A_v \beta V_d}{1 - A_v\beta} + V_d$$

The last two terms in this equation must be the distortion voltage since the other term, $A_v V'_g/(1 - A_v\beta)$, contains only input signal V'_g and the constants A_v and β.

So the total distortion with feedback is

$$V'_d = \frac{A_v \beta V_d}{1 - A_v\beta} + V_d = \frac{A_v \beta V_d}{1 - A_v\beta} + \frac{V_d(1 - A_v\beta)}{1 - A_v\beta}$$

$$V'_d = \frac{V_d}{1 - A_v\beta} \tag{8--20}$$

Not too surprisingly, this shows that feedback reduces distortion by the same factor that it affects a number of other amplifier characteristics.

The use of equal output signal levels as a basis for comparison has another practical aspect to it. Since distortion in general is greatest in large-signal amplifiers, feedback employed for the purpose of reducing distortion is usually applied to final, high-signal-level stages. Its effect on gain is compensated for by providing more gain in the preceding stages, so that the final output signal level is the same.

PROBLEMS

8-1. (a) An amplifier has a voltage gain, without feedback, equal to 100. Negative feedback is used, with a feedback factor, β, of 0.008. What will the voltage gain be?

(b) If the same amplifier employed positive feedback (with $\beta = 0.008$) instead of negative feedback, what would the voltage gain be?

8–2. A transistor amplifier has a voltage gain without feedback of 50. It uses negative feedback, with a feedback factor of 0.1.

(a) What is the gain with feedback?

(b) Suppose the transistor is damaged and replaced with another of the same type which happens to have higher h_{fe}, so that its voltage gain without feedback is 80. The feedback factor, β, is determined by circuit components and remains constant at $\beta = 0.1$. What is the value of the gain with feedback after the transistor is changed?

(c) What is the percent change in the gain with feedback, and what would the percent change have been if there were no feedback?

8–3. A two-stage amplifier employing negative feedback has a voltage gain without feedback of 2000. The value of β is 0.01 for feedback over the two stages. What is the gain with feedback?

8–4. In Problem 8–3 above, $A\beta = 20$. $A\beta$ is quite large compared to 1, and in many such cases the approximation of Equation (8–4) is a convenient one.

(a) What is the gain with feedback in Problem 8–3 as calculated by Equation (8–4)?

(b) Suppose you wanted to analyze the effect of a change in transistor characteristics on the gain with feedback (as you did in Problem 8–2). Would you use Equation (8–3) or (8–4)? Why?

8–5. In a circuit such as that of Figure 8–3(a), the signal voltage V_g is 0.1 v, while the signal voltage across R_1 is 0.09 v. The total output voltage is 1.0 v.

(a) What is the value of the base-emitter signal voltage?

(b) From the given information, without using Equation (8–3), find the value of the voltage gain with feedback (i.e. from A-B to the output).

(c) What is the value of the gain without feedback (i.e. from the base-emitter terminals to the output)?

8–6. Show that Equation (8–3) holds true for the circuit of Problem 8–5.

8–7. (a) In the circuit of Figure 8–3(a), if the signal voltage V_g increases by 10 percent without any change in transistor parameters or circuit component values, what will happen to the output voltage and to the feedback voltage? How will the percentage changes in all these voltages compare with each other?

(b) In the same circuit, assume that the amplifier's voltage gain without feedback increases by a small amount, without any change in V_g. Explain what will happen to the output voltage, the feedback voltage, and the base-emitter voltage as a result. How will the effect on the output voltage compare with what would have happened without feedback?

8–8. (a) In the circuit of Figure 8–3(b), if the signal voltage V_g increases by 10 percent without any change in transistor parameters or circuit component values, what will happen to the output voltage, and to the feedback current? How will the percentage change in output voltage and feedback current compare with the change in the voltage V_g?

(b) In the same circuit, if the amplifier's current gain without feedback increases by a small amount, without any change in V_g, what will happen to the output current and output voltage? What will happen to the feedback current, and the base current?

8–9. (a) In the circuit of Figure 8–3(c), where is the feedback voltage developed? Is the feedback proportional to the output voltage or the output current?

(b) If the transistor's h_{fe} should increase due to temperature or transistor replacement, what would happen to the output signal voltage and the feedback voltage? What will happen to the base-emitter voltage?

(c) How will the change in output current and output voltage compare with what would have happened without feedback?

8–10. In the circuit of Figure 8–3(c), if R_c should double in value without any other change in component values or transistor parameter values, what would happen to the feedback voltage? As a result, what would happen to the base-emitter voltage? How would the change in output voltage compare with what would have happened without feedback?

8–11. Find the feedback factor for the indicated circuits of Figure 8–4 if circuit values are as follows:

Circuit

(a) $R_g = 1000 \ \Omega$ $R_c = 3900 \ \Omega$
     $R_1 = 10 \ \text{K} \ \Omega$ $R_2 = 90 \ \text{K} \ \Omega$

(b) $R_g \gg R_i$ $R_f = 75 \ \text{K} \ \Omega$
     $R_c = 4700 \ \Omega$
     R (final load connected across output) $= 2200 \ \Omega$

(c) $R_g = 4000 \ \Omega$ $R_f = 75 \ \text{K} \ \Omega$
     $R_i = 2000 \ \Omega$ $R_c = 4700 \ \Omega$
     R (across output) $= 2200 \ \Omega$

(d) $R_g = 4000 \ \Omega$
     $R_c = 5000 \ \Omega$
     R (final load across the output) $= 3000 \ \Omega$
     $R_e = 470 \ \Omega$

8–12. (a) Find the approximate voltage gain of the following amplifier if $h_{fe} = 50$ and $h_{ie} = 1000 \ \Omega$.

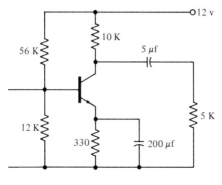

FIGURE P8–12

(b) Find the approximate voltage gain of the above amplifier if the $330\,\Omega$ emitter resistor is left unbypassed.

8-13. (a) In the circuit of Figure 8–4(a), $\beta = 0.05$; the voltage gain without feedback is 100, and the current gain without feedback is 50. What is the voltage gain with feedback?

(b) In the circuit of Figure 8–4(b), $\beta = -0.09$. The current gain without feedback is 100. What is the current gain with feedback?

8-14. In the circuit of Figure 8–4(b), the voltage gain without feedback is 200, and the current gain without feedback is 150. The feedback factor is -0.03. What are the voltage gain and current gain with feedback?

8-15. (a) What is the input resistance R_i' of this circuit, if the values without feedback are:

$$R_i = 800 \text{ ohms}$$
$$R_o = 40 \text{ kilohms}$$
$$A_i = 50$$
$$A_v = 100$$

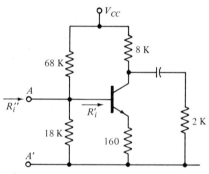

FIGURE P8–15

(b) What is the input resistance of the above circuit looking into terminals $A\text{-}A'$? (i.e., What is the input resistance defined in the figure as R_i''?)

8-16. What is the input resistance of the following circuit, if current gain without feedback is 80, and input resistance without feedback is 2000 ohms?

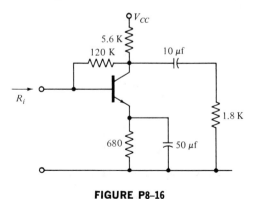

FIGURE P8–16

8–17. Find the input resistance of the circuit in Problem 8–15(a) if the values without feedback are:

$$h_{ie} = 1500 \text{ ohms}$$
$$A_i = 50$$
$$A_v = 100$$

8–18. (a) What is the approximate input resistance of the following circuit measured at the base of the transistor?

$$h_{ie} = 1100 \text{ ohms}$$
$$h_{fe} = 50$$

(b) What is the input resistance looking into the junction of the bias divider resistance?

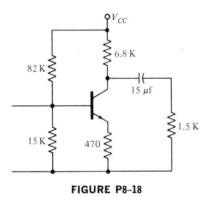

FIGURE P8–18

8–19. (a) What is the approximate input resistance of the following circuit at the input terminals, if $h_{fe} = 100$, and $h_{ie} = 1800$ ohms?

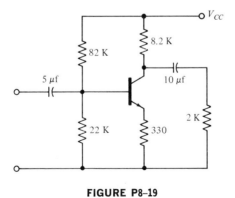

FIGURE P8–19

(b) What output quantity is being stabilized in this circuit, voltage or current?

(c) Is voltage gain or current gain being controlled (i.e. affected) in order to stabilize the output?

(d) What is the current gain of this circuit?

(e) What is the voltage gain of this circuit?

(f)   What kind of bias stabilizing is this circuit using? What circuit component provides the stabilizing action?

8–20. (a)   What is the value of resistance providing dc stabilizing in the following circuit?

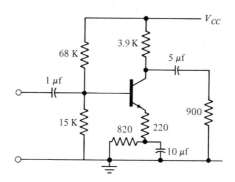

FIGURE P8–20

(b)   What value of resistance is being used for signal feedback in this circuit? What is the value of β?

8–21. (a)   What output quantity is stabilized in the following circuit, voltage or current?

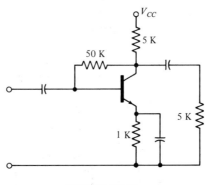

FIGURE P8–21

(b)   Is voltage gain or current gain being controlled (i.e. affected) in order to stabilize the output?

(c)   What is the current gain of the above circuit, from input terminals as indicated, to the *collector*, if current gain without feedback is 100?

(d)   What is the voltage gain of the above circuit if $R_i = 2000$ ohms without feedback?

(e)   What is the input resistance (at the input terminals indicated) for the above circuit?

(f)   What kind of bias stabilizing is being used in this circuit? List the circuit element or elements providing the bias stabilizing.

(g) Does this circuit have a higher or lower output resistance than it would without feedback?

8–22. An amplifier having midrange gain without feedback of -150, and a feedback factor, β, of 0.133 has an upper 3-db frequency of 60 kHz without feedback. What is its upper 3-db point with the feedback (assuming β is constant with frequency)?   *1.6 mHZ*

8–23. The upper 3-db point of the following amplifiers would be 100 kHz without feedback. What is the upper 3-db point of the circuits as shown? (Assume constant β.) The voltage gain without feedback in each case is 100.

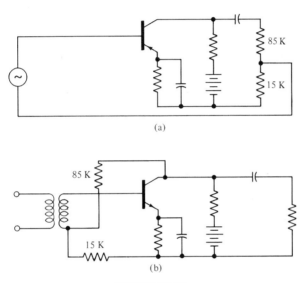

FIGURE P8–23

8–24. An amplifier has gain without feedback of -140 and feedback factor -0.1. With an output voltage of 10 v rms, it has 10 percent distortion without feedback (i.e. the distortion voltage V_d equals 1 v). What is the distortion voltage and distortion percentage with feedback, assuming the same amplitude of undistorted output?

CHAPTER 9

The Emitter Follower and Common-Base Circuits

9.1 Introduction to the Emitter Follower

The *CE* amplifier, which has been our principal subject so far, is the most commonly used junction transistor circuit. There are, however, other ways of connecting the transistor which provide advantages for certain applications. One of these is the emitter follower, or common-collector circuit, illustrated in Figure 9–1.

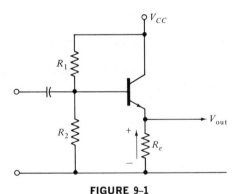

FIGURE 9–1
RC-coupled emitter follower amplifier

This circuit is called a *common-collector amplifier* because the collector is grounded (for signal) rather than the emitter. The emitter, instead of being connected to ground or common, is connected to the load so that it is above ground by the amount of the output signal voltage. It is called an emitter follower because the emitter potential tends to follow the base potential.

Consider, for example, the basic relationships that are indicated by Figure 9–1. Emitter current (electron flow) is in the direction shown by the arrow, and it causes a voltage drop with a polarity as indicated. In order for any emitter current to flow (other than leakage), the base-emitter junction must be biased so that the base is more positive than the emitter. Now the total "input" voltage, from base to common, is the sum of the base-emitter voltage and the voltage across R_e. If the applied signal causes the base voltage to change in the positive direction, the forward-bias will increase, causing an increase in the emitter current and therefore causing the voltage across R_e to change in the positive direction. If the signal causes the base voltage to decrease, this will decrease the forward-bias, decreasing the emitter current and causing the voltage across R_e to decrease. Thus the emitter will be following the base — rising when the base rises, falling when the base falls, but always slightly less positive than the base.

Figure 9–2 shows the waveforms of these signal voltages for the case of a

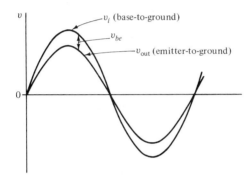

FIGURE 9–2
Signal components of emitter-follower voltages

sine wave input, demonstrating why the emitter is said to "follow" the base. This points up an important aspect of this amplifier — that the output voltage is in phase with the input voltage. When the input rises, the output rises; when the input falls, the output falls. The 180° phase inversion that characterizes the common-emitter is not present in the emitter follower.

More careful consideration of this circuit reveals that it is a feedback circuit, with the entire output signal voltage $I_e R_e$ fed back in series with the input. In order to evaluate such feedback, it is necessary to know the gain without feedback. Figure 9–3 shows that the circuit is basically a *CE* amplifier in which the load has been "slid" around until it is in series with the input. Thus the gain without feedback is the gain that the same transistor with the same load would have in the *CE* configuration.

Standard feedback relations (Chapter 8) may be used to evaluate the characteristics of the emitter follower. In this section we shall draw some general conclusions in this way, but later, in Section 9.5, we shall make an individual circuit analysis because that will provide an opportunity to become more familiar with the circuit.

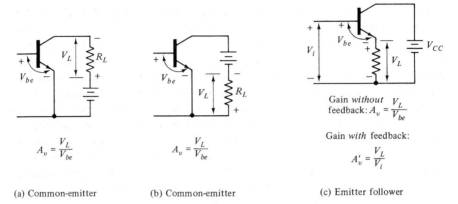

(a) Common-emitter $\qquad$ (b) Common-emitter $\qquad$ (c) Emitter follower

FIGURE 9–3
Development of emitter follower from CE *circuit*

Emitter Follower Output Impedance

Since this circuit involves voltage feedback, its output impedance is much lower than that of the common-emitter.

Input Impedance

Since the feedback is in series with the input, the input impedance is much higher than that of the common-emitter. This combination of high input impedance and low output impedance makes the emitter follower useful as an impedance transformer. Where a high input impedance is needed, it can serve as the input stage preceding a common-emitter; where a low output impedance is needed, it can serve as an output stage.

Voltage Gain

Reference to Figure 9–3(c) shows that the input signal V_i is greater than the output signal V_L by the amount of the base-emitter junction voltage V_{be}. Thus the voltage gain must be less than one. This is borne out by the equation for voltage gain with feedback from Chapter 8:

$$A'_v = \frac{A_v}{1 - A_v\beta} \qquad (8\text{–}3)$$

Since the entire output voltage is fed back, $\beta = -1$. (The negative sign here is due to the fact that $\beta = V_f/V_o$, and V_o in this circuit has the opposite polarity from that of the circuits studied in Chapter 8. Therefore the ratio V_f/V_o has the opposite polarity. For the same reason — the polarity of V_o — the gain A_v will have a positive sign. The gain with feedback then becomes

$$A'_v = \frac{A_v}{1 - (A_v)(-1)} = \frac{A_v}{1 + A_v} \qquad (9\text{–}1)$$

which shows that the voltage gain for this circuit must always be less than 1.

Current Gain

The current gain is approximately the same as that of the common-emitter. In the emitter follower the total output signal current is the emitter signal current, or the sum of the base signal current and the collector signal current, while in the *CE* amplifier the total output current is the collector signal current only. Thus with the same input (base) current, the emitter follower output current exceeds that of the common-emitter only by the amount of the small base current.

9.2   Load Line Construction

The load line technique for the emitter follower is essentially the same as for the common-emitter. The only difference is that the dc load line depends upon R_e only (since there is no resistance between the collector and V_{CC}), and the ac load line depends upon the parallel combination of R_e and whatever load is connected to R_e. Figure 9–4 illustrates the general case for an *RC-*

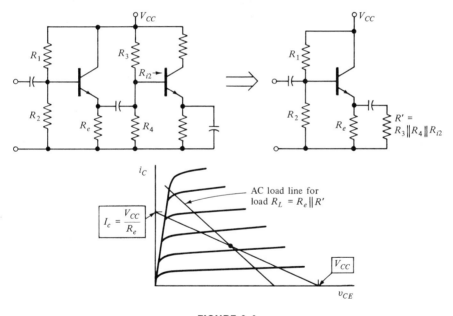

FIGURE 9–4
Emitter follower load line

coupled circuit in which the load is a *CE* amplifier's input circuit. The effective ac load for the emitter follower is therefore the parallel combination of R_e with the second stage's bias divider resistors and input resistance R_{i2}.

The technique for drawing the ac load line is covered in Section 2.12, while the dc operating point (at which the ac load line intersects the dc load line) may be found by the method of Section 3.9.

Drawing the Load Line

Load line construction and location of the operating point is illustrated in the following problem.

Example 9–1

The 2N1924 transistor is to be used in the circuit shown in Figure 9–5.

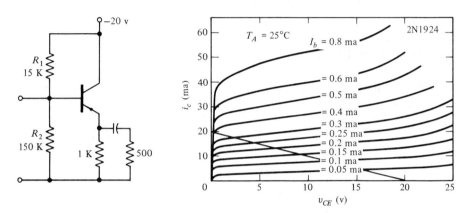

FIGURE 9–5
Emitter follower circuit for load line example

The collector characteristics of the 2N1924 are reproduced here for convenience.

1. The dc load line for the 1000-ohm dc load is shown in the figure. This has been drawn in the normal way from V_{CC} on the voltage axis to

$$I_C = \frac{V_{CC}}{R_e} = \frac{20}{1000} = 20 \text{ ma}$$

on the current axis.

2. The expected operating point for the circuit as shown may be found by solving the bias circuit voltage equation for the base current. This may be done by Thevenizing the bias divider, to give the dc equivalent circuit of Figure 9–6. For the circuit values given in Figure 9–5 we have

$$R = \frac{(15,000)(150,000)}{15,000 + 150,000} \cong 13,600 \text{ ohms}$$

$$V = \frac{R_2}{R_1 + R_2} V_{CC} = \frac{150,000}{165,000} (20) \cong 18.2 \text{ v}$$

Then, ignoring the collector cutoff current,

$$V \cong I_B R + V_{BE} + (h_{FE} + 1)I_B R_e$$

so that

$$I_B \cong \frac{V - V_{BE}}{R + (h_{FE} + 1)R_e}$$

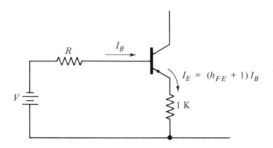

FIGURE 9–6
Thevenized bias circuit of emitter follower example

V_{BE} may be estimated as 0.2v, and h_{FE} measured on the collector characteristics, in the vicinity of $V_{CE} = 5$ to 10v and $I_C = 10$ to 15 ma, as approximately 67. This leads to

$$I_B \cong \frac{18.2 - 0.2}{13,600 + (67 + 1)(1000)}$$

$$I_B \cong 0.22 \text{ ma}$$

The intersection of the 0.22 ma base current curve with the dc load line places the operating point. The ac load line may then be drawn through this point. The ac load will be the parallel combination of 1000 ohms and 500 ohms.

9.3 Design of the Bias Circuit

If it were necessary to design the bias divider to give a particular operating point (instead of analyzing an already existing circuit as we did above), the procedure would be as follows.

Example 9–2

The same transistor and load circuit as above is to be used. The operating point is to be approximately at

$$V_{CE} = 5 \text{ v}$$

$$I_C = 15 \text{ ma}$$

With $h_{FE} = 67$, this requires a base current of

$$I_B \cong \frac{I_C}{h_{FE}} \cong \frac{0.015}{67} \cong 0.224 \text{ ma}$$

Consequently the quiescent emitter current will be

$$I_E = I_C + I_B$$

$$I_E \cong 15.22 \text{ ma}$$

The base voltage will then be

$$V_B = V_{BE} + I_E R_e$$

$$V_B \cong 0.2 + (0.01522)(1000)$$

$$V_B \cong 15.42 \text{ v}$$

Assuming that bias stabilizing design requirements have set the necessary value of R at 15,000 ohms or less, the required voltage V in Figure 9–6 will then be

$$V = I_B R + V_{BE} + I_E R_e$$
$$v = (0.22 \times 10^{-3})(15,000) + 15.42$$
$$v \cong 18.72 \text{ v}$$

The necessary voltage divider ratio is then

$$\frac{R_2}{R_1 + R_2} = \frac{V}{V_{CC}}$$

$$\frac{R_2}{R_1 + R_2} = \frac{18.72}{20} \cong 0.935$$

A choice of standard 10 percent resistor values of $R_1 = 15$ kilohms and $R_2 = 150$ kilohms gives a divider ratio of

$$\frac{R_2}{R_1 + R_2} = \frac{150}{165} \cong 0.91$$

and an effective parallel resistance of 13,600 ohms as noted above. If this effective resistance is not considered too low, the operating point resulting from this choice of standard resistor values may be checked by the methods of the first example above, to ensure that it is close enough to the design objective.

9.4 Large-Signal Graphical Analysis

Input-output signal current relations can be analyzed graphically in the same manner as with the common-emitter, since the emitter follower output current is emitter current, and this normally differs from collector current by only a small percentage. Thus the common-emitter output characteristics will usually be satisfactory when used as illustrated in Figure 9–7.

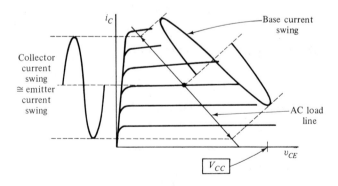

FIGURE 9–7

CE output characteristics used for emitter follower analysis

Graphical analysis showing voltage relations is not so direct, since the emitter follower input voltage is the sum of the signal voltages across the base-emitter junction and the load. The procedure is as follows. For each of a number of base current values along a load line such as in Figure 9–7, the value of load voltage $i_E R_L \cong i_C R_L$ may be found. This may be done by dropping down from the intersection of each base current line with the load line, and reading the value of v_{CE} at that point. The value of $i_C R_L$ is then $V_{CC} - v_{CE}$, or the distance from V_{CC} to the point in question on the voltage axis. *For the same values of base current,* values of v_{BE} may be taken from the base-emitter curve. These corresponding values of v_L and v_{BE} are then added to give values of v_i for each value of i_B. The dynamic input characteristic can then be constructed from these values. Figure 9–8 illustrates the general appearance of such a graph.

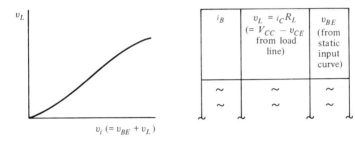

FIGURE 9–8
Form of dynamic input characteristic for emitter follower

9.5 Small-Signal Analysis of the Emitter Follower

A simple but practical form of emitter follower circuit is shown in Figure 9–9(a). V_s represents the open-circuit output voltage of the signal source, and R_s is the output resistance of the signal source. In part (b) of the figure the combination of V_s, R_s, R_1, and R_2 has been Thevenized and is represented by V_g and R_g. The dc load resistor R_e and final load R' have been combined into

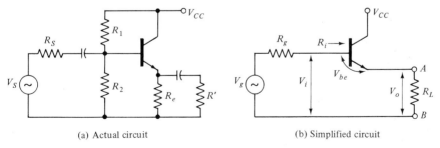

(a) Actual circuit   (b) Simplified circuit

FIGURE 9–9
Emitter follower circuit

their parallel equivalent, R_L. Blocking capacitors, assumed to be ideal short-circuits for signal frequencies, have been omitted.

Current Gain

The current gain is

$$A'_i = \frac{I_o}{I_b} = \frac{I_b + I_c}{I_b} = \frac{I_b + A_i I_b}{I_b}$$

$$A'_i = A_i + 1 \tag{9-2}$$

in which A'_i designates the emitter-follower current gain, and A_i is the common-emitter gain. Thus the emitter-follower current gain is

$$A'_i \cong A_i = \frac{h_{fe}}{1 + h_{oe} R_L}$$

and for small values of load resistance

$$A'_i \cong h_{fe} \tag{9-3}$$

Input Resistance

By using the method of Section 8.6,

$$R'_i = \frac{V_i}{I_b} = \frac{V_{be} + A'_i I_b R_L}{I_b} \tag{9-4}$$

$$R'_i = \frac{I_b R_i + A'_i I_b R_L}{I_b}$$

in which R'_i stands for the emitter-follower input resistance and R_i designates the input resistance of the common-emitter. Therefore

$$R'_i = R_i + A'_i R_L \tag{9-5}$$

This leads to the following approximations:

$$R'_i \cong h_{ie} + h_{fe} R_L \tag{9-6}$$

$$R'_i \cong h_{fe} R_L \tag{9-7}$$

A very helpful interpretation of this input resistance effect may be obtained by considering the term $A'_i I_b R_L$ in Equation (9-4). This term represents the output signal voltage. Since this voltage is in series with the input loop where the current is I_b, it produces the same effect as a resistance there having the value $A'_i R_L$. That is, it causes a signal voltage drop $I_b(A'_i R_L)$. Consequently, the resistance R_L is "multiplied" by A_i' (or h_{fe}). The input resistance, Equation (9–6), therefore indicates that the equivalent circuit of the emitter-follower, as seen from the input, can be represented by the circuit in Figure 9–10.

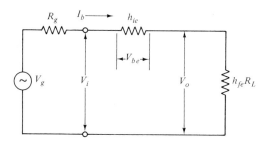

FIGURE 9–10
Approximate equivalent circuit of emitter follower as seen from input

Voltage Gain

From Figure 9–10, the voltage divider ratio V_o/V_i is

$$A_v' = \frac{V_o}{V_i} \cong \frac{h_{fe}R_L}{h_{fe}R_L + h_{ie}} \tag{9–8}$$

Also since

$$h_{ie} = (h_{fe} + 1)h_{ib} \cong h_{fe}h_{ib} \tag{4–7}$$

we have

$$A_v' \cong \frac{R_L}{R_L + h_{ib}} \tag{9–9}$$

Equation (9–8) can also be obtained from

$$A_v' = A_i' \frac{R_L}{R_i}$$

with appropriate substitution of Equations (9–3), (9–6), and (4–7).

Output Resistance

Looking back from the load into the emitter in Figure 9–9, the voltage drops across elements in series with the generator are:

$$V \cong I_b R_g + I_b h_{ie}$$

The source resistance as seen looking into the emitter (that is, in terms of the current flowing in the emitter circuit) therefore is

$$R_o = \frac{V}{I_e} \cong \frac{I_b R_g + I_b h_{ie}}{I_e}$$

but

$$I_e = (A_i + 1)I_b \cong h_{fe}I_b$$

so that

$$R_o \cong \frac{I_b R_g + I_b h_{ie}}{h_{fe}I_b}$$

$$R_o \cong \frac{R_g + h_{ie}}{h_{fe}} \tag{9–10}$$

Example 9–3

The 2N335A is to be operated in the circuit shown in Figure 9–11. The quiescent collector current is 1 ma. The data sheet in Appendix B lists the following typical *h*-parameter values:

$$h_{fe} = 52$$
$$h_{ie} = 2000 \text{ ohms}$$

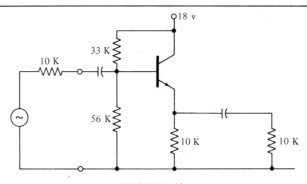

FIGURE 9–11
Emitter follower example

These values give the following results for this amplifier.

Input Resistance

$$R'_i \cong h_{ie} + h_{fe}R_L \qquad (9\text{–}6)$$
$$R'_i \cong 2000 + (52)(5000)$$
$$R'_i \cong 262{,}000 \text{ ohms}$$

Output Resistance

$$R_o \cong \frac{R_g + h_{ie}}{h_{fe}} \qquad (9\text{–}10)$$

First R_g must be evaluated. This represents the effective source or "generator" resistance *of the circuit to the left of the emitter follower base*. This is the parallel combination of 10 kilohms, 33 kilohms, and 56 kilohms.

$$R_g \cong 6750 \text{ ohms}$$

Then

$$R_o \cong \frac{6750 + 2000}{52}$$
$$R_o \cong 168 \text{ ohms}$$

Voltage Gain

$$A_v \cong \frac{h_{fe}R_L}{h_{fe}R_L + h_{ie}} \qquad (9\text{–}8)$$
$$A_v \cong \frac{(52)(5000)}{(52)(5000) + 2000}$$
$$A_v \cong \frac{260{,}000}{262{,}000} \cong 0.99$$

9.6 High Input Resistance Circuits

If very high input resistance were needed, such as 100 or 200 kilohms, the circuit of the above example could not provide it. In spite of the value of 262,000 ohms for R_i', the bias resistors shunting the input would lower the effective stage input resistance to approximately 20 kilohms in this case. For operating point stability this bias resistance cannot usually be made very large.

Bootstrapping

The effective resistance that the bias network presents to signal frequencies can be raised, without raising its dc resistance, by bootstrapping. Figure 9–12 illustrates how this might be applied in the case of the above example.

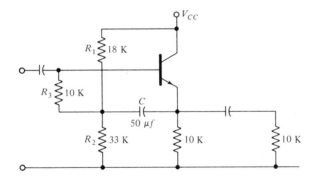

FIGURE 9–12
Bootstrapping of the bias resistance

The capacitor C connects $R3$ to the emitter for signal frequencies. Since the voltage gain is approximately 0.99, the signal voltage at the emitter is 0.99 times that at the base (the other end of $R3$). Therefore, the voltage across $R3$ is about 0.01 times the input voltage, and $R3$ draws only about 0.01 the current it would draw if the full input voltage were impressed on it. Consequently, it appears as a resistance of about 100 $R3$ or approximately 1 megohm. Bootstrapping here has made the bias circuit appear as 1 megohm instead of 20 kilohms as it was originally, and the effective input resistance of the stage is now the parallel combination of 1 megohm and the 262 kilohms emitter follower input.

The capacitor C that provides the bootstrapping should be large enough so that its reactance is small compared to the resistance of $R1$ and $R2$ in parallel, at the lowest frequency.

Shunting Effect of the Collector Resistance on Emitter Follower Input

Equation (9–7) for the emitter follower input resistance did not include the effect of the collector-base junction resistance of the transistor. Since the collector is ac grounded, this resistance $(1/h_{ob})$ is effectively shunted from the input to ground, in parallel with R_i' of Equation (9–7). At low current levels (say 1 ma) $1/h_{ob}$ may be in the range of 1 to 5 megohms, and it decreases as the current increases. Thus it acts as a limiting factor when attempting to obtain very high values of input resistance.

Bootstrapping the Collector Resistance

The bootstrapping technique can be used to raise the effective resistance of $1/h_{ob}$, and is illustrated in Figure 9–13. The capacitor places the collector

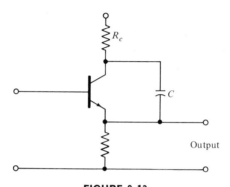

FIGURE 9–13
Bootstrapping the collector resistance

at the emitter signal potential so that the collector-base potential is very small. The resistor R_c is needed to decouple the collector from ac ground — so the bootstrapping voltage will not be shorted to ground. The bootstrapping circuits shown here are the simplest versions. More refined methods are discussed in the literature.

The Darlington, or Cascaded Emitter Follower Circuit

The input resistance of the emitter follower is directly proportional to its emitter resistance, but obtaining extremely high values of input resistance by

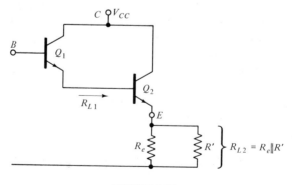

FIGURE 9–14
Darlington circuit

simply increasing the emitter resistance is impractical. Operating at normal values of emitter current with very large R_e requires very large supply voltage. Using normal values of supply voltage with very large values of R_e would require operating at very low emitter current which often means lowered h_{fe} values. Finally, the actual load coupled to the emitter often prevents obtaining a large effective ac load resistance.

A solution to this problem is to use the input resistance of a second emitter follower as the emitter resistance for the first stage. This is illustrated in Figure 9–14 and is called the *Darlington circuit*. The input resistance of the second stage ($Q2$) is approximately $h_{fe2}R_{L2}$. The load for the first stage is therefore $R_{L1} \cong h_{fe2}R_{L2}$. The input resistance to the first stage, then, is

$$R_i \cong h_{fe1}R_{L1}$$

Therefore
$$R_i \cong h_{fe1}h_{fe2}R_{L2} \tag{9–11}$$

This is a very crude approximation, since it is based on using h_{fe} as an approximation for the current gain of each emitter follower. Since the load for $Q1$ here is a very large resistance (the high input resistance of $Q2$), the h_{fe} approximation for $Q1$ has a very large error. But the expression $h_{fe1}h_{fe2}R_L$ provides a convenient, easily remembered rule-of-thumb, and more exact equations are available.

The total current gain for the Darlington pair is roughly $h_{fe1}h_{fe2}$. Again, this is a very rough approximation for the same reason. Darlington pairs are supplied by some manufacturers in a single package with three leads (E, B, and C in Figure 9–14) and with a composite h_{fe} specified by the manufacturer.

9.7 The Common-Base Amplifier

The *CB* connection of the transistor, discussed originally in Chapter 1, has provided a useful amplifier circuit for a number of special applications. Figure 9–15 shows the basic circuit. The *h*-parameter equivalent circuit of the *CB*

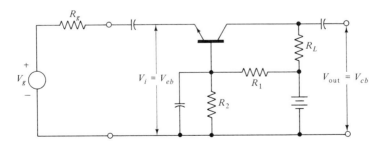

FIGURE 9–15
Basic RC-*coupled* CB *amplifier*

amplifier is the same form as that of the common-emitter, and is shown in Figure 9–16.

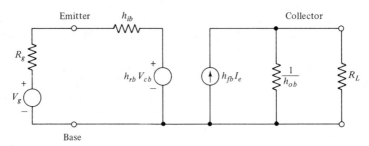

FIGURE 9–16
Hybrid equivalent circuit of the CB *amplifier*

The voltage and current gain and input and output resistance equations are the same as the common-emitter, but with the *CB* parameters substituted for the *CE* parameters. For reference, the equations are listed here with the *CB* parameters.

$$A_i = \frac{h_{fb}}{1 + h_{ob}R_L} \tag{9–12}$$

$$A_v = -\frac{h_{fb}R_L}{h_{ib} + R_L\Delta^{hb}} \tag{9–13}$$

$$R_i = \frac{h_{ib} + R_L\Delta^{hb}}{1 + h_{ob}R_L} \tag{9–14}$$

$$R_o = \frac{h_{ib} + R_g}{\Delta^{hb} + R_g h_{ob}} \tag{9–15}$$

The simplified equivalent circuit is commonly more useful than the exact equivalent. This is similar to that given in Chapters 2 and 4 for the common-emitter, and is shown in Figure 9–17. From this equivalent circuit the approximate performance equations may be obtained:

$$A_i \cong h_{fb} \cong 1 \tag{9–16}$$

$$A_v = A_i\left[\frac{R_L}{R_i}\right] \cong \frac{R_L}{h_{ib}} \tag{9–17}$$

$$R_i \cong h_{ib} \tag{9–18}$$

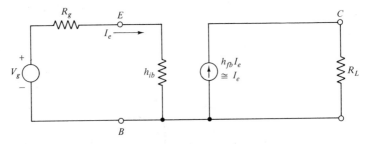

FIGURE 9–17
Simplified equivalent circuit of CB *amplifier*

Many data sheets give only the *CE* parameters. These must be converted to *CB* parameters to use the above equations. The relations between the parameters are

$$h_{fb} = \frac{h_{fe}}{h_{fe} + 1} \tag{9-19}$$

$$h_{ib} = \frac{h_{ie}}{h_{fe} + 1} \tag{9-20}$$

$$h_{ob} = \frac{h_{oe}}{h_{fe} + 1} \tag{9-21}$$

$$h_{rb} = \frac{h_{ie}h_{oe}}{h_{fe} + 1} - h_{re} \tag{9-22}$$

Example 9–4

A 2N3250 is to be used in a *CB* circuit with an ac load resistance of 4000 ohms. The operating point is to be approximately $I_C = 1$ ma, $V_{CE} = 10$ v. The data sheet (see Appendix B) lists the following parameters for the 2N3250:

	Min.	Max.
$h_{fe} =$	50	200 ohms
$h_{ie} =$	1000	6000 ohms

Using the average of the Min. and Max. values, we obtain for the corresponding *CB* parameters

$$h_{fb} = \frac{h_{fe}}{h_{fe} + 1} = \frac{125}{126}$$

$$h_{fb} \cong 0.992$$

$$h_{ib} = \frac{h_{ie}}{h_{fe} + 1} = \frac{3500}{126}$$

$$h_{ib} \cong 28 \text{ ohms}$$

Thus the approximate amplifier performance is

$$A_i \cong h_{fb} \cong 1$$

$$A_v = A_i \left(\frac{R_L}{R_i}\right) \cong \frac{R_L}{h_{ib}} \cong \frac{4000}{28} \cong 143$$

$$R_i \cong h_{ib} \cong 28 \text{ ohms}$$

The same transistor and load in a *CE* circuit would give

$$A_i \cong h_{fe} = 125$$

$$A_v \cong h_{fe}\left(\frac{R_L}{h_{ie}}\right) \cong (125)\left(\frac{4000}{3500}\right) \cong 143$$

$$R_i \cong 3500 \text{ ohms}$$

PROBLEMS

9–1. Draw the circuit of a simple emitter-follower amplifier with RC coupling to a resistive load.

9–2. Refer to Figure 9–1. Assume that a small voltage change occurs at the base and draw arrows indicating electron-flow direction for the resulting emitter current change. From this deduce the phase of the output voltage relative to the phase of the input voltage, and indicate this by showing polarity signs at the base-ground and emitter-ground terminals. Show also the polarity of the base-to-emitter voltage.

9–3. Write the Kirchhoff voltage equation for the voltage from base to ground in Figure 9–1 in terms of the base-emitter voltage and the voltage across the emitter resistor.

9–4. Recall the polarities deduced in Problem 9–2, and the voltage equation of 9–3. If the signal voltage drop across the base-emitter junction, in a circuit such as Figure 9–1, is 0.15 v, and the signal voltage drop across R_e is 1.65 v, what is the base-to-ground voltage? If this base-to-ground voltage is the signal input to the stage, and the voltage from emitter to ground is the output, what is the value of the voltage gain?

9–5. Considering the emitter-follower as a negative feedback amplifier with the feedback factor, β, equal to 1 (i.e., "100% feedback"), what signal voltage in Problem 9–4 above would be considered the input to the amplifier without feedback? What would be the value of the gain without feedback? Using these figures and the feedback equation ($A_v' = A_v/(1 - A_v B)$), calculate the gain with feedback and compare with the gain you found in Problem 9–4.

9–6. (a) Draw the dc load line for the following circuit. (Use the 2N1924 curves in Figure 9–5 or in Appendix B.)

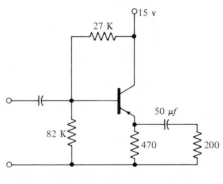

FIGURE P9-6

(b) Using the method of Section 9.2, find the quiescent base current I_B. Mark this operating point on the dc load line, and draw the ac load line.

(c) Check the correctness of your calculations above by reading the quiescent collector current from the load line, and using this as necessary to calculate the dc voltage drop across the emitter resistor in the circuit of part (a). From this and the base-emitter voltage you used in (b) above, find the dc base-to-ground voltage. Then find the current in the 82-kilohm resistor, the current in the 27-kilohm resistor, and the voltage drop in the 27-kilohm resistor.

9-7. (a) How does the emitter-follower output signal current compare with that of the *CE* amplifier? What then is a good approximate expression for the current gain of the emitter follower, *regardless of size of load*?

(b) When the load resistance is small, what is a good approximation for the current gain of the emitter follower?

9-8. An emitter follower has a load resistance of 1000 ohms, a current gain of 50, and h_{ie} = 500 ohms. What is the value of its input resistance?

9-9. (a) What is the approximate input resistance of the following circuit (directly at the base) if h_{ie} = 2000 ohms, and h_{fe} = 50?

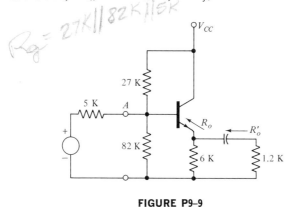

FIGURE P9-9

(b) What is the approximate input resistance of the above circuit at point *A*?

9-10. What is the voltage gain of the circuit of Problem 9-8? The circuit of Problem 9-9? Compare these gain figures and explain the difference.

9-11. (a) What is the approximate output resistance R_o of the circuit of Problem 9-9?

(b) What is the approximate output resistance R_o' of the same circuit?

9-12. Draw the basic circuit of a "bootstrapped" emitter-follower amplifier.

9-13. Expain why bootstrapping makes the bias divider network appear as a higher resistance.

9-14. Consider the following circuit in which h_{ie} = 4000 ohms, h_{ob} = 0.5 × 10⁻⁶ mhos, and h_{fe} = 100.

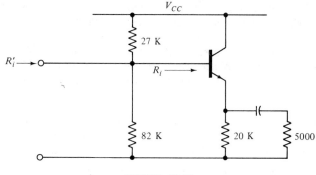

FIGURE P9–14

    (a)   What is the approximate input resistance R_i, taking into account the effect of h_{ob}?

    (b)   What is the input resistance R'_i?

9–15. Consider the following circuit:

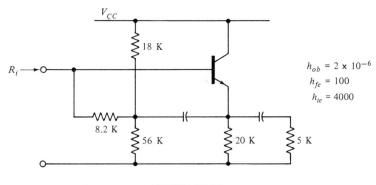

$h_{ob} = 2 \times 10^{-6}$

$h_{fe} = 100$

$h_{ie} = 4000$

FIGURE P9–15

820K   (a)   What is the effective resistance presented by the *bias network* to the signal?

    (b)   What is the approximate effective input resistance R_i (as defined in the figure)?   *176K*   *820K // hob // Ri*

9–16. Draw the basic circuit of a Darlington amplifier. Include the necessary bias network to make it a practical working circuit.

9–17. Explain, in terms of emitter-follower ideas, how the presence of the second transistor (the one whose base is connected to the emitter of the other transistor) helps to make the input resistance of the first transistor higher than it would be in the case of a single transistor emitter-follower circuit.

9–18. Draw a practical working circuit of a *CB, RC*-coupled amplifier.

9–19. Draw the complete equivalent circuit of the *CB* amplifier.

9–20. Draw the approximate equivalent circuit of the *CB* amplifier, and on the basis of this equivalent, write the approximate equations for voltage gain, current gain, and input resistance.

9-21. A 2N3250 is used in a *CB* amplifier at a quiescent collector current of 1 ma. The load is 1500 ohms. Find the approximate current gain, voltage gain, and the input resistance.

9-22. Find the approximate current gain, voltage gain, and input resistance for the same transistor and operating point as in Problem 9-21 but in the *CE* circuit. Compare these figures with the figures obtained in Problem 9-21.

9-23. Use the *CE* and *CB* approximate voltage gain equations to show why the voltage gain is about the same for common-base and common-emitter amplifiers using the same transistor and the same load.

REFERENCES

Fitchen, Franklin C., *Transistor Circuit Analysis and Design*, Second edition. Princeton, New Jersey: D. Van Nostrand Company, Inc., 1966.

Millman, Jacob and Christos C. Halkias, *Electronic Devices and Circuits*. New York: McGraw-Hill Book Company, 1967.

Schilling, Donald L. and Charles Belove, *Electronic Circuits: Discrete and Integrated*. New York: McGraw-Hill Book Company, 1968.

Towers T. D., "High Input-Impedance Amplifier Circuits," *Wireless World*, (July 1968).

CHAPTER 10

Field Effect Transistors

10.1 Introduction

There are two major types of field-effect transistor, the junction-gate type (JFET) and the insulated-gate type (IGFET). The insulated-gate FET is also known as the metal-oxide-semiconductor transistor (MOS, or MOSFET). Both kinds of FET operate by voltage control of an electric field which in turn controls the flow of current through a portion of the device. The electric field is set up in an insulating region, however, so that very little current flow occurs where the controlling voltage is applied. As a result, the input resistance of the FET is typically quite high. It is in this respect that the FET differs fundamentally from the bipolar transistor, which controls output current by means of the current flow across a forward-biased, low-resistance junction, and which herefore has quite a low input resistance.

10.2 The Junction FET

A basic structure for a junction field-effect transistor is illustrated in Figure 10–1. The type shown is an *n*-channel FET. It consists of a bar of *n*-type semiconductor with a region of *p*-type material on each side, and contacts arranged at the two ends and at the *p*-type regions. If a voltage is applied between the two ends of the bar, current will flow. The current within the bar is a result of the free electrons in the *n*-type material.

Recall from Section 1.3 that a reverse-biased *pn* junction has a *depletion region* on both sides of the junction. This is a region which has lost most of its free electrons and holes, and therefore has very low conductivity. The width of the depletion region varies with the amount of applied reverse-bias. Consequently, in the FET if a voltage is connected between the *p*-regions and one end of the bar so as to reverse-bias the *pn* junctions, the resulting depletion

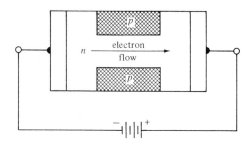

FIGURE 10–1
Elemental construction of the junction FET

regions will tend to decrease the width of the effective conducting portion of
the bar. This condition is illustrated in Figure 10–2. If the reverse-bias voltage
is made greater, the conductivity of the bar is decreased, and the current flow

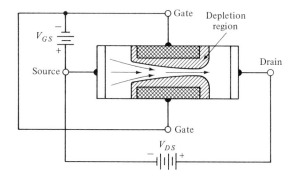

FIGURE 10–2
Depletion region in the FET

decreases. If the reverse-bias is decreased, the current flow will increase. This
control of the current flow can be used to provide signal amplification as in the
bipolar transistor. But since the control voltage is a reverse-bias, very little
current is drawn by the FET input.

Standard notation for the FET is illustrated in Figure 10–2. The terminal
where the electrons enter the bar is called the *source*, and the current through
this terminal is the *source current*, I_s. The terminal where the electrons leave
the bar is the *drain*, and the current through this terminal is the *drain current*,
I_D. The two *p*-regions are called gates. The voltage applied between gate and
source is the gate-to-source voltage, V_{GS}; that from drain to source is V_{DS}.

The physical form shown for the junction FET in Figures 10–1 and 10–2
is difficult to fabricate because it requires diffusion into both sides of the wafer.
A more practical structure, which is very commonly used, is shown in Figure
10–3. This is known as a single-ended type. The substrate would normally

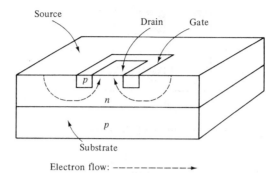

Electron flow: ----------→

FIGURE 10-3
Single-ended FET structure

be connected to the lowest potential point in the circuit, that is, to the circuit ground or common. It may also be operated as a second gate, for gain control or other special purposes.

Drain Characteristics of the Junction FET

Typical static characteristic curves of the *n*-channel junction-gate FET are illustrated in Figure 10–4. With the gate connected directly to the source,

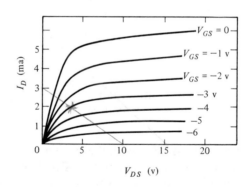

FIGURE 10-4
Typical junction-gate field-effect transistor output curves

so that the gate-to-source voltage is zero, and with low values of drain-to-source voltage V_{DS}, the current rises approximately linearly with V_{DS}. The body of the FET is acting like a resistor, with the current proportional to the drain-source voltage. But as the voltage is increased, the IR drop along the body of the FET, which is positive relative to the gate voltage, serves to increase the reverse-bias on the junction. Consequently, the depletion regions grow wider as V_{DS} is increased. When they become wide enough, the constriction of the effective conducting region slows down the rise of current. This is the region approaching the "knee" of the curves in Figure 10–4. At some sufficiently high drain-source voltage the two depletion regions come close enough together to prevent any further appreciable rise of current, and the curve becomes nearly horizontal.

If the gate is biased so it is negative to the source, the levelling off of the drain current will occur at a lower current value. The reverse-bias applied to the gate adds to that produced by the IR drop in the material so that the "pinching off" of the conducting region happens sooner. As Figure 10–4 shows, this effect is proportional to the amount of reverse-bias applied to the gate, so that for any given drain-to-source voltage, the drain current is proportional to gate voltage. This set of curves is therefore quite similar to the collector characteristic of the bipolar transistor, except that the control parameter in the case of the bipolar transistor is a current (base or emitter current).

Amplifying Action

As in the case of the bipolar transistor, a load line can be drawn on these curves to show that signal amplification is possible when a resistive load is connected in the drain circuit. Figure 10–5 shows such a circuit arrangement along with the load line drawn on the drain characteristics.

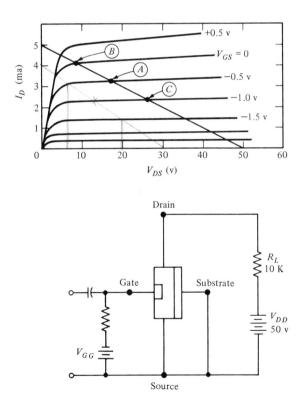

FIGURE 10–5
Basic circuit of the FET amplifier

If the quiescent value of V_{GS} in this circuit were -0.5 v, the operating point would be at A. A signal of 0.5 v peak amplitude applied between the input terminals (1 and 2) would then cause the operating point to move along the load line between the two extreme points B and C. The voltage gain would be found by dividing the peak-to-peak drain voltage swing (approximately $27\text{-}9 = 18$ v) by the peak-to-peak voltage swing (1 v).

When the input voltage change is in the positive direction, the output voltage change is in the negative direction, as is evident from Figure 10–5. This is due to the fact that a positive change of gate voltage causes an increase of drain current. This causes an increase in the voltage drop $i_D R_L$ so that the drain voltage (which is $V_{DD} - i_D R_L$) is lowered. Thus this amplifier is characterized by the same 180° phase shift from input to output as the CE amplifier.

10.3   The p-Channel Junction FET

The junction-gate field-effect transistor is also made as a p-channel type. In this construction the main body is a p-type material, and the gates are n-material. The current within the device is hole flow, and all supply voltages are of opposite polarity from those of the n-channel FET.

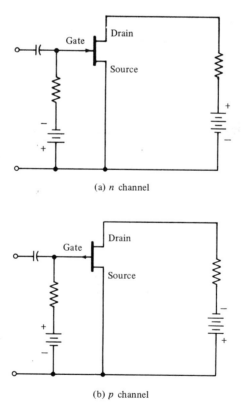

(a) n channel

(b) p channel

FIGURE 10–6
Schematic symbols for junction-gate field-effect transistors

10.4   Schematic Symbols for the Junction-Gate FET

Figure 10–6 gives the symbols used for the junction field-effect transistors, and shows each type connected in an elementary amplifier circuit in order to illustrate the correct voltage polarities. The gate voltages shown are the polarity which would provide reverse-bias of the gate junction as described above.

10.5   The Insulated-Gate FET

The insulated-gate field-effect transistor (IGFET or MOSFET) also controls output current by means of an electric field. However, in the insulated-gate type the field is set up by a voltage applied across a thin layer of insulating material instead of by reverse-biasing a *pn* junction. As a result, the input resistance of the MOSFET is much higher than that of the JFET.

The Depletion-Type MOSFET

Figure 10–7 illustrates the basic construction of a depletion type *n*-channel MOSFET. Two pockets of n^+ (highly doped) material are diffused into a *p*-type substrate. These two regions form the source and drain. Between them

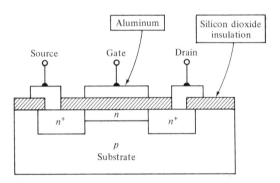

FIGURE 10-7
Basic structure of a depletion-type n-*channel insulated-gate FET*

is diffused a channel of *n* material. Over this channel is deposited a very thin layer of insulation — commonly silicon dioxide. On top of the oxide is placed a thin layer of metal such as aluminum. This metal layer is the gate electrode. The name MOSFET, for metal-oxide-semiconductor FET, comes from this combination of materials.

With the gate-to-source voltage, V_{GS}, equal to zero, a positive drain-to-source voltage will cause electron flow from source to channel through the channel. If the gate is biased negatively, however, the electric field set up by this voltage causes a redistribution of charges in the channel, resulting in a depletion region analagous to that of the JFET. The resulting volt-ampere characteristic is very similar to that of the JFET shown in Figure 10–4. For a given value of gate voltage, the drain current rises as the drain voltage is raised from zero, and the current levels off into a horizontal (constant current) region after the drain voltage reaches a certain value. For a fixed value of drain voltage, the drain current is decreased as the gate voltage is made more negative. This type of IGFET is called a *depletion type* because control of the drain current is by the depletion process.

The Enhancement-Type MOSFET

An enhancement-type IGFET can also be made. This type uses essentially the same construction as the depletion type except that the *n*-channel between the source and the drain is omitted. With zero gate voltage the current from source to drain is extremely low because the drain-to-source voltage (of either polarity) causes one of the two *pn* junctions to be reverse-biased. However, if the gate is biased positive to the source, the resulting electric field in the material causes minority carriers in the substrate (electrons in this case) to move into the region between the source and drain just under the gate-insulating material. These charges thus form an *induced n-channel*, capable of supporting electron flow from source to drain. The greater the gate-bias voltage, the greater the conductivity of this induced channel. Thus the drain

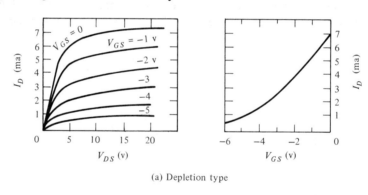

(a) Depletion type

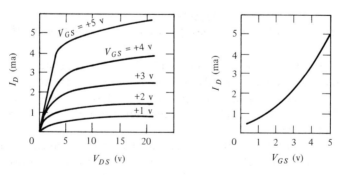

(b) Enhancement type

FIGURE 10–8
Static characteristics of MOSFETS

current is controlled by the gate voltage. This type of insulated-gate FET is called the *enhancement type* because the drain current is very low with zero gate voltage, and is "enhanced" by positive gate voltage.

Characteristic Curves of Depletion and Enhancement MOSFET Types

Figure 10–8 illustrates typical drain characteristics and transfer curves (I_D versus V_{GS}) for the two MOSFET types. The depletion type MOSFET may also be operated in the enhancement mode. In the *n*-channel type discussed so far this simply requires that the gate voltage be made positive. This causes more negative charges to move into the region of the channel, raising its conductivity, and thus "enhancing" the drain current. Typical drain and transfer characteristics for units used in this way are shown in Figure 10–9.

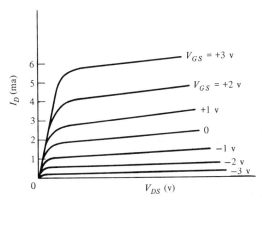

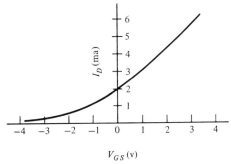

FIGURE 10–9
MOSFET operated in both depletion and enhancement modes

The p-Channel MOSFET

The insulated-gate field-effect transistor can be made in the *p*-channel type, by making the substrate of *n*-type semiconductor, and the drain and source regions of p^+ material. For this type of FET all voltage polarities must be reversed from those used with the *n*-channel type, and all current directions will be reversed.

Typical Dimensions in the MOSFET

To provide some notion of the dimensions of these structures, Figure 10–10 is a sketch of a typical unit, drawn roughly to scale and with some of the dimensions shown.

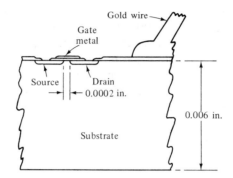

FIGURE 10–10
Dimensions of a typical MOSFET unit (From MOSFET in Circuit Design *by Robert H. Crawford)*

10.6 Schematic Symbols Used for the Insulated-Gate FET

Some of the circuit symbols for the MOSFET which may be encountered in the literature are shown in Figure 10–11. Those illustrated are *n*-channel type; for the *p*-channel type the arrows would point outward.

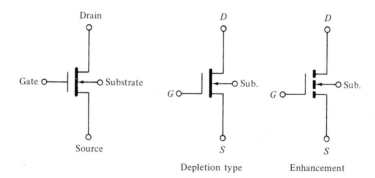

FIGURE 10–11
Circuit symbols for the MOSFET

10.7 FET Ratings and Characteristics

Operating limitations, significant operating voltages and currents, and equivalent-circuit parameters are listed by manufacturers of field-effect transistors for each type, just as with bipolar transistors. Those ratings and characteristics which have no counterpart in bipolar transistor work, or for which the notation differs enough to justify comment, are listed here with brief explanations and with some indication of typical values.

Input Resistance

In the JFET this is the resistance of a reverse-biased *pn* junction and may be in the range of 1 to 1000 megohms. In the MOSFET this is the insulation resistance of the silicon dioxide layer between the gate and the channel and is typically 1000 megohms or more.

The dc input resistance may be specified in terms of the gate leakage current at a specified gate voltage. The signal input resistance is often listed using the symbol R_e (Y_{is}) indicating the real part (i.e. resistive part) of the common-source input admittance. (The admittance-parameter equivalent circuit, or *y*-parameter circuit, is often used in the analysis of high-frequency amplifiers. Manufacturer's specifications for devices intended for high frequency operation commonly include such parameters. Although detailed discussion of *y*-parameters is outside the scope of this book, further comment will be made in Section 10.9 when the FET equivalent circuit is discussed.)

Input Capacitance

This is usually specified as the input capacitance in the common-source circuit with the drain shorted to circuit ground for signals. Consequently it is gate-to-source capacitance. In the JFET this capacitance may lie in the range of 5 to 100 pf, while in the insulated-gate type it may range from 1 to 10 pf. This capacitance will often be listed using the notation C_{iss}, meaning input capacitance in the common-source configuration with the output shorted.

Reverse Transfer Capacitance

The reverse transfer capacitance, or feedback capacitance, is the capacitance from drain to gate. It has the same significance with regard to effective input capacitance of an operating amplifier (the Miller effect) as the bipolar transistor's collector-base capacitance. A commonly used notation in the case of the FET is C_{rss}. Typical values in the JFET may fall in the range of 1 to 20 pf. In the MOSFET, values as low as 0.02 to 0.2 pf are available.

I_{DSS}

This is the drain current that flows with zero gate bias. In a depletion-type unit it represents a "full-on" condition in a sense. See Figure 10–12(a).

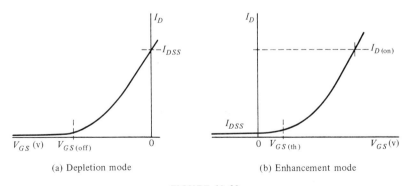

(a) Depletion mode   (b) Enhancement mode

FIGURE 10–12

Transfer curves defining the current and voltage notation encountered in FET specifications

In the enhancement-type unit I_{DSS} is essentially the cutoff condition (because zero gate bias gives low current in enhancement units), and the "full-on" condition will be specified by a rating for $I_{D(ON)}$.

$I_{D(ON)}$

This is the "ON" condition for the enhancement mode. It is the drain current that flows when the gate voltage is some specified value, and is usually near the maximum rated drain current. See Figure 10–12(b).

$V_{GS(OFF)}$

This is the gate-source voltage required to cut off the drain current. Since there is a small leakage current even when the device is cut off, $V_{GS(OFF)}$ is specified as the gate voltage required to reduce the drain current to some specified low value. See Figure 10–12(a).

$V_{GS(th)}$

In the insulated-gate FET of the enhancement type, the *gate-source threshold voltage* may be specified. This is the gate cutoff (i.e. "turn-off") voltage: the gate voltage at which the drain current will be at or below a specified low value. See Figure 10–12(b).

$V_{DS(ON)}$

In field-effect transistors used in switching circuits (for example in chopper and commutator applications), it is important that the drain-source voltage be low when the FET is "turned-on." This requires that the drain voltage in the region below the knee of the drain curves be low, even at high values of I_D. This is similar to the requirement for low $V_{CE(SAT)}$ in power transistors and switching transistors. $V_{DS(ON)}$ is specified for zero gate voltage and a specified high value of drain current.

10.8 Handling Precautions for the MOSFET

The insulation between the gate and the channel in an insulated-gate field-effect transistor is very thin, so that it is susceptible to voltage breakdown. In addition, the leakage current is extremely low, so that electrostatic charge due to friction in handling can readily build up dangerous voltage levels.

Electrostatic charge acquired by the human body may also cause damage. Potentials of hundreds of volts are frequently encountered. If an FET is held by the case and the gate is permitted to touch ground, this potential is impressed across the case-to-channel and channel-to-gate capacitances in series, and thus may cause voltage breakdown of the insulation between channel and gate.

Because of these factors, MOSFETS should be handled with care. They will usually be shipped from the manufacturer with the leads shorted together by metal clips, or otherwise conductively connected. A conductive container may be used. When the FET is removed from its container, a grounding strap should be employed so that the hand being used, or the tool being used, is grounded. Soldering iron tips should be grounded. Finally, the device should never be inserted into or removed from a circuit while the power is on.

10.9 The Low-Frequency Equivalent Circuit of the FET

At low frequencies (as in the audio range) and for amplifier use in the normal operating region of its characteristics, the FET can be represented by the simple equivalent circuit shown in Figure 10–13(b). Part (a) of this figure is the elementary amplifier circuit, shown without any biasing circuitry.

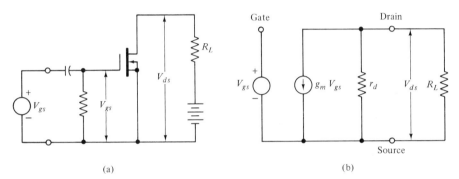

FIGURE 10–13
Elementary amplifier and its equivalent circuit

At first glance the appearance of the input portion of the equivalent circuit may seem strange since the source of signal is shown connected to a terminal (indicated as the gate) which is completely isolated from any other parts of the circuit. There is no input resistance shown — either in series with the signal or shunting it. This is because the FET is essentially an electric-field-operated device; the applied voltage controls the output by means of an electric field set up in an insulating material. The dielectric used for this insulation is an excellent one, so that the input resistance is very high at low frequencies. In addition, the capacitance between the gate and the channel is quite small. Thus the input impedance can be omitted from the equivalent circuit at low frequencies.

The effect that the input voltage has on the output conditions can be expressed as an output current controlled by the input voltage. At low frequencies it is sufficient to show the output resistance r_d, and the effect of the input voltage on the output current in the form of a constant current generator $g_m V_{gs}$. The *drain resistance* r_d is defined by

$$r_d = \frac{\Delta V_{DS}}{\Delta I_D}\bigg|_{\Delta V_{GS}\,=\,0} = \frac{V_{ds}}{I_d}\bigg|_{V_{gs}\,=\,0} \qquad (10\text{–}1)$$

while the *transconductance* g_m is

$$g_m = \frac{\Delta I_D}{\Delta V_{GS}}\bigg|_{\Delta V_{DS} = 0} = \frac{I_d}{V_{gs}}\bigg|_{V_{ds} = 0} \tag{10-2}$$

The term g_{fs} is often used instead of g_m. g_{fs} stands for "transfer conductance in the *forward* direction" (i.e., from gate to output) with the device in the common-*source* configuration. This term is the real part of the forward transfer admittance Y_{fs} (transfer admittance in the forward direction with the device operated in the common-source connection). At high frequencies Y_{fs} may be separated into in-phase and out-of-phase parts:

$$y_{fs} = g_{fs} + jb_{fs}$$

At low frequencies the out-of-phase part is not significant, and the forward transfer admittance has the value

$$y_{fs} = g_{fs}$$

Since the in-phase or resistive part of an admittance is a conductance, this is commonly called the *transconductance* when applied in low-frequency work.

The drain resistance r_d represents the resistive part of the more general term y_{os} — the output admittance — but is usually expressed as a resistance r_d, in low-and medium-frequency work, rather than as a conductance.

Wth a load R_L connected to the output terminals and an input signal voltage V_{gs} applied to the input terminals, the output signal voltage is the product of the total current $g_m V_{gs}$ and the parallel impedance through which it flows — R_L in parallel with r_d. Thus

$$V_{ds} = -g_m V_{gs}\left(\frac{r_d R_L}{r_d + R_L}\right)$$

The voltage gain therefore is

$$A_v = \frac{V_{ds}}{V_{gs}} = -g_m\left(\frac{r_d R_L}{r_d + R_L}\right) \tag{10-3}$$

When $R_L \ll r_d$ this simplifies to

$$A_v = -g_m R_L \tag{10-4}$$

As an example of the use of these equations, consider the 3N139 FET. Appendix B shows that for operation with a self-bias source resistance of 360 ohms and a supply voltage of 15 v, the g_m is 4500 μmhos and $r_d = 20$ kilohms.

Example 10-1

An effective load impedance of 2000 ohms is to be used. Since this load is much smaller than r_d, the approximate gain equation is adequate for routine work:

$$A \cong -g_m R_L$$
$$A \cong -(4500 \times 10^{-6})(2000)$$
$$A \cong -9$$

This approximate result is, of course, about 10 percent greater than the value that the complete equation would give, since the complete equation involves the parallel combination of r_d and R_L.

Example 10–2

An effective load impedance of 15,000 ohms is used. The approximation would obviously give such large error as to be worthless even for rough work. The exact equation gives the following results:

$$A = -g_m\left[\frac{r_d R_L}{r_d + R_L}\right]$$

$$A = -(4500 \times 10^{-6})\left[\frac{(20 \times 10^3)(15 \times 10^3)}{35 \times 10^3}\right]$$

$$A \cong -39$$

(*Note:* The approximate equation would have given a gain figure of about 68.)

Typical values of g_m (or g_{fs}) may range from below 1000 μmhos to above 10,000 μmhos depending upon FET type and on the operating point. Typical values of r_d may range from below 5 kilohms to above 100 kilohms, again depending upon type and operating point.

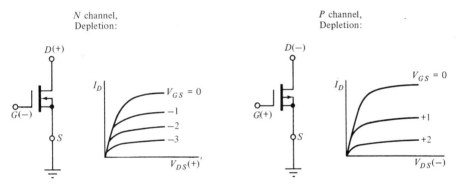

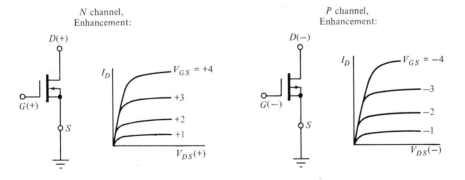

FIGURE 10–14
Gate and drain polarities

10.10 Bias Methods

As in the case of the bipolar transistor, the dc design of the FET amplifier is of basic importance since it is only through the control of the operating point that the desired signal conditions can be maintained. Due to the greater number of modes of operation, the choice of bias circuits and polarities may initially seem confusing, but the basic relationships are direct and simple. Figure 10–14 summarizes the FET types and indicates the bias polarity commonly used in each case for amplifier circuits.

Note that the polarity of the drain supply depends upon the channel type — positive for n-channel and negative for p-channel — while the relation of the gate polarity to the drain polarity depends upon whether the unit is a depletion or an enhancement type. For depletion types the gate is of *opposite* polarity from the drain; for enhancement types the gate is the *same* polarity as the drain.

Figure 10–15 illustrates a general method of achieving these bias voltages

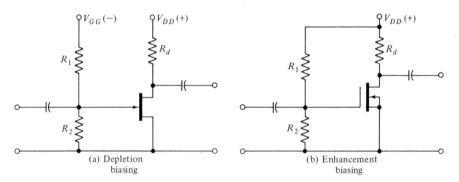

(a) Depletion biasing

(b) Enhancement biasing

FIGURE 10–15
Elementary FET biasing

for n-channel devices. In the case of p-channel units, all polarities would be reversed. The two circuits shown in this figure are the same except that the depletion type requires a separate supply voltage for the bias because of the polarity. If the desired bias, in the case of the depletion type, happens to be zero, then of course V_{GG} and R_1 are eliminated.

The polarity requirement of the depletion type permits the use of a bias circuit called "self-bias," shown in Figure 10–16. In this arrangement the gate is connected through R_g to ground or common. Since there is no gate current, there is no IR drop across R_g, and the gate is therefore at ground potential. The source, however, is above ground by the amount of the IR drop in the resistor R_s that results from the dc drain current. Thus the gate is below the source by the voltage $I_D R_s$, or the gate-to-source voltage V_{GS} is negative in the n-channel FET, as required. In the case of a p-channel FET, the current direction and polarity of the IR drop would be reversed. The gate would then be *above* the source by the voltage $I_D R_s$, and V_{GS} would be positive as required.

If negative signal feedback is not desired, the resistor R_s is bypassed as shown in part (b) of the figure. Negative feedback of course then still exists for dc or very slow changes. This provides stabilizing action against temperature-

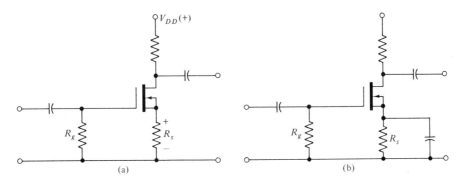

FIGURE 10–16
Self-bias, used with deletion-type units

caused drift of the operating point, or unit-to-unit differences in dc characteristics, just as does emitter-resistor stabilization in bipolar transistor amplifiers. Stabilizing methods will be considered in the next section.

The above simple form of self-bias is not available to enhancement type units since the polarity of the resulting bias is not correct for such devices, but the use of the source resistor for stabilizing purposes is possible in conjunction with the arrangement of Figure 10–15(b). When this is done, the enhancement bias provided by the voltage divider $R_1 - R_2$ must of course be increased by the amount of the voltage drop across R_s, since the latter opposes the desired bias. The resulting circuit is the biasing arrangement so familiar from bipolar transistor work, and is shown in Figure 10–17.

Since the fixed bias arrangements generally provide no stabilizing effect, the more commonly employed circuits will be those of Figures 10–16 and 10–17, and a drain feedback circuit which will be discussed in connection with stabilizing methods.

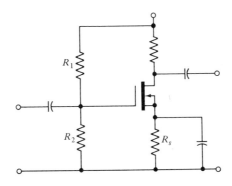

FIGURE 10–17
Source resister used with enhancement type FET

10.11 Bias Stabilizing

The major source of variation of operating point in a FET may well be the unit-to-unit or manufacturing variation in the transfer characteristic. The value of I_{DSS} may vary by as much as 10 to 1 among units of some types. The minimum and maximum values are usually specified on the manufacturer's data sheets.

Temperature effects may also be important. Because of two opposing temperature-dependent effects in the physical processes that take place within the FET (one of which causes an increase in drain current with temperature increases, while the other causes a decrease), the FET may have a positive, zero, or negative temperature coefficient. Figure 10–18 illustrates this in terms

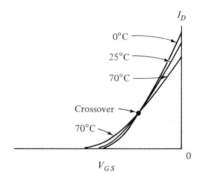

FIGURE 10–18
Temperature effects in the FET

of the transfer curve. This figure shows drain current versus gate-to-source voltage at three different temperatures.

In one region of the transfer characteristic a rise in temperature causes drain current to decrease, while in the other region the opposite effect occurs. The operating point determines which of the opposing internal temperature-sensitive effects is the greatest. At the crossover, a zero temperature coefficient exists. FET circuits may be designed so as to take advantage of this. By operating with the correct value of bias, the drift of operating point with temperature may be eliminated or minimized. The value of this optimum gate bias differs among FET types, and some FET types may not have such a zero temperature coefficient point. In general, stabilizing methods are similar to those employed for bipolar transistors, but are simpler to analyze since the gate circuit draws negligible current.

Source Resistor Stabilizing

The first method to be considered will be that of employing a source resistor; that is, the general type of circuit illustrated above in Figures 10–16 and 10–17. For complete generality, the circuit used will be as shown in Figure 10–19, with the polarity of the gate supply voltage V_{GG} determined by the bias and stability requirements.

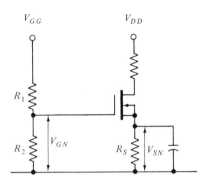

FIGURE 10–19
Basic stabilizing circuit

In this circuit the voltage from gate to ground, V_{GN}, is fixed, while the voltage from source to ground, V_{SN}, varies with the drain current I_D. The gate-to-source bias is the difference between these voltages, or

$$V_{GS} = V_{GN} - V_{SN} = V_{GN} - I_D R_s \qquad (10\text{–}5)$$

Thus if I_D attempts to increase, V_{SN} will increase, and the bias, V_{GS}, will therefore decrease. This change will oppose the increase of I_D.

For example, consider the case of a depletion mode, n-channel unit, with circuit and drain characteristics such that $I_D = 5$ ma when $V_{GS} = 0$. If $R_s = 500$ ohms, then

$$V_{SN} = I_D R_s = (0.005)(500)$$

$$V_{SN} = 2.5 \text{ v}$$

and to have $V_{GS} = 0$, the gate-to-ground voltage must be

$$V_{GN} = 2.5 \text{ v}$$

If this unit should be replaced with a higher current unit, say one that has $I_D = 10$ ma at $V_{GS} = 0$, the drain current cannot rise to 10 ma since that would produce

$$V_{SN} = I_D R_s = (0.01)(500) = 5 \text{ v}$$

giving a bias of

$$V_{GS} = V_{GN} - V_{SN}$$

$$V_{GS} = 2.5 - 5.0 = -2.5 \text{ v}$$

which would of course not permit 10 ma to flow. Obviously the bias and drain current condition that will actually result must be somewhere between 0 and -2.5 v for V_{GS}, and between 5 and 10 ma for I_D.

The following discussion will show how to determine the size of source resistor R_s that is necessary to prevent the drain current from changing more than some predetermined amount.

The crux of the method is having information as to the expected variations. Although data sheets usually give the upper and lower manufacturing limits for I_{DSS}, this may not be the operating condition involved in the actual circuit to be used. It may be necessary to test units representing maximum and minimum drain currents — and where temperature effects are expected to be significant, to conduct these tests at the expected maximum and minimum temperatures. The result of such tests would be two transfer curves such as (a) and (b) in Figure 10–20.

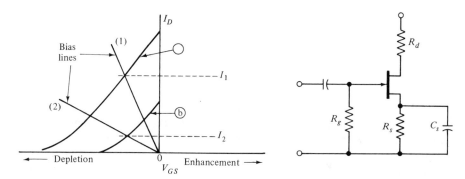

FIGURE 10–20

Depletion-type FET using source resistor for dc stability

Assume that a depletion-type FET is to be used, so that it is hoped that the bias circuit shown in Figure 10–20 will be possible. Assume also that the application requires that I_D never exceed I_1 or fall below I_2. Then a source resistor chosen so as to produce a bias line between (1) and (2), will produce operation meeting your requirement. (The bias line is simply the graph of bias voltage versus drain current. For this type of circuit the bias is $V_{GS} = I_D R_s$ so that the bias line is drawn from the origin through a point whose coordinates are the expected values of V_{GS} and I_D.)

In this case, a point is chosen representing a desired value of I_D between the two limits I_1 and I_2, and the bias line drawn through this point. The necessary value of R_s is then V_{GS}/I_D for any point on this line.

A source resistor without any additional fixed bias will be satisfactory in many cases. But if the transfer curve limits and your operating requirements are as in Figure 10–21, the required bias line can not go through zero.

In this case some enhancement bias must be added as indicated by V_{GG} in Figure 10–21. This bias may of course be added by use of a voltage divider as in Figure 10–22. The voltage divider $R_1 - R_2$ must satisfy the relation

$$\left(\frac{R_2}{R_1 + R_2}\right)V_{DD} = V_{GG}$$

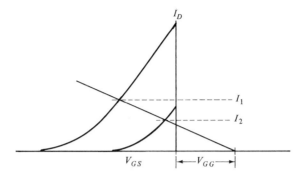

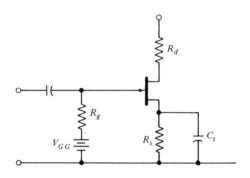

FIGURE 10–21
*Depletion-type FET requiring some enhancement bias (V_{GG}) because
stability requirement forces the use of too large a source resistor*

If an enhancement type unit is being used, fixed bias in the enhancement
direction will always be required, since the source resistor provides depletion
bias. The general situation will be as pictured in Figure 10–23.

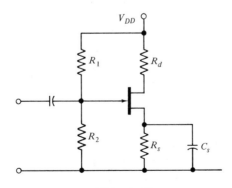

FIGURE 10–22
Use of voltage divider for V_{GG} requirement of Figure 10–21

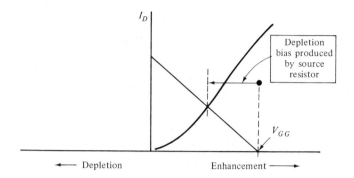

FIGURE 10–23
Enhancement type FET with source resistor for dc stabilizing

Drain Feedback Stabilizing

It is possible to stabilize the operating point with one less resistor, if the FET is an enhancement type so that V_{GG} and V_{DD} can be the same polarity. The arrangement is illustrated in Figure 10–24.

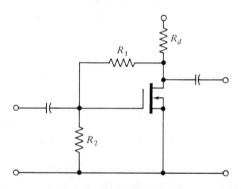

FIGURE 10–24
Drain feedback stabilizing

The saving of one resistor would result only if signal feedback were desired. If not, decoupling would be necessary as discussed previously in connection with bipolar transistor bias circuits. Then the number of resistors and capacitors would be the same for the two circuits. However, the capacitor value needed in the drain feedback case would usually be much smaller than for source resistor bypassing, and this would represent a considerable cost saving even with the same number of parts.

Since the coupling resistor R_d is usually determined by other factors in the design of the amplifier, and the voltage divider ratio is determined by the required bias voltage, the degree of operating point stability achieved will not be under the control of the designer in this version of the circuit. However, in RC-coupled amplifiers such as shown above, the size of R_d will often be such that good stability will prevail, particularly if the required value of bias, or at least an acceptable value of bias, happens to be near the value of V_{DS}, so that the divider does not greatly attenuate the dc feedback. Amplifiers with low values of resistance in the drain circuit, however — such as transformer-coupled amplifiers, tuned amplifiers, and the like — would have poor dc stability using this stabilizing method.

10.12 FET Feedback Amplifiers

Feedback techniques in FET circuits are essentially the same as in bipolar transistor circuits. They may in many respects be easier to apply, and easier to analyze, because of the very high input resistance of the FET.

As with bipolar transistors, the type of feedback may be classified as voltage feedback or current feedback. Voltage feedback tends to lower the output resistance, that is, to produce a more constant output voltage. Current feedback tends to produce more constant output current, that is, to raise the output resistance. In addition, the feedback may be arranged to be in series with the input, which will increase the input resistance, or to be in shunt with the input, which will lower the input resistance. In order to indicate the general aspects of feedback in FET circuits, two basic forms will be discussed briefly.

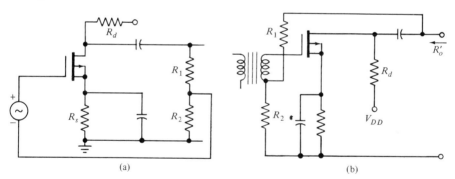

(a)   (b)

FIGURE 10–25
Voltage feedback

Voltage Feedback in Series with the Input

Figure 10–25 (a) illustrates a rather generalized form of this arrangement, the circuit action of which was described in Section 8.3. Part (b) shows one way in which it might be applied. The feedback factor is

$$\beta = \frac{R_2}{R_1 + R_2} \qquad \qquad \textbf{(10–6)}$$

and the gain with feedback is

$$A' = \frac{A}{1 - A\beta} \qquad \qquad \textbf{(10–7)}$$

where

$$A = -g_m\left(\frac{r_d R_L}{r_d + R_L}\right) \qquad \qquad \textbf{(10–3)}$$

is the gain without feedback measured from gate-source terminals to drain-source terminals. The output resistance of an FET amplifier is reduced by voltage feedback, in accordance with Equation (8–12):

$$R'_o = \frac{R_o}{1 - A\beta} \qquad\qquad (8\text{–}12)$$

Example 10–3

Find the gain and output resistance of the circuit of Figure 10–25 (b) if the following values apply:

$$g_m = 6000 \ \mu\text{mhos}$$
$$r_d = 15 \ \text{kilohms}$$
$$R_d = 30 \ \text{kilohms}$$
$$R_1 = 1 \ \text{megohm}$$
$$R_2 = 180 \ \text{kilohms}$$

The gain without feedback is

$$A = -g_m\left(\frac{r_d R_L}{r_d + R_L}\right)$$

in which $R_L = R_d \ \| \ (R_1 + R_2)$. But $(R_1 + R_2)$ is large enough so that it may be neglected. Then

$$A \cong -g_m\left(\frac{r_d R_d}{r_d + R_d}\right)$$

$$A \cong -(0.006)\left(\frac{(15)(10^3)(30)(10^3)}{(45)(10^3)}\right)$$

$$A \cong -60$$

The feedback factor is

$$\beta = \frac{R_2}{R_1 + R_2}$$

$$\beta = \frac{(180)(10^3)}{(1.18)(10^6)} = -.152$$

Then the gain with feedback is

$$A' = \frac{A}{1 - A\beta}$$

$$A' = \frac{-60}{1 - (-60)(0.152)}$$

$$A' \cong \frac{-60}{10.15} \cong -5.9$$

and the output resistance is

$$R'_o \cong \frac{R_o}{1 - A\beta} \cong \frac{R_o}{10.15}$$

in which

$$R_o = \frac{r_d R_d}{r_d + R_d} = 10 \ \text{kilohms}$$

Thus

$$R'_o \cong \frac{10,000}{10.15} \cong 1 \ \text{kilohm}$$

Current Feedback in Series With the Input

Another frequently encountered feedback circuit is shown in Figure 10–26. The basic action of this arrangement was also explained in Section 8.3.

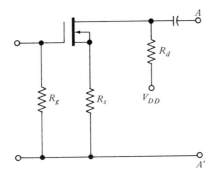

FIGURE 10–26
Basic source resistor feedback circuit

The feedback factor is

$$\beta = \frac{R_s}{R_d} \qquad (10\text{–}8)$$

while the gain is given by the same equations as for the voltage feedback case:

$$A' = \frac{A}{1 - A\beta}$$

10.13　The Source-Follower Circuit

The common-drain, or source-follower, amplifier is the FET version of the common-collector or emitter-follower circuit discussed in Chapter 9. The basic circuit is illustrated in Figure 10–27.

Since this is a negative feedback amplifier with $\beta = -1$, the gain can be expressed as

$$A' = \frac{A}{1 - A\beta} = \frac{A}{1 + A} \qquad (10\text{–}9)$$

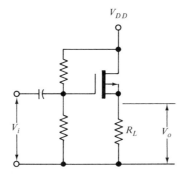

FIGURE 10–27
Basic circuit of the source follower

where A' is the gain with feedback, that is, the source follower gain, and A is the gain without feedback, or the gain *from the gate-source terminals* to the load. That is, A is the gain as a common-source amplifier with a load having the value R_L.

Thus
$$A = g_m\left(\frac{r_d R_L}{r_d + R_L}\right) \tag{10-3}$$

Substituting this expression for A into Equation (10–9) then leads to

$$A' = \frac{\dfrac{r_d R_L}{r_d + R_L}}{\dfrac{r_d R_L}{r_d + R_L} + \dfrac{1}{g_m}} \tag{10-10}$$

This equation shows that the gain is less than one, but that if r_d and R_L are large and g_m is large, the gain will approach one.

Example 10–4

When
$$r_d = 10,000 \text{ ohms}$$
$$R_L = 200 \text{ ohms}$$
$$g_m = 2000 \text{ } \mu\text{mhos}$$

Then
$$A' \cong \frac{196}{196 + 500}$$
$$A' \cong 0.282$$

Note the effect of low R_L and low g_m. Note also that even if a FET having g_m as great as 10,000 were used, the above value of R_L would give a gain of only about 0.66. In contrast note how a high r_d, a high g_m, *and* a high value of effective load resistance provide a gain of almost 1 in the following.

Example 10–5

When
$$r_d = 10,000 \text{ ohms}$$
$$R_L = 10,000 \text{ ohms}$$
$$g_m = 10,000 \text{ } \mu\text{mhos}$$

Then
$$A' \cong \frac{5000}{5000 + 100}$$
$$A' \cong 0.98$$

Output Resistance and Source-Follower Equivalent

Equation (10–10) can be rewritten in the following form:

$$A' = \frac{g_m\left[\dfrac{r_d}{g_m r_d + 1}\right]R_L}{\left[\dfrac{r_d}{g_m r_d + 1}\right] + R_L} \tag{10-11}$$

Comparing this equation with Equation (10–3) for the gain of the common-source circuit reveals that they are of the same form if $r_d/(g_m r_d + 1)$ replaces r_d in the common-source equation.

$r_d/(g_m r_d + 1)$ can then be considered to be the output resistance of the FET when used in the *source-follower* circuit. The equivalent circuit for the source-follower might then be drawn as shown in Figure 10–28. When this

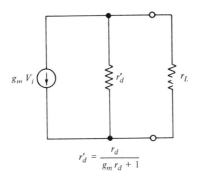

$$r'_d = \frac{r_d}{g_m r_d + 1}$$

FIGURE 10–28
Equivalent circuit for source follower

equivalent circuit representation is used, the gain equation is in the same simple form as that of the common-source amplifier, except that r_d as specified in the FET data sheet is replaced by $r'_d = r_d/(g_m r_d + 1)$, or

$$A' = g_m\left(\frac{r'_d R_L}{r'_d + R_L}\right) \qquad (10\text{--}12)$$

As an example of the use of these relationships, consider the circuit of Figure 10–29 (a). The output equivalent circuit is shown in part (b). The FET characteristics are

$$g_m = 6000 \ \mu\text{mhos}$$
$$r_d = 15{,}000 \ \text{ohms}$$

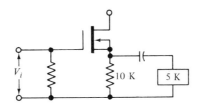

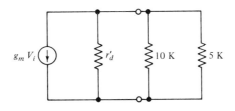

FIGURE 10–29
Use of the source follower equivalent circuit

Therefore

$$r'_d = \frac{r_d}{g_m r_d + 1} = \frac{15 \times 10^3}{(6 \times 10^{-3})(15 \times 10^3) + 1} = \frac{15 \times 10^3}{90 + 1}$$

$$r'_d \cong 165 \text{ ohms}$$

The gain is

$$A' = g_m \left(\frac{r'_d R_L}{r'_d + R_L} \right)$$

$$A' \cong (6 \times 10^{-3}) \left[\frac{(165)(3333)}{165 + 3333} \right] \cong (6 \times 10^{-3})(157)$$

$$A' \cong 0.94$$

The necessity for two equations here certainly does not seem an advantage over the gain calculation performed with the one Equation (10–10). However, the method using r'_d permits the ready "characterization" of different FETs, so that you may conveniently compare their expected performance with respect to both gain and output resistance — both of which are important operating characteristics. Equation (10–10) is not so convenient in this regard.

10.14   High Input Resistance FET Circuits

One of the principal advantages of the FET is its high input impedance. In the junction FET this is the result of the fact that the input is a reverse-biased junction; in the insulated-gate FET the reason is the isolation provided by the silicon dioxide layer between the gate electrode and the channel material.

The biasing resistor R_g connected to the gate, however, is directly in parallel with the input and therefore acts to lower the effective input resistance. Extremely high values of R_g may not be permissible in a junction-gate FET circuit due to the gate leakage current. With modest values of R_g (for example, below 10 megohms) the effect of this very small current may be negligible. This is why the input resistance effect is left out of the low-frequency equivalent circuit. But if one were to attempt to build a high-input-resistance circuit by using an R_g value of, say, 100 megohms, then a leakage current of only 0.01

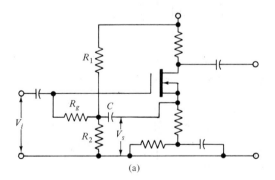

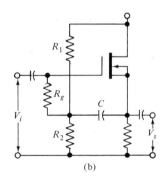

(a)   (b)

FIGURE 10–30
Bootstrapping variations

μa would cause an IR drop of $(0.01)(10^{-6})(100)(10^6) = 1$ v. Recalling that semiconductor leakage current approximately doubles with each $10°C$ rise leads to the conclusion that temperature effects on this IR drop would cause drastic drift of the bias point. Consequently, R_g may have to be kept moderate in value.

When this is the case, high values of input resistance at signal frequencies may be obtained by bootstrapping, as discussed in Chapter 8 in connection with Figure 8–12. Figure 10–30 here provides a simple example of such a technique in an FET amplifier. Part (a) of the figure shows bootstrapping applied to a common-source circuit in which some unbypassed source resistance is being used for negative feedback. Part (b) illustrates its use in a source-follower circuit. In both cases C is a large capacitance which serves to effectively connect one end of R_g to the unbypassed source resistor for signal frequencies. The signal voltage across the source resistor is in phase with the signal voltage at the gate, and somewhat smaller in amplitude. Since the gate voltage is the potential at one end of R_g, and the source resistor voltage is the potential at the other end of R_g, the signal voltage across R_g is the difference between the two, or $V_i - V_s$. This voltage is smaller than V_i, and so the signal current flowing in R_g is smaller than would flow in such a resistor due to the input signal alone. That is, the resistor R_g has been made to appear like a larger resistance, by drawing less current from the circuit to which it is connected.

The *effective* input resistance due to R_g in parallel with the very much higher gate-to-source resistance R_{gs} of the FET is

$$R_i = \frac{V_i}{I_{Rg} + I_{gs}}$$

and where I_{gs} is very small, as in IGFETS and low-leakage JFETS, we may neglect I_{gs}:

$$R_i = \frac{V_i}{I_{Rg}}$$

but

$$I_{Rg} = \frac{V_{Rg}}{R_g} = \frac{V_i - V_s}{R_g}$$

so that

$$R_i = \left(\frac{V_i}{V_i - V_s}\right)R_g \qquad \text{(10–13)}$$

This equation indicates that R_i is indeed larger than R_g, since $V_i - V_s$ is smaller than V_i. To illustrate the use of this equation, consider a circuit such as Figure 10–30 (a) in which R_g is 5 megohms; V_i is 0.6 v, and V_s is 0.45 v. Then

$$R_i = \left[\frac{V_i}{V_i - V_s}\right]R_g \qquad \text{(10–13)}$$

$$R_i = \left[\frac{0.6}{0.6 - 0.45}\right](5)(10^6)$$

$$R_i = 20 \text{ megohms}$$

Where this technique is applied to source-follower circuits, the input resistance may be expressed in terms of the gain of the source-follower circuit. Thus, in the source follower with gain A'

$$V_s = A'V_i$$

so that

$$R_i = \left[\frac{V_i}{V_i - A'V_i}\right]R_g$$

$$R_i = \left[\frac{1}{1 - A'}\right]R_g \qquad (10\text{--}14)$$

With a source follower having a gain of 0.95 and using a resistor $R_g = 5$ megohms, the effective input resistance would be

$$R_i = \left[\frac{1}{1-A'}\right]R_g = \left[\frac{1}{1 - 0.95}\right](5 \times 10^6)$$

$$R_i = 100 \text{ megohms}$$

FET circuits *without* bootstrapping can provide high-input resistance; *with* bootstrapping, extremely high resistances are possible for special needs. In bipolar transistor circuits the low-input resistance and the relatively low

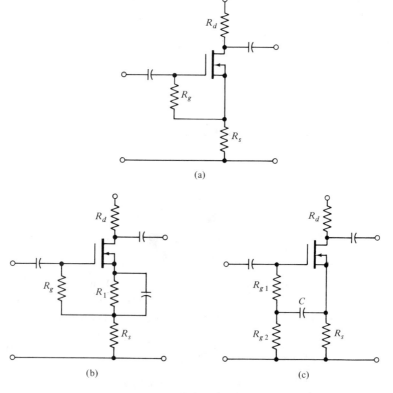

(a)

(b)   (c)

FIGURE 10–31
Bootstrapping arrangements suitable for depletion-mode operation

values of bias resistors (necessary for operating point stability) limit the magnitude of effective input resistance that can be achieved even with boot-strapping.

The circuits of Figure 10–30 are quite general in form. The voltage divider $R_1 - R_2$ provides enhancement bias, to illustrate the arrangement that would be needed to operate an enhancement-type FET or to provide the additional enhancement bias required in a bias stabilizing situation such as Figure 10–22. Figure 10–31 illustrates various arrangements that may be used where there is no need for enhancement bias. In (a), the bias is zero. In (b), resistor R_1 and a bypass capacitor are added to provide depletion biasing. The bypass capacitor could be omitted if this did not make the total feedback (due to $R_1 + R_s$) too great. Part (c) illustrates an arrangement that is possible if the size of R_s is satisfactory for the bias requirement. This circuit may be more economical than that of (b) because the required value of C would usually be much smaller.

10.15 The FET as a Voltage-Controlled Resistor

In the lower portion (well below the knee) of the FET's drain character-istics the curves tend to be quite linear, with a slope that is determined by the gate voltage. This is illustrated in the typical curves shown in Figure 10–32.

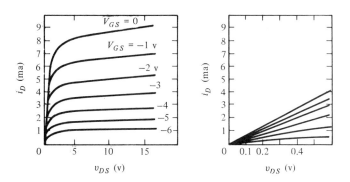

FIGURE 10-32
FET drain curves showing the slope below the knee

In part (a) of this figure, the full extent of the curves is shown. In part (b) the horizontal scale has been expanded, and only the region well below the knee is presented. Notice that the lines are quite straight. Note also that the slope of the lines is controlled by the gate-to-source bias. That is, with a given gate voltage the slope is constant, and when the gate voltage is changed to a different value, the FET operates along a new curve, having a different slope.

Since the slope of these curves is $\Delta I_D / \Delta V_{DS}$, it represents the reciprocal of the drain-to-source resistance. Constant slope indicates a constant resistance, for a given gate bias, and the change of slope with change of bias indicates the gate's control over this resistance. This region of the FET curves is sometimes called the *ohmic region*. The ohmic region of the FET extends into the region of reversed drain voltage, so that it tends to be symmetrical about zero. This is illustrated in Figure 10–33.

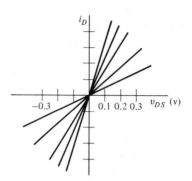

FIGURE 10–33
Ohmic region of FET on both sides of zero drain voltage

The Voltage-Controlled Attenuator

The gate-controlled resistance of the FET makes it very useful as a voltage-controlled attenuator. Figure 10–34 illustrates this. In this circuit the drain-to-source resistance is in series with a resistor R so that the combination forms

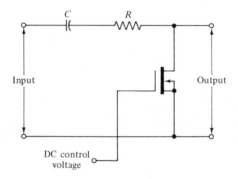

FIGURE 10–34
FET used as a voltage-controlled attenuator

a voltage divider. If r_D denotes the drain-source resistance, the output of this divider is

$$V_o = \left[\frac{r_D}{R + r_D}\right]V_i$$

Thus the signal output level can be varied by means of the dc control voltage applied as a gate-to-ground voltage (that is, as a gate-to-source voltage, since the source is grounded).

Note the capacitor C. This serves as a blocking capacitor, and is necessary if there is a dc component in the signal being applied to the attenuator. There would be a dc component, for example, in the output of an amplifier, and such a dc voltage would tend to move the operating point of the attenuator FET up above the knee of the drain curves — out of the ohmic region. Even a small dc component might move the operation far enough away from zero so that it would be out of the linear region. If this happens — or if too large an input signal is used — the nonlinearity of the upper portion of the ohmic region (where the curves begin to approach the knee) can introduce distortion.

10.16 The Dual-Gate MOS

Insulated-gate field-effect transistors can be made with two independent insulated gates, so that a number of different kinds of operation requiring two separate input or control points are possible. Figure 10–35 shows the essential

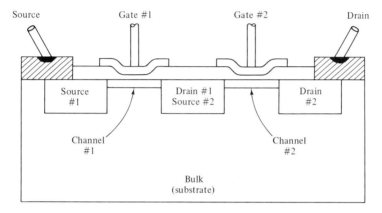

FIGURE 10–35
Construction of the dual-gate FET

nature of the construction of this dual-gate FET. This construction results in what is essentially a series combination of two single-gate units with the central region acting as the drain for the first unit and the source for the second unit. The bias voltage on each gate affects not only the drain current and the forward transconductance of that gate, but also affects the forward trans-conductance of the other gate. The control that each gate exercises over the drain current permits either portion of the dual-gate FET to be used as a voltage-controlled resistor, so that the combination can be used as in Figure 10–36 (a) or as in (b).

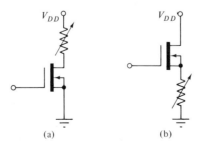

FIGURE 10–36
Use of dual-gate FET to form FET/resistance combinations

PROBLEMS

10-1. Make two sketches of a JFET illustrating the depletion regions for two different values of gate-to-source voltage. Use the type of JFET structure shown in Figure 10-2, and assume the same drain-to-source voltage for the two cases. Indicate which sketch is for the more negative gate bias.

10-2. An n-channel JFET having the characteristics shown in Figure 10-4 is operated with a drain-source voltage of 15 v and a gate bias of -1 v. What is the quiescent drain current? $4,75 ma$

10-3. The same JFET as in Problem 10-2 is operated so that $V_{DS} = 10$ v, and $V_{GS} = -3$ v. What is the value of I_D? $2.5 ma$

10-4. Draw the basic amplifier circuit for a p-channel FET. Use the schematic symbol for the device. Show all supply polarities. Show the direction of electron flow in the circuit connected to the FET, by means of arrows.

10-5. Draw the load line and graphically determine the voltage gain for a circuit of the same general type as that used in Figure 10-5, if the device has the characteristics shown in that figure, and the following values apply:

$$V_{DD} = 30 \text{ v}$$
$$R_L = 7.5 \text{ kilohms}$$
$$V_{GS} = -1.0 \text{ v}$$
$$V_{gs} = 0.5 \text{ v peak}$$

$A_v = 12.5$

10-6. Use the Appendix to obtain the following information concerning the indicated FETs.

(a) The 3N138:
     Input capacitance (max value)
     Reverse transfer capacitance (max value)
     Gate leakage current
     Drain cutoff current

(b) The 3N140:
     DC input resistance
     Gate leakage current (max)
     I_{DSS} (min, typ, and max)
     Gate-to-source cutoff voltage

(c) The 2N4416:
     Gate leakage current (max)
     $V_{GS(OFF)}$
     I_{DSS} (min, typ, and max)
     C_{iss} (max)

10-7. A FET is operated as an RC-coupled amplifier. Draw the equivalent circuit, designating each part of the circuit by its customary notation. Show the resistor in the drain circuit, the coupling capacitor, and the load.

10–8. The device and circuit values used in Problem 10-7 are:

$$r_d = 20 \text{ kilohms}$$
$$g_m = 5000 \text{ } \mu\text{mhos}$$
$$R_d = 10 \text{ kilohms}$$
$$R_L = 15 \text{ kilohms}$$
$$V_g = 0.1 \text{ v rms}$$

    (a) Mark these values on the equivalent circuit in the appropriate places. In the case of the current generator, compute its value and mark it on the generator, using the correct unit.

    (b) Calculate the voltage gain.

10–9. Use Appendix B to obtain the typical forward transconductance and the output resistance of the 3N139 under the indicated conditions.

    (a) $V_{DS} = 15$ v, $R_s = 0$, $f = 1$ kHz (This is a zero gate-bias condition: note the test circuit shown in the specification sheet.)

    (b) $V_{DD} = 15$ v, $R_s = 360$ ohms, $f = 1$ kHz. (This is a specified gate-bias condition. Depletion bias is produced by R_s as discussed in Section 10.10.)

10–10. Obtain the following information:

    (a) G_{fs} of the 3N138 with $V_{GS} = 0$, $V_{DS} = 12$ v.

    (b) Forward transconductance of the 2N4416 at $V_{DS} = 15$v, $V_{GS} = 0$, $f = 1$ kHz.

    (c) Output resistance of the 2N4416 at $V_{DS} = 15$ v, $V_{GS} = 0$, $f = 1$ kHz.

10–11. A FET is operated so that its $g_{fs} = 10,000$ μmhos, and $r_d = 5$ kilohms. The amplifier circuit is as shown here. (C_s is a perfect bypass at signal frequency, so that the source is effectively connected to ground for signals.) What is the gain?

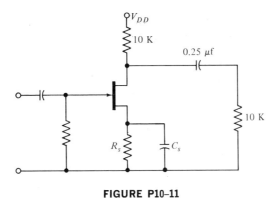

FIGURE P10–11

10–12. A 3N139 is operated in a circuit similar to that used in Problem 10–11. The drain-to-ground voltage is 15 v, $R_s = 360$ ohms, and $f = 1$ kHz. The effective signal load resistance is 20 kilohms. What is the gain?

10–13. A 3N139 is operated at $V_{DN} = 15$ v; $R_s = 360$ ohms, and the effective signal load resistance is 1 kilohm. Find the gain by the exact Equation (10–3) and by the approximation Equation (10–4) and compare them.

10–14. Notice that Equation (10–3) involves the parallel combination of r_d and R_L while the approximation Equation (10–4) uses only R_L. From your knowledge of parallel resistance combinations, approximately what is the maximum permissible size of R_L relative to r_d, if Equation (10–4) is to be accurate within 10 percent?

10–15. Brief listings of electrical characteristics may often be used for making initial estimates of performance. The listing of FET characteristics in Appendix B shows g_{fs} figures but does not show r_d. On the assumption that $R_L \ll r_d$, calculate the expected approximate gain for the following FET types, used in a circuit in which the effective load is 5000 ohms:

$$3N128$$
$$3N139$$
$$3N140$$

10–16. Indicate the required drain supply polarities for each of the following devices, assuming conventional amplifier operation.

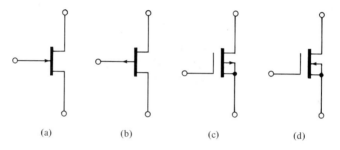

(a)   (b)   (c)   (d)

FIGURE P10–16

10–17. Identify the following FET types as to JFET or IGFET, p-channel or n-channel, and enhancement or depletion. Assume that the bias polarities shown are for conventional amplifier operation.

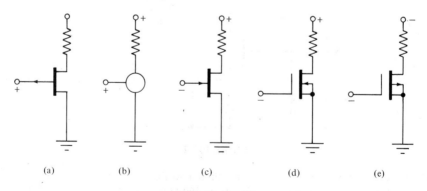

(a)   (b)   (c)   (d)   (e)

FIGURE P10–17

10–18. If possible, where should the following FET be biased in order to minimize temperature effects?

10–19. In the circuit of Figure 10–16(b); $R_s = 270$ ohms, and $I_D = 3$ ma. What is the effective gate bias, V_{GS}? Is this enhancement or depletion bias?

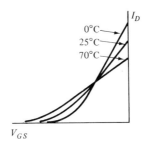

FIGURE P10-18

10-20. In the circuit of Figure 10-15(b); $V_{DD} = 20$ v, $R_1 = 6$ megohms, and $R_2 = 4$ megohms. What is the effective gate bias, V_{GS}?

10-21. In a circuit of the general type shown in Figure 10-17, $R_1 = 27$ megohms; $R_2 = 1.0$ megohm; $R_s = 360$ ohms; $I_D = 4.5$ ma, and $V_{DD} = 30$ v. What is the effective gate bias V_{GS}? Is this enhancement or depletion bias?

10-22. In a circuit of the type shown in Figure 10-17, $R_1 = 1.8$ megohms; $R_2 = 1.2$ megohms, and the rest of the values are as given in Problem 10-21. What is the gate bias V_{GS}? Is this enhancement or depletion bias?

10-23. An *n*-channel FET is operated in the depletion mode in the circuit of Figure 10-16(b). The quiescent drain current is 5 ma. The quiescent gate-to-source bias is -0.5 v. What value of source resistor R_s is being used?

10-24. The 3N138 is to be used in the circuit of Figure 10-16(b) with the following component values:

$$V_{DD} = 30 \text{ v}$$
$$R_d = 2 \text{ kilohms}$$
$$R_g = 1 \text{ megohm}$$
$$V_{GS} = -1 \text{ v}$$

Draw the dc load line; locate the operating point, and calculate the value of R_s needed to provide this operating point.

10-25. What is the advantage of circuit (a) over (b) in addition to its use of only one power supply?

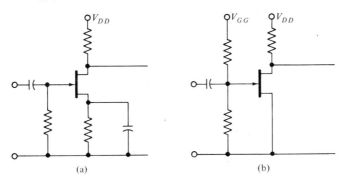

(a)   (b)

FIGURE P10-25

10–26. What is the advantage of circuit (a) over circuit (b)?

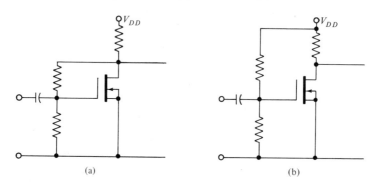

(a)   (b)

FIGURE P10–26

10–27. Identify and explain the method(s) of bias stabilizing used in these circuits.

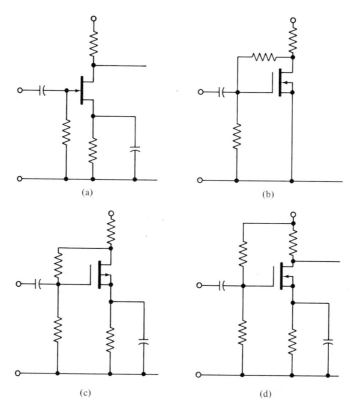

(a)   (b)

(c)   (d)

FIGURE P10–27

10–28. A certain depletion transistor type when tested under expected extremes of operating temperature, showed maximum and minimum current transfer curves as given below. The units tested included the highest current and lowest current units from a large quantity, so that it is hoped that these curves include the maximum unit-to-unit variations that may be expected. A source resistor is to be chosen to provide bias stabilizing that will keep the drain current within the limits of 2 to 7 ma. If a circuit such as that in Figure 10–16(b) is to be used, what should the value of R_s be?

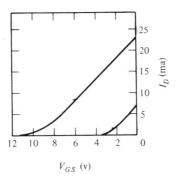

V_{GS} (v)

FIGURE P10-28

10–29. If the drain current is to be kept within the limits of 4 to 7 ma, what value of R_s will be required? How much enhancement bias will be required to offset the additional depletion bias produced by this value of R_s? Draw a circuit diagram illustrating the type of circuit that will be needed.

10–30. Identify the output quantity that is being sampled in the following feedback amplifier circuits and find the value of the feedback factor β.

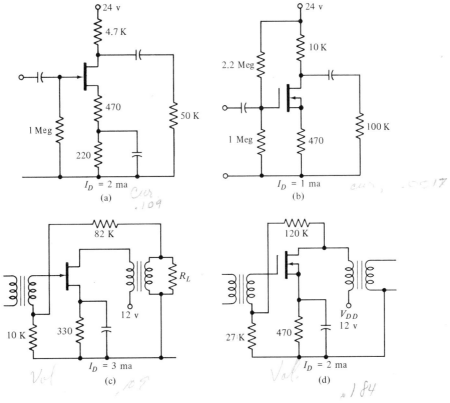

FIGURE P10-30

10–31. Assuming that the gain without feedback is 30 in each of the circuits in 10–30 above, what is the gain with feedback?

10–32. Calculate the value of the bias voltage V_{GS} in each of the circuits of Problem 10–30, and state whether it is depletion or enhancement.

10–33. Calculate the output resistance of circuits (a) and (b) of Problem 10–30, if $r_d = 10$ kilohms in each case.

10–34. In the circuit of Figure 10–27, what is the gain when the values are:

$$A_v = .732$$

$$R_L = 1000 \text{ ohms}$$
$$r_d = 10,000 \text{ ohms}$$
$$g_m = 3000 \ \mu\text{mhos}$$

10–35. In a source-follower circuit, the effective load is 10,000 ohms; $r_d = 20,000$ ohms, and $g_m = 7000 \ \mu\text{mhos}$. What is the gain?   .98

10–36. What is the source resistance of the circuit of Problem 10–34? $R_s = 323 \Omega$

10–37. What is the source resistance of the circuit of Problem 10–35? 142Ω

10–38. Calculate the signal input resistance of the following stages:

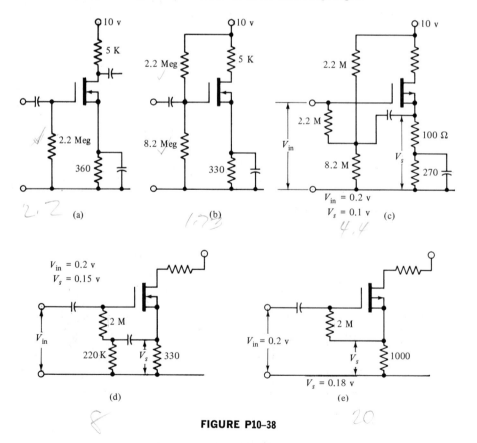

FIGURE P10–38

10–39. Assume that a source-follower circuit has the gate resistor R_g connected from the gate directly to the source (as in circuit (e) of Problem 10–38). Let $R_g = 2.2$ megohms.

(a) If the gain of the source follower is 0.8, what is the input resistance?

(b) If the gain of the source follower is 0.98, what is the input resistance?

REFERENCES

Crawford, Robert H., *MOSFET in Circuit Design*. New York: McGraw-Hill Book Company, 1967.

Griswold, D. M., *RCA Insulated-Gate MOS Field-Effect Transistors*. RCA Technical Publication ST-2990A.

Kane, James F. and Donald L. Wollesen, *Field Effect Transistors in Theory and Practice*. Motorola Application Note AN-211.

Millman, Jacob and Christos C. Halkias, *Electronic Devices and Circuits*. New York: McGraw-Hill Book Company, 1967.

Todd, Carl David, *Junction Field-Effect Transistors*. New York: John Wiley & Sons, Inc., 1968.

Wallmark, J. Torkel and Harwick Johnson, eds., *Field-Effect Transistors*. Englewood Cliffs, New Jersey: Prentice-Hall, Inc., 1966.

CHAPTER 11

Vacuum Tubes

11.1 Introduction

As a result of the fundamental advantages of the transistor and the integrated circuit, only a small portion of the design and development work being done today in electronics is concerned with vacuum tube amplifiers. However, there is tube equipment still operating in the field. In addition, vacuum tubes are still important in certain applications, such as high-frequency high power amplifiers. Consequently, a familiarity with the principles of vacuum tube amplifiers is still important to the technician and the engineer.

11.2 Construction and Characteristics of Vacuum Tubes

The operation of vacuum tubes depends on a stream of electrons in an evacuated space. This stream or flow of electrons can be adjusted and controlled by potentials applied to electrodes placed in the region of flow to alter the electric field conditions in the region. The flow can be increased or decreased by the voltages applied to particular electrodes. As a result, just as in the transistor, an applied signal voltage can cause variations in the current, and thereby cause larger voltage variations across a load resistance in series with the device. In the transistor it is the base region and the back-biased collector-base junction which prevent the high voltage output from interfering with the low voltage output. In the vacuum tube it is the fact that the electrode connected to the input is much closer to the source of electrons than the electrode connected to the input, so that the output electrode has much less control on the electron flow than the input electrode.

Construction of the Triode

The simplest tube capable of amplification is the triode. This consists of a *cathode* which emits electrons when heated, a *control grid* made of a grid-work or open spiral of wire usually surrounding the cathode and quite close to it, and an *anode*, at a greater distance from the cathode, to collect the electrons. All of this is usually mounted within a glass or metal container from which the air has been evacuated to prevent the air molecules from interfering with the electron flow and to prevent the heated cathode from burning up due to the presence of oxygen.

The anode is placed at a positive potential relative to the cathode, so that the electric field in the intervening space will attract the electrons from the cathode to the anode. The control grid is usually at a potential which is somewhat negative relative to the cathode. The cathode is heated by an electric current provided by a separate *heater supply* or *filament supply*. Figure 11–1(a) illustrates one common form of the triode.

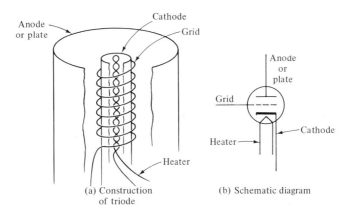

FIGURE 11-1
Construction and symbol of vacuum triode

The construction diagram in this figure shows a cylindrical cathode and anode, cut open to reveal the interior. Inside the cathode is a spiral heater wire or filament. The cathode is a cylinder of material specifically chosen for efficient emission of electrons and long life. Surrounding the cathode is the spiral control grid, and outside of this at a much greater distance is the anode, or plate. In part (b) of the figure the standard schematic diagram symbol of the triode is illustrated. The heater or filament is often omitted from this schematic symbol.

Function of the Control Grid

Due to the large spacing between the wires of the control grid, electrons can pass through the grid structure if its potential is not made too negative. The negative voltage on the grid does tend to cause those electrons which might otherwise hit the grid wires, to veer around them so that there is practically no current flow to the grid. In addition, the grid voltage has sufficient effect on the electric field between the grid wires, to counteract some of the field set up

by the positive plate. The strength of the electric field which accelerates the
electrons toward the plate, therefore, is a function of both the plate voltage
and the grid voltage. Consequently, the magnitude of the plate current flow is
dependent upon both voltages.

The Basic Triode Circuit

Figure 11–2 shows the triode and a load resistance connected to dc operating voltages so that the anode is positive to the cathode, and the control grid is
negative to the cathode. With the cathode heated to emission temperature by

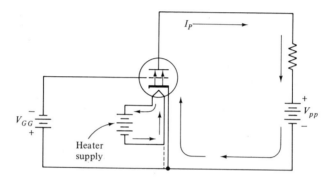

FIGURE 11–2
Triode tube with plate-to-cathode, grid-to-cathode, and heater
supply voltages

the heater or filament, the plate connected to a positive potential, and the grid
not too negative, electrons will flow as indicated by the arrows, from the
cathode to the plate and from there to the positive terminal of the plate
supply voltage V_{PP}. From the negative terminal of V_{PP} electrons flow to the
cathode to replace those which were emitted by the cathode. Because of the
negative potential of the grid wires, as mentioned above, very few of the electrons from the cathode hit the grid, so that there is essentially no grid current.
The heater current flow is separate from the plate current flow although the
heater circuit is usually "grounded" to the same common line as the amplifier,
as shown by the dashed-line connection, in order to minimize the effects of
stray electric fields.

In many types of low- and medium-power equipment the heater supply is a
low-voltage winding on the main power transformer; in transformerless equipment a number of tube heaters may be operated in series, connected directly
to the 117 v, 60-Hz power input. In high-power equipment, the tube heaters
are often fed from a separate power supply. Small receiving-type tubes intended for heater operation from a low-voltage winding are very commonly
designed for 6.3 or 12.6 v (rms), but tubes are also available with heater voltages ranging from less than 2 to 117 v.

Output Characteristics of the Triode Tube

The output characteristics of a typical small triode are shown in Figure 11–3. Note the plate-to-cathode voltage, which goes to much higher values than in most transistors. (High-power vacuum tubes use even higher plate voltages, up to tens of kv, and have dissipation ratings up to hundreds of kw.)

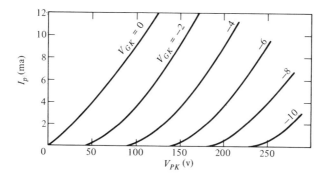

FIGURE 11–3
Typical triode characteristics

The vacuum triode curves clearly show the dependence of the plate current I_P upon both the plate voltage and the grid voltage. For example, at $V_{PK} = 150$ v and $V_{GK} = -4$ v, I_P is approximately 3.5 ma. Increasing V_{PK} to 200 v without changing V_{GK} causes I_P to increase to about 9 ma. If, instead of increasing V_{PK}, the grid voltage is changed from -4 to -2 while V_{PK} is kept at 150, the plate current increases from 3.5 ma to about 9 ma. In other words, a 2 v change on the grid causes about the same magnitude of change in plate current as a 50 v change at the plate.

Construction and Characteristics of Tetrodes

The capacitance existing between the control grid and the plate in the triode is great enough to act as a severe limitation on high-frequency operation. The addition of another grid between the control grid and the plate serves to reduce this capacitance by acting as a shield or screen between the control grid and the plate. This second grid, known as a screen grid, is operated at a relatively high positive dc voltage — usually equal to or less than the plate voltage — but is grounded for ac by a large capacitor. Thus the control-grid-to-plate capacitance of the triode is replaced by capacitance from the control grid to the screen (which is ac grounded) and from the plate to the screen. The result is a great reduction in Miller effect capacitance at the input to tube amplifiers, and less feedback from output to input.

In normal operation, due to its positive potential, the screen grid intercepts a portion of the current flowing from the cathode toward the plate. The screen grid current is often in the range of 25 to 40 percent of the plate current. The schematic symbol of the tetrode is shown in Figure 11–4(a), and the basic circuit showing dc voltages and currents is illustrated in (b).

In addition to reducing the control-grid-to-plate capacitance, the shielding effect of the screen grid prevents the plate from having as much effect on the

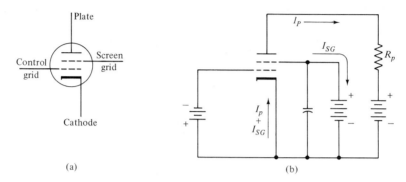

FIGURE 11-4
Tetrode symbol

plate current as it does in the triode. In other words, an even greater increment of plate voltage is required to cause a given change of plate current. This is revealed in the output characteristics of the tetrode shown in Figure 11–5. Note

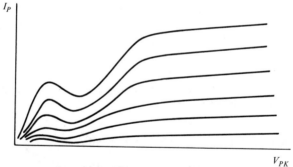

FIGURE 11-5
Static characteristics of tetrode vacuum tube

the almost horizontal region of the curves. In this region the plate voltage has very little effect on the plate current.

The large dip in the curves is caused by *secondary emission* of electrons from the plate. When the electrons from the cathode strike the plate with sufficient velocity, they cause electrons to be emitted by the plate. Many of these secondary electrons are collected by the screen grid due to its positive voltage. At higher plate voltages, secondary emission still occurs, but the plate voltage is high enough to attract them back to the plate before they can reach the screen.

The Pentode Vacuum Tube

The large dip in the tetrode curves severely limits the operating voltage range. To eliminate this effect, another grid was added, between the screen and the plate. This grid, called the *suppressor*, is generally operated at the same potential as the cathode. This voltage is low enough to provide a barrier to the secondary electrons being emitted by the plate. In other words they are repelled back to the plate instead of being collected by either the screen or the suppressor. It is not a great enough barrier to stop the electrons coming from the cathode since these are traveling at a much higher velocity.

The presence of the suppressor grid effectively eliminates the dip of the tetrode curves, resulting in characteristics such as those illustrated in Figure 11–6. These curves are quite similar in general shape to those of the bipolar transistor and the FET.

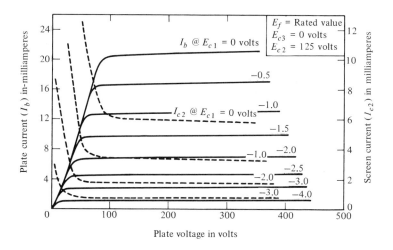

FIGURE 11–6
Typical pentode output characteristics

Amplifying Action of the Vacuum Tube

A simple triode amplifier circuit is shown in Figure 11–7(a). Typical output curves are given in (b). The load line shown on the curves was drawn in the usual way, extending from V_{PP} on the voltage axis to $I = V_{PP}/R_p$ on the cur-

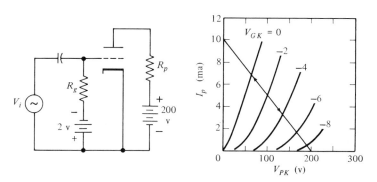

FIGURE 11–7
Amplifier circuit and output curves

rent axis. The operating point at the intersection of the load line and the 2-v grid bias curve is set by the 2-v bias supply shown in (a). If the applied input signal V_i has a peak amplitude of 2 v, it will cause the grid to rise to a peak value of zero volts in one direction, and fall to a peak value of -4 v in the other direction, as shown by the arrowheads on the load line. Projecting from these two extreme points downward to the plate voltage axis shows that this grid voltage excursion causes the plate voltage to swing downward to about 65 v and upward to about 135 v. The voltage gain therefore is

$$A_v = \frac{\Delta V_o}{\Delta V_i} \cong \frac{65 - 135}{0 - (-4)}$$

$$A_v = -\frac{70}{4} \cong -17.5$$

Note that when the grid voltage is at its *maximum* value (zero), the plate voltage is at its *minimum* value (65). Similarly, when the grid voltage is at its minimum peak, the plate is at its maximum peak. This circuit provides 180° phase inversion just as the common-emitter and the common-source circuits do. The tube circuit of this type, in which the cathode is the grounded, or common, element is known as a grounded-cathode or common-cathode amplifier.

11.3 DC Circuits and Graphical Analysis

A typical common-cathode triode amplifier is illustrated in Figure 11–8. The arrangement is the same as that of an *n*-channel depletion-mode FET in the common-source circuit, since tubes use positive plate voltages and negative

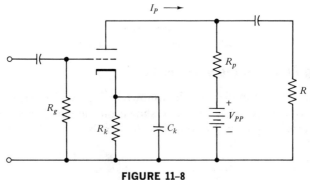

FIGURE 11–8
Basic RC-coupled triode amplifier

grid voltages. The grid is shown connected to ground through R_g. Since there is no grid current, the dc voltage across R_g is zero, so the grid is at ground potential. But the cathode is at a positive voltage relative to ground as a result of the voltage drop caused by the plate current I_P flowing in the cathode resistor R_k. Consequently, the grid, at ground potential, is negative relative to the cathode.

The rest of the circuit is familiar, being of the same form as transistor output circuits. The dc plate current flows through R_p to the positive terminal of the supply voltage V_{PP}, and from the negative terminal of V_{PP} through R_k to the cathode. The ac component of plate current divides up between R_p and R and, assuming that C_k is a good bypass, then flows through C_k to the cathode.

Figure 11–9 gives the basic circuit of an *RC*-coupled pentode amplifier.

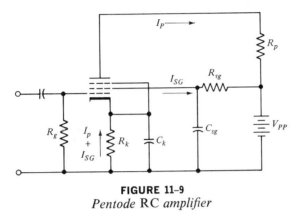

FIGURE 11–9
Pentode RC amplifier

Note that the suppressor grid is connected directly to the cathode. In some tubes this connection is made internally. The screen grid is connected to the plate supply voltage through the resistor R_{sg}, and the capacitor C_{sg} is connected from the screen to ground to provide the ac grounding of the screen.

The resistor R_{sg} is a voltage-dropping resistor which permits obtaining the desired dc operating voltage for the screen from the same supply voltage as the plate. The value of this resistor is determined by the voltage V_{PP}, the required screen grid voltage V_{SG}, and the screen grid current at the desired operating point. The following example illustrates the method.

Example 11–1

A 6AU6A pentode is to be operated in a *RC*-coupled circuit with a plate voltage of 150 v and a screen grid voltage of 150 v. The control-grid-to-cathode bias is to be -1.0 v. Under these conditions, according to the manufacturer's data, the plate current is 10.6 ma, and the screen grid current is 4.3 ma. The plate supply voltage is 250 v. Figure 11–10 shows the circuit; the voltages and currents are indicated on the diagram.

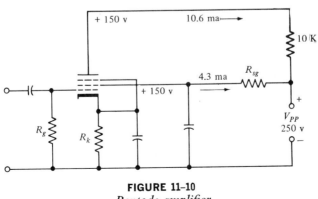

FIGURE 11–10
Pentode amplifier

The voltage drop across R_{sg} is $V_{PP} - V_{SG} = 250 - 150 = 100$ v. Since the current through R_{sg} is the 4.3 ma screen grid current, the required value of the screen dropping resistor is

$$R_{sg} = \frac{V_{PP} - V_{SG}}{I_{SG}}$$

$$R_{sg} = \frac{250 - 150}{(0.0043)} = \left(\frac{100}{4.3}\right)(10^3)$$

$$R_{sg} \cong 23.2 \text{ kilohms}$$

A standard value of 22 kilohms would probably be used.

Graphical Analysis of Triode Circuits

Construction of the load line on the output characteristics is the same for tubes as for transistors. Calculations related to finding the operating point are different for tubes, however, since their bias methods differ. Figure 11–11

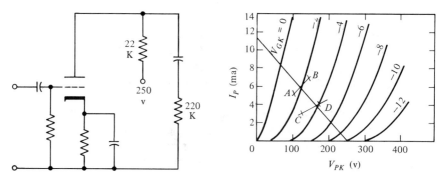

FIGURE 11–11
Triode circuit and output curves of tube being used

shows a typical triode circuit and the output characteristics of the tube used in the circuit. The dc load line extends from V_{PP}, or 250 v, on the voltage axis, to $I_P = V_{PP}/R_p = 250/22,000 \cong 11.37$ ma on the current axis.

Choice of Cathode Resistor Value

If this circuit were being designed, and the necessary value of R_k for a grid-cathode bias of -2 v were needed, the procedure would be as follows. At the intersection of the -2 v bias line with the load line, the plate current value is noted. In this example $I_P \cong 5.7$ ma at this operating point. Then, since

$$V_{GK} = |I_P R_k| \tag{11–1}$$

we have
$$R_k = \left|\frac{V_{GK}}{I_P}\right| = \frac{2}{0.0057}$$

$$R_k \cong 351 \text{ ohms}$$

For most practical cases a standard value of 330 ohms would probably be used.

Finding the Operating Point in an Existing Circuit

It is sometimes required to analyze a circuit that is already in existence. Perhaps the most common instance of this in engineering work is verifying the acceptability of the choice of a nearest standard value instead of the exact value, as above, or the evaluation of the effect of component tolerances or variations upon circuit performance.

In the example above, the value of R_k has now been chosen, and it is necessary to find out whether the resulting operating point is near enough to the original design objective. The procedure in such a case is to arbitrarily pick several values of I_P and, using the chosen value of R_k, calculate the bias that would result from each value of I_P. Each point corresponding to each plate current value and its associated bias voltage is then plotted on the output characteristics, and the points joined by a line. The intersection of this line with the load line is the operating point.

Example 11–2

In verifying the above choice of $R_k = 330$ ohms, we would multiply several arbitrarily chosen values of I_P by 330, as follows:

I_P (ma)	$V_{GK} = -I_P R_k$ (v)
5	−1.65
7	−2.31

These two points ($V_{GK} = -1.65$ v, $I_P = 5$ ma, and $V_{GK} = -2.3$ v, $I_P = 7$ ma) have been plotted in Figure 11–11, interpolating bias voltage values between the given bias curves whenever necessary. The points are shown in the figure as A and B respectively. Note that the bias resulting from the use of 330 ohms is only slightly less than the originally desired −2 v.

Example 11–3

An identical circuit is used except that R_k is 1000 ohms. Locate the operating point.

I_P (ma)	$V_{GK} = -I_P R_k$ (v)
3	3
4	4

These points are shown in Figure 11–11 as C and D, and the bias line joining the two points has been drawn. The bias resulting from the use of 1000 ohms for R_k is slightly less than 4 v. The construction of the ac load line corresponding to the ac load of 22,000 ∥ 220,000 ohms follows the same methods as used previously.

Graphical Analysis of Pentode Circuits

Figure 11–12 shows a pentode RC-coupled amplifier using a 6CB6A tube. The output curves for this tube are also shown. The dc load line is shown on the figure. If it were necessary to choose the value of cathode resistor to produce a

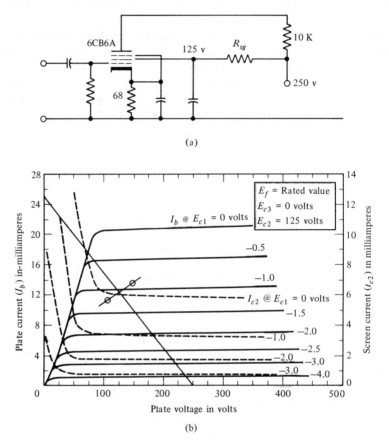

(a)

(b)

FIGURE 11–12

Pentode circuit and output curves

given bias voltage, the method would be the same as with the triode, except that the screen current flowing in R_k would have to be included in the bias calculation:

$$R_k = \left| \frac{V_{GK}}{I_P + I_{SG}} \right| \tag{11–2}$$

The values of I_P and I_{SG} for the desired operating point would be obtained from the manufacturer's information. Data sheets often list such values for one or two recommended operating points. If a different operating point is required, values must be taken from the characteristic curves. Often on these curves the screen grid current is shown only for a grid bias of zero volts. However, screen current is approximately proportional to plate current, so that if it is known at $V_{GK} = 0$, it can be found for other bias values. That is, I_{SG} will have the same ratio to I_P at other bias values as it does at zero bias, if the plate and screen voltages are not changed much.

Finding the dc Operating Point in a Pentode Circuit

As in the case of the triode, an arbitrary choice of values is made for the current in R_k, so that several values of $V_{GK} = -I_k R_k$ can be calculated and the bias line drawn. But with the pentode, the screen current must be included. Also, since the plate current horizontal lines and the grid voltage curves are nearly parallel, graphically locating their intersection is very inaccurate. Instead of using I_P and V_{GK}, V_{PK} and V_{GK} can be used, since we have

$$V_{PP} = V_{PK} + I_P R_c + (I_P + I_{SG})R_k$$
$$V_{PP} \cong V_{PK} + I_P R_C$$
$$V_{PK} \cong V_{PP} - I_P R_C$$

Thus, V_{GK} and V_{PK}, both dependent upon I_P, can be used to plot points for the bias line.

Example 11–4

The operating point of the circuit of Figure 11–12 is to be obtained. The 6CB6A curves show that $I_{SG} \cong 0.28\ I_P$. Arbitrary values of I_P will be chosen, corresponding values of I_{SG} calculated, and from this information, values of V_{GK} will be obtained. Values of V_{PK} will be obtained from $V_{PK} \cong V_{PP} - I_P R_c$ (or directly from the load line).

TABLE 11–1

I_P (ma)	I_{SG} (ma)	$V_{GK} = -I_k R_k$ (v)	$V_{PK} = V_{PP} - I_P R_c$ (v)
10	2.8	−0.87	150
14	3.9	−1.22	110

When the two points ($V_{GK} = -0.87$, $V_{PK} = 150$; and $V_{GK} = -1.22$ and $V_{PK} = 110$) are plotted and connected by a line as in Figure 11–12, the intersection of this bias line with the load line shows that the operating point is at $V_{GK} \cong -1.1$ v, $V_{PK} \cong 125$ v, $I_P \cong 12.1$ ma.

11.4   Tube Equivalent Circuits and Gain Equations

The triode and the pentode differ strikingly in their output characteristics. The pentode output current is almost constant throughout much of its range, so that the curves in this region resemble the output characteristic of a constant current generator. The pentode curves, in other words, are much like those of the bipolar transistor and the FET. The triode curves, being more vertical than horizontal, could be said to resemble the output characteristics of a constant voltage generator. For this reason the two devices are represented by different equivalent circuits.

The Triode Equivalent Circuit

The voltage-generator form of equivalent circuit, which is used to represent the triode tube amplifier at low frequencies, is pictured in Figure 11–13. The input portion of this equivalent is the same form as in the FET equivalent

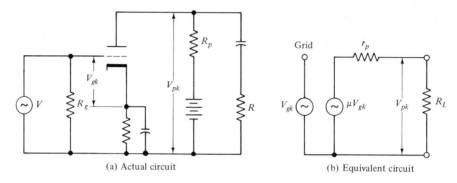

(a) Actual circuit   (b) Equivalent circuit

FIGURE 11–13
Actual and equivalent circuits of triode tube amplifier

because the vacuum tube, like the FET, is an electric-field operated device. The grid is well isolated from the rest of the tube at low frequencies, drawing negligible current as far as conventional amplifier use is concerned, if it is maintained negative with respect to the cathode.

The output portion is a constant voltage generator having the value μV_{gk}, in series with an output resistance r_p. The voltage μV_{GK} represents the control that the input voltage has on the output voltage, as revealed in the output curves. It expresses the fact that the open-circuit output voltage is μ times the voltage V_{GK}. Note, for example, in Figure 11–11, that for any given value of I_P, a small change in V_{GK} is accompanied by an appreciable change in V_{PK}.

The parameter μ is called the *amplification factor*, and is defined by

$$\mu = \frac{\Delta V_{PK}}{\Delta V_{GK}}\bigg|_{\Delta I_P = 0} \tag{11–3}$$

It can be measured in a test circuit as illustrated in Figure 11–14(a), by setting V_{GK} and V_{PK} to the values desired, noting the value of I_P, then changing V_{GK}. This will cause a change in I_P. If then V_{PK} is readjusted so as to restore I_P to its original value (thus complying with the requirement that $\Delta I_P = 0$), the change in V_{PK} divided by the change in V_{GK} will be the value of μ. μ can also be determined graphically by drawing a horizontal line (for $\Delta I_P = 0$) through the desired operating point and noting the change in V_{PK} corresponding to a given small change in V_{GK} along this line.

The resistance r_p represents the regulation of the output — the decrease in output that occurs as it is loaded more heavily. Load lines for several values of load resistance, drawn on the output curves, show that for a given magnitude

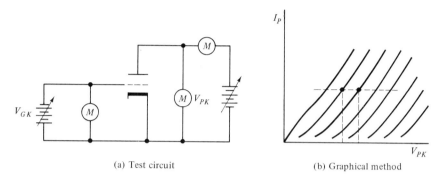

(a) Test circuit   (b) Graphical method

FIGURE 11–14
Two basic methods of determining the μ of a tube

of input signal voltage, the output signal voltage decreases as the load resistance is made smaller.

The parameter r_p is called the *plate resistance*, and is defined by

$$r_p = \frac{\Delta V_{PK}}{\Delta I_P}\bigg|_{\Delta V_{GK} = 0} \tag{11-4}$$

The plate resistance may similarly be measured in a test circuit or obtained graphically from the output curves for the tube. The gain equation for the triode may be obtained from the equivalent circuit, and is

$$A_v = \frac{V_{pk}}{V_{gk}} = \frac{\mu R_L}{r_p + R_L} \tag{11-5}$$

Typical values of r_p for triodes may range from 500 to 100,000 ohms. Typical values of μ may range from 5 to 100.

The Pentode Equivalent Circuit

The pentode is usually represented by the current-generator form of equivalent circuit as shown in Figure 11–15. This is the same form as used for the FET. The current generator $g_m V_{gk}$ is used to represent the control that the input voltage has over the output current, as revealed in the output curves. The parameter g_m is called the transconductance or mutual conductance; it is defined by

$$g_m = \frac{\Delta I_P}{\Delta V_{GK}}\bigg|_{\Delta V_{PK} = 0} \tag{11-6}$$

This is the same as Equation (10–2) for the FET, except for the subscripts identifying the currents and voltages.

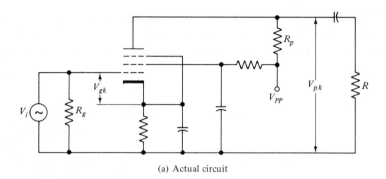

(a) Actual circuit

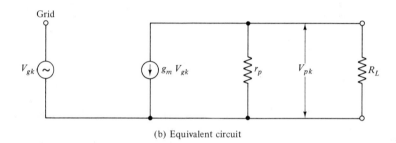

(b) Equivalent circuit

FIGURE 11-15
Actual and equivalent circuits for pentode amplifier

The resistance r_p represents the effect of the pentode's departure from perfect constant current characteristics. It serves the same purpose as $1/h_{oe}$ in the bipolar transistor equivalent, and r_d in the FET equivalent. It is defined by

$$r_p = \frac{\Delta V_{PK}}{\Delta I_P}\bigg|_{\Delta V_{GK} = 0} \tag{11-7}$$

The pentode's voltage gain equation is obtained from the equivalent circuit as follows. The output signal voltage is produced by the current $g_m V_{gk}$ flowing through the resistance of r_p and R_L in parallel, or

$$V_{pk} = g_m V_{gk}\left(\frac{r_p R_L}{r_p + R_L}\right)$$

The voltage gain therefore is

$$A_v = \frac{V_{pk}}{V_{gk}} = g_m\left(\frac{r_p R_L}{r_p + R_L}\right) \tag{11-8}$$

and when $R_L \ll r_p$, as often happens with pentodes, this simplifies to the very convenient approximation

$$A_v \cong g_m R_L \tag{11-9}$$

Typical values of g_m for small pentodes are in the range of 1000 to 10,000 μmhos. Typical values of r_p are in the range of 100 kilohms to 1 megohm.

Other Parameters for the Triode and Pentode

Although the Thevenin (voltage generator) form of equivalent is most commonly used to represent the triode, it is perfectly possible to use the Norton (current generator) form. Similarly, the voltage generator equivalent may be used for the pentode, although the current generator form is usually more convenient. The three parameters are related according to

$$\mu = r_p g_m \qquad\qquad (11\text{--}10)$$

PROBLEMS

11-1. A triode vacuum tube is to be operated in a circuit of the type shown in Figure 11-8. Load line construction shows that at a grid-cathode bias of -1 v the plate current is 10 ma. What value of cathode resistor R_k will be required to provide this bias?

11-2. A triode circuit is being checked. The dc voltage from cathode to ground is 0.34 v. The cathode resistor size is 68 ohms. What is the plate current?

11-3. Find the approximate operating point that a 560 ohm cathode resistor would produce in the circuit of Figure 11-11.

11-4. A pentode vacuum tube is to be operated in a circuit of the type illustrated in Figure 11-10. The following values apply:

$$V_{PP} = 300 \text{ v}$$
$$R_p = 4.7 \text{ kilohms}$$
$$R_k = 68 \text{ ohms}$$
$$I_P = 10 \text{ ma}$$
$$I_{SG} = 3 \text{ ma}$$

(a) What is the quiescent plate voltage, V_{PK}?

(b) What is the grid-cathode bias, V_{GK}?

(c) If the screen voltage is to be 150 v, what value of screen dropping resistor will be required?

11-5. Using the 6J6-A output curves in Appendix B, graphically calculate the μ and r_p in the vicinity of $V_{GK} = -2$ v, $I_p = 10$ ma.

11-6. Using the curves in Appendix B, graphically calculate the approximate values of g_m and r_p for the 6CB6-A pentode, in the vicinity of a grid bias of zero to -1 v and a plate voltage of 200 v.

11-7. Graphically find the value of g_m for the 6J6-A in the vicinity of $V_{GK} = -2$ v, $I_p = 10$ ma.

11-8. Graphically try to calculate the μ of the 6CB6-A in the vicinity of $V_{GK} = -1$ v. Discuss your difficulties.

11–9. A triode tube is used in a circuit of the type shown in Figure 11–13. When the following values apply, what is the gain of this amplifier?

$$\mu = 100$$
$$r_p = 70 \text{ kilohms}$$
$$R_p = 220 \text{ kilohms}$$
$$R = 1 \text{ megohm}$$

11–10. A triode tube is used in the circuit of Figure 11–13. When the following values apply, what is the gain?

$$\mu = 20$$
$$r_p = 7000 \text{ ohms}$$
$$R_p = 20 \text{ kilohms}$$
$$R = 470 \text{ kilohms}$$

11–11. The following circuit is a two-stage amplifier. The same tube is used for both stages. Its parameters are:

$$\mu = 50$$
$$r_p = 10 \text{ kilohms}$$

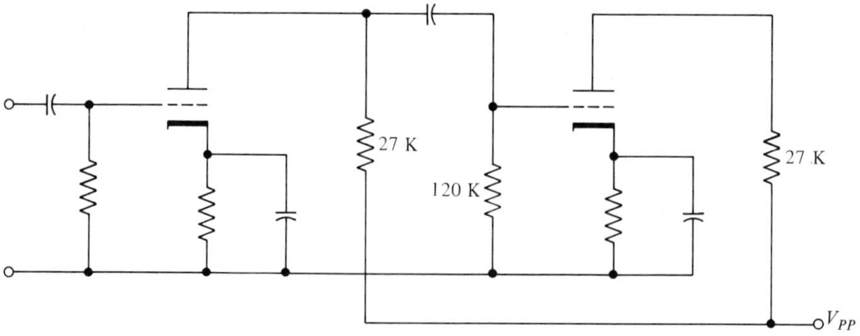

FIGURE P11–11

Find the gain of each stage and the overall gain. Assuming a 50-mv peak input to the first stage, what is the output signal voltage amplitude?

11–12. A pentode is to be used in a transformer-coupled circuit. The effective load presented to the tube by the transformer is 15 kilohms. What is the voltage gain when the tube parameters are:

$$g_m = 4000 \text{ } \mu\text{mhos}$$
$$r_p = 30 \text{ kilohms}$$

11–13. A pentode is to be used in the circuit of Figure 11–15(a). The following values apply:

$$g_m = 7000 \text{ } \mu\text{mhos}$$
$$r_p = 250 \text{ kilohms}$$
$$R_p = 10 \text{ kilohms}$$
$$R = 470 \text{ kilohms}$$

(a) Calculate the gain using the exact equation.

(b) Calculate the gain using the approximation of Equation (11–9).

11–14. A pentode is to be used in a cascaded amplifier consisting of three identical stages. Two of the stages are shown below. The same tube is used for all stages. The tube parameters are:

$$g_m = 10,000 \ \mu\text{mhos}$$

$$r_p = 300 \ \text{kilohms}$$

Find the individual stage gain and the overall gain for the three stages.

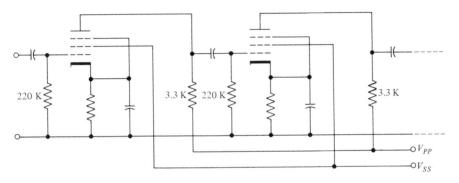

FIGURE P11–14

APPENDIX A

Power Supplies

A.1 Introduction

Electrical power distribution is most commonly done by means of alternating current. This fact permits the use of simple transformers to convert the high voltages needed for efficient long-distance power transmission to the lower voltages needed by users. However, most electronic equipment requires direct current. Although some of this equipment can use batteries, most of the power is more conveniently supplied by converting the alternating current of the power lines to direct current which is then used to operate the electronic circuits.

The most common method of conversion from ac to dc is by the use of diodes. The process is called *rectification* and is illustrated in its simplest form in Figure A–1. In this figure the resistor represents the equipment requiring the dc power. Since current can flow in only one direction through a diode, the presence of this element in series with the load prevents the load current from reversing its direction. Diodes used for this purpose are called *rectifiers*.

Although the rectifier circuit shown does prevent alternation of the load current, the current fluctuates greatly. For most applications a steady dc voltage and current are required, such as would be supplied by a battery. The waveform of Figure A–1 may be changed to a very steady value by the use of suitably designed low-pass filters. Such circuits store energy from the rectifier during the peaks of the input and release it to the load in a smooth flow between peaks.

Transformers in Rectifier Circuits

The available ac power line voltage is usually not the correct value to provide the desired dc voltage. A transformer is therefore often used to step it up or down before rectifying. This is illustrated in Figure A–2.

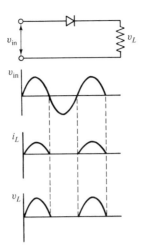

FIGURE A-1
Simple rectifier circuit

A.2 The Half-Wave Rectifier Circuit

This is the name usually given to the circuit illustrated in Figures A–1 and A–2 above. Its unfiltered output simply consists of one-half of the sine wave.

DC and RMS Values of the Half-Wave Rectifier Output

When the input ac waveform is a sine wave, and rectification is achieved by an ideal diode, the unfiltered output in Figure A–1 has an average value equal to the peak value divided by π:

$$V_{\text{ave}} = \frac{1}{\pi}(V_m) \cong 0.318 \ V_m \qquad\qquad \textbf{(A–1)}$$

$$I_{\text{ave}} = \frac{1}{\pi}(I_m) \cong 0.318 \ I_m \qquad\qquad \textbf{(A–2)}$$

The average value is also referred to as the "dc" value.

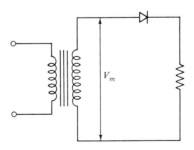

FIGURE A-2
Use of a transformer to provide desired voltage value

The rms value of this waveform is one-half its peak value:

$$V_{\text{rms}} = 0.5\, V_m \tag{A-3}$$

$$I_{\text{rms}} = 0.5\, I_m \tag{A-4}$$

Note that this is not the same as the rms value of the unrectified sine wave, which is 0.707 times the peak value.

A.3 Full-Wave Rectification

Since current only flows during one-half of the input cycle in the half-wave circuit, the average output is low relative to the peak current and voltage. This limits the efficiency and economy of the power supply. To improve this, *full-wave rectification* may be used. In this arrangement, the circuit is made to cause current flow into the output during each half of the input cycle. This is achieved, in effect, by operating two rectifier circuits connected so that their inputs are 180° out-of-phase, and their outputs are connected to the same load. Figure A–3 illustrates the basic idea (although the arrangement shown is not

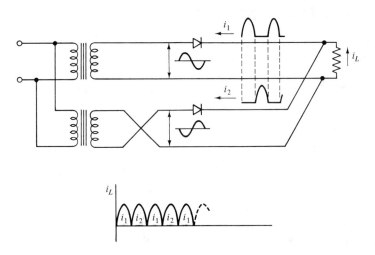

FIGURE A-3
Basic idea of full-wave rectifier principle

normally employed as a practical circuit). The arrows in this figure show the direction of electron flow.

Note that when one of the two out-of-phase inputs is causing current flow through the load, the other is cut off due to its diode, and vice-versa. Both half-waves of current, however, *are in the same direction through the load.* Thus the load current is unidirectional but flowing during both halves of the input cycle.

The Full-Wave Rectifier Using Center-Tapped Transformer

The two out-of-phase inputs are readily achieved in practical circuits by using a single transformer with center-tapped secondary, as shown in Figure A–4. In the center-tapped winding, the potentials across the entire winding at

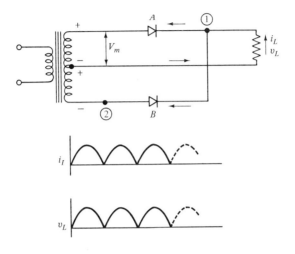

FIGURE A–4
Full-wave center-tapped rectifier circuit

any one instant are such that when one end is positive relative to the center, the other end is negative relative to the center. Thus if one end of the load is connected to the center-tap, the two halves of the winding provide out-of-phase voltages to the rectifiers. Each diode permits current flow only when the end of the transformer to which it is connected is positive relative to the center tap.

DC Value of the Full-Wave Rectifier Output

The average or dc value of voltage and current in the unfiltered full-wave output, assuming sine wave input and an ideal diode, is twice that of the half-wave output:

$$V_{\text{ave}} = \frac{2}{\pi}V_m \cong 0.636\ V_m \qquad \textbf{(A–5)}$$

$$I_{\text{ave}} = \frac{2}{\pi}I_m \cong 0.636\ I_m \qquad \textbf{(A–6)}$$

A.4   The Full-Wave Bridge Circuit

Another arrangement providing full-wave rectified output is the bridge circuit shown in Figure A–5. When input terminal *A* is positive relative to *B*, the current (electron flow) is from *B* through rectifier 1, through the load, and through rectifier 2 to terminal *A*. When the input polarity reverses so that *B* is

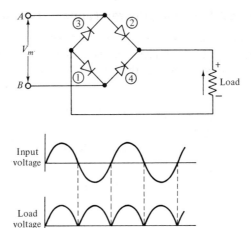

FIGURE A–5
Bridge rectifier circuit

positive, the electron flow is from A through rectifier 3, the load, and rectifier 4 to terminal B. In both cases the direction of flow in the load is the same — in the direction indicated by the arrow. The resulting load voltage polarity is as indicated.

A.5 Ripple in the Rectifier Output

Fourier analysis of the half-wave rectifier output waveform illustrated in Figure A–1 shows it to consist of a sine wave at the frequency of the input, plus sine waves at all even multiples of this frequency. The amplitude of these ripple components is inversely proportional to frequency. The most important components of the ripple are indicated by the following equation for the output current.

$$i = \frac{I_m}{\pi} + \frac{I_m}{2} \sin \omega t - \frac{2I_m}{\pi 3} \cos 2\omega t - \frac{2I_m}{15\pi} \cos 4\omega t - \cdots \qquad \textbf{(A–7)}$$

The first term in this equation represents the dc value of the output, and was given originally in Equation (A–2). The next three terms represent ripple components at frequencies f, $2f$, and $4f$, where f is the frequency of the input to the rectifier. Thus, where the input is a 60-Hz sine wave, the output ripple consists of components at 60 Hz, 120 Hz, 240 Hz and so on, with the amplitude being greatest at 60 Hz. If 400-Hz power input were used, the output ripple would of course be at 400 Hz, 800 Hz, 1600 Hz and so on.

The output of the full-wave rectifier differs significantly from that of the half-wave circuit. It contains no ripple at the frequency f, but instead has components at $2f$, $4f$, $6f$, and so on. The most important components are given by:

$$i = \frac{2I_m}{\pi} - \frac{4I_m}{3\pi} \cos 2\omega t - \frac{4I_m}{15\pi} \cos 4\omega t - \frac{4I_m}{35\pi} \cos 6\omega t - \cdots \qquad \textbf{(A–8)}$$

Thus the ripple in the output of the full-wave rectifier, when operating from a 60 Hz input, would be 120 Hz, 240 Hz, and so on. In the case of a 400 Hz input, the lowest ripple frequency would be 800 Hz. The voltage equation would of course have the same form:

$$v = \frac{2V_m}{\pi} - \frac{4V_m}{3\pi}\cos 2\,\omega t - \frac{4V_m}{15\pi}\cos 4\,\omega t - \cdots \tag{A-9}$$

Ripple Factor

The amount of ripple in the output of a power supply is often expressed by comparing the rms value of the ripple to the dc voltage. This rms value of ripple is the sum of all the ripple components. However, in the output of most power supplies the ripple components at frequencies above the lowest are negligible, so that for practical purposes the ripple factor in such cases represents the lowest ripple frequency. The ripple factor is defined as:

$$r = \frac{\text{rms value of ac components in output}}{\text{average (dc) value of output}} \tag{A-10}$$

A.6 Isolated Filter Circuits

The simplest example of a low-pass filter is the series RC circuit shown in Figure A–6. When the load impedance is very much greater than X_C, the voltage divider action of this circuit gives

$$V_{\text{out}} = \frac{X_C}{\sqrt{R^2 + X_C^2}}(V_{\text{in}}) \tag{A-11}$$

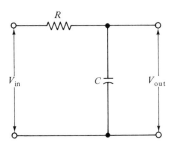

FIGURE A–6
RC *low-pass filter*

This indicates that at dc ($f = 0$) $V_{\text{out}} = V_{\text{in}}$, so that there is no attenuation, while at very high frequencies $V_{\text{out}} \to 0$. If the values of R and C are made fairly large, the attenuation will be quite great even at 60 Hz. For example, using $R = 27$ kilohms, and $C = 10$ μf gives, at 60 Hz,

$$X_C = \frac{1}{2\pi f C}$$

$$X_C \cong \frac{0.159}{(60)(10^{-5})} \cong 265 \text{ ohms}$$

so that

$$V_{out} = \frac{X_C}{\sqrt{R^2 + X_C^2}}(V_{in})$$

$$V_{out} \cong \frac{265}{\sqrt{(27,000)^2 + (265)^2}}(V_{in})$$

$$V_{out} \cong 0.01\ V_{in}$$

If a complex wave which is the combination of a dc component and sine wave components is applied to the input, the results are as illustrated in Figure A–7.

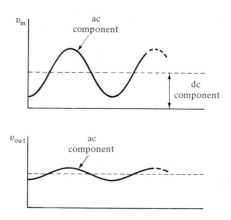

FIGURE A-7
Effect of low-pass RC filter on dc and ac components

Another basic low-pass filter form is the series *LR* circuit illustrated in Figure A–8. The voltage-divider expression for this circuit is:

$$V_{out} = \frac{R}{\sqrt{R^2 + X_L^2}}(V_{in}) \qquad\qquad \textbf{(A–12)}$$

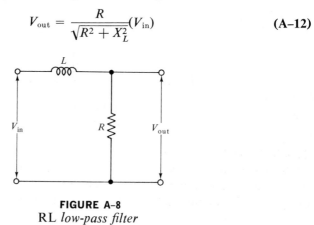

FIGURE A-8
RL *low-pass filter*

Again, this indicates that for dc the output is equal to the input, while at high frequency $V_{out} \rightarrow 0$.

A.7 Practical Filters

Effect of Rectifier

The filter characteristics noted above are altered somewhat when the filter is connected to the output of a rectifier. One major effect is that the dc output voltage of the filter is not necessarily the same value as the dc component of the unfiltered rectifier output. In one type of filter the dc output can be almost as great as the peak of the unfiltered rectified output. In other filter circuits the dc output will tend to approach the dc value of the input (minus any series losses as described below).

Losses in Filter Circuits

The reactive elements used in power supply filters do not have the ideal characteristics assumed in the above discussion. Inductances must have winding resistance, and capacitances suffer from leakage which has the effect of resistance in parallel with the capacitance. Both of these tend to reduce the dc output amplitude. Figure A–9 illustrates the effect for the filter inductor case

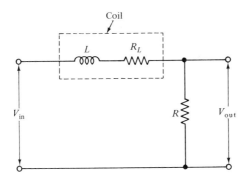

FIGURE A–9
Loss of dc voltage due to resistance of filter inductance

with R_L designating the coil's resistance. The dc output is reduced by the voltage-divider action of the resistances.

A.8 Inductor Filters

Figure A–10 illustrates a half-wave rectifier with a simple choke or inductor filter. This type of filter is not usually used with a half-wave rectifier. The filtering is very ineffective due to the current being cut off from the load for a large part of each cycle.

Figure A–11 shows the use of the simple choke filter with the full-wave rectifier. The analysis of this circuit can be simplified by assuming that the input to the filter consists only of the dc value and the lowest frequency ac component from the rectifier. This is reasonable in view of the fact that the

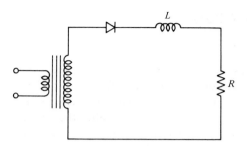

FIGURE A–10
Choke filter with half-wave rectifier (not often used)

next largest ac component is only 20 percent of the first [see Equation (A–9)], and the filter has greater effect on the higher frequency components so that they will be reduced even further.

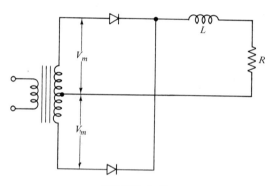

FIGURE A–11
Choke filter used with full-wave rectifier

The voltage drop and the nonlinearity in the rectifier may also be neglected for an initial analysis of this circuit. Thus the input to the filter can be considered to be as shown in Figure A–12: a dc component equal to the average

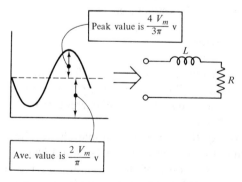

Peak value is $\dfrac{4\,V_m}{3\pi}$ v

Ave. value is $\dfrac{2\,V_m}{\pi}$ v

FIGURE A–12
Approximate input to choke filter from full-wave rectifier

value of the rectifier input, and an ac component at twice the frequency of the rectifier's input, and with a peak value equal to two-thirds of the dc.

The dc current in R (assuming no dc losses in L) is

$$I_{\text{ave}} = \frac{V_{\text{dc}}}{R} \cong \frac{0.636 \, V_m}{R} \qquad \textbf{(A–13)}$$

since $X_L = 0$ at dc.

The ac current in the load is

$$I_{\text{rms}} \cong \frac{0.707 \, \dfrac{4 \, V_m}{3\pi}}{\sqrt{R^2 + X_L^2}} \qquad \textbf{(A–14)}$$

in which V_m is the peak value of the input to the rectifier, and $4 \, V_m/3\pi$ is the peak value of the lowest frequency ripple component in the output of the rectifier according to Equation (A–9).

The ripple factor is $I_{\text{rms}}/I_{\text{ave}}$ and therefore can be seen to be proportional to $R/\sqrt{R^2 + X_L^2}$. This shows that ripple decreases as the inductance is increased and as the load resistance is decreased (i.e., as the load current is increased).

A.9 The Shunt Capacitance Filter

A common form of power supply filter utilizes a large capacitance across the output of the rectifier circuit, directly in parallel with the load. A simple version is shown in Figure A–13. The capacitor receives charge from the recti-

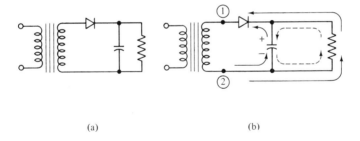

(a)   (b)

FIGURE A–13
Shunt-capacitance filter

fier during the time that the diode permits current to flow, and then during the nonconducting parts of the cycle, it discharges through the load. Thus the shunt capacitance serves to change the pulsating load current waveform of Figure A–1 to a smoother, more continuous flow.

The action of this circuit is as follows. When the input voltage polarity is such as to cause the diode to conduct, the path for electron flow is through the capacitor and the load in parallel as indicated by the solid arrows in Figure A–13. Since the diode and the transformer winding are normally low impedance, and the reactance of C is low at the applied frequency, the capacitor charges up quickly. When the applied voltage causes the diode to become non-

conducting, C attempts to discharge but can do so only through the load resistance, since current cannot flow (in any appreciable amount) in the other
direction through the diode.

On each succeeding cycle it recharges the small amount of charge lost
between the cycles. The result of this is that the capacitor voltage rises to some
high value, often close to the peak value of the applied sine wave.

This is shown in Figure A–14. During the time from B to C in this figure,

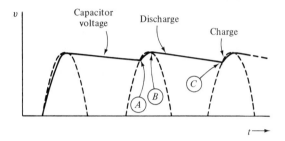

FIGURE A–14
Capacitor voltage in shunt-C filter

the input voltage (shown dashed for reference) is less than the capacitor
voltage. Since the positive side of the input is connected to the anode end of the
diode and the positive side of the capacitor is connected to the cathode end of
the diode, the diode is back-biased during this time interval. Thus no current
can flow from the rectifier to the capacitor. During intervals such as A to B, the
input is greater than the capacitor voltage, and the diode is forward-biased,
permitting diode current to flow. During the A to B intervals the capacitor re-
plenishes the charge it loses to the load during the B to C intervals.

Figure A–15 illustrates two extremes of dc output and ripple, depending
upon the size of the load resistance. The smaller the load resistance, the greater
the discharge current and the lower the capacitor voltage drops between peaks.
Thus the smaller load resistance results in a lower dc output voltage and
greater ripple.

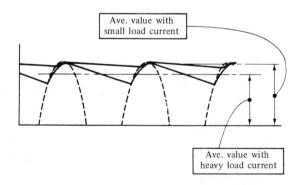

FIGURE A–15
Effect of load on dc output and on ripple

Pulse Nature of Rectifier Current in Shunt Capacitance Filters

Figure A–14 shows that this type of filter permits only a short interval of rectifier current flow during each cycle of the input. Thus the entire output of the power supply — released to the load at a more or less steady rate — must be supplied by an input current which may flow for only a fraction of the time. Because of this, the rectifier, transformer, and capacitor are subjected to high peak values of current. For example, with a 100 ma load current, and an input current pulse lasting only 10 percent of the cycle, the input current would have to be greater than ten times the load current, or greater than 1 amp. Figure A–16 illustrates the pulse nature of this current.

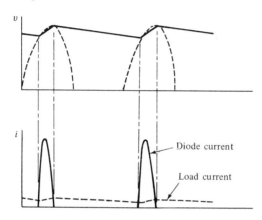

FIGURE A–16
Typical diode current pulses with shunt-C filter

Analysis of the Shunt Capacitor Filter

An approximate analysis of this circuit, which will provide good results for practical work, may be based on the assumption that the ripple will be small and the capacitor charge and discharge approximately linear, as shown in Figure A–17. The ripple is then a triangular wave, and the dc voltage output is the rectifier peak voltage V_m minus one-half of the peak-to-peak ripple voltage:

$$V_{dc} = V_m - \frac{V_r}{2} \tag{A–15}$$

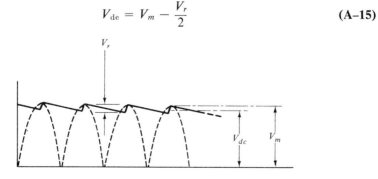

FIGURE A–17
Waveform assumed for approximate analysis of the shunt-capacitance filter

The above approximations permit expressing the relationship between the dc load current and the change of capacitor voltage during discharge as

$$I_{dc} = C\frac{\Delta V}{\Delta t} = C\frac{V_r}{\Delta t}$$

which leads to

$$V_r = \frac{I_{dc}}{fC} \text{ for the half-wave rectifier} \tag{A-16}$$

and

$$V_r = \frac{I_{dc}}{2fC} \text{ for the full wave case} \tag{A-17}$$

since when the ripple is small, the discharge time Δt approaches the time between peaks, $1/f$ and $1/2f$, respectively for the two types of rectifiers.

Consideration of Equations (A–15), (A–16), and (A–17) leads to the following conclusions concerning performance of the shunt-capacitance filter.

Output Voltage

With adequate filtering and light load (that is, small load current, or high value of load resistance) the dc output voltage is high, approaching the peak value of the input to the rectifier.

Ripple

The ripple is low with large value of capacitance and small load current.

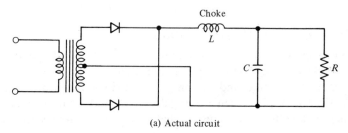

(a) Actual circuit

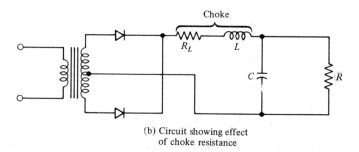

(b) Circuit showing effect
of choke resistance

FIGURE A–18
L-section filter

Regulation

Equations (A–15) and (A–16) show that good regulation requires a large capacitance.

Design of the Simple Shunt Capacitor Filter

The value of capacitance needed to meet a given ripple requirement may be found by solving Equation (A–16) or (A–17) for C.

A.10 The L-Section Filter

Figure A–18 illustrates an L-section filter, which combines an inductance and a capacitance. Although this filter may be used with either half-wave or full-wave rectifier circuits, the following discussion will be based upon full-wave rectification. The series inductor presents a high impedance in series with the load at ripple frequencies while the capacitance provides a very low impedance. The combination therefore acts as a voltage divider or attenuator for the ripple frequencies. The reactance X_L is usually large compared with the coil losses R_L, and X_C is usually very small compared to either R or X_L, so that the voltage divider ratio for each ripple component may be taken as

$$\frac{V_{\text{out}}}{V_{\text{in}}} = \frac{X_C}{\sqrt{R_L^2 + (X_L - X_C)^2}} \cong \frac{X_C}{X_L} \qquad \text{(A–18)}$$

Taking the ripple to be only the first term of the harmonic series as a practical approximation gives, as the ripple output,

$$V_{r(\text{peak})} \cong \frac{4V_m}{3\pi}\left(\frac{X_C}{X_L}\right)$$

or

$$V_{r(\text{rms})} \cong \frac{4V_m}{3\sqrt{2}\pi}\left(\frac{X_C}{X_L}\right) \qquad \text{(A–19)}$$

If the filter series resistance R_L is neglected, the dc output voltage is considered equal to the dc component of the rectifier output $(2V_m/\pi)$, and the ripple factor may then be expressed as

$$r = \frac{V_{r(\text{rms})}}{V_{\text{dc}}} \cong \frac{\sqrt{2}}{3}\left(\frac{X_C}{X_L}\right) \qquad \text{(A–20)}$$

Note that in Equations (A–18), (A–19), and (A–20), the reactances X_C and X_L must be calculated at the ripple frequency — which in the case of the full-wave rectifier is twice the input frequency. From the above we obtain (for full-wave rectification operating from a 60-Hz input)

$$r \cong \frac{0.83}{LC} \qquad \text{(A–21)}$$

in which C is in microfarads and L is in henries (h).

Ripple

Note that while the shunt-capacitance filter suffers increasing ripple with increasing load current, the L-section filter's ripple output is essentially unaffected by the load current.

Output Voltage

The dc output voltage tends to approach the dc value of the unfiltered rectifier output. It does not approach the peak value of the input as with the filter having a capacitor at the input, because the inductor prevents the rapid charging of the capacitor which occurs in the input capacitor case.

Regulation

Although the approximate dc output voltage may be taken as the dc component of the input, the actual value is affected by voltage drops in the transformer, rectifier and choke. Representing the resistances of these components by R', we have

$$V_{\mathrm{dc}} = \frac{2V_m}{\pi} - I_{\mathrm{dc}}R'$$ (A–22)

Critical Inductance

If the inductance L of Figure A–18 is not large enough, the circuit performs more like a simple shunt-capacitance filter than an L-section filter. In the shunt-C case, current flows through the diodes only during the brief charging time, while in the L-section case, current flows all the time, through one diode or the other.

The minimum value of inductance necessary to provide the continuous current characteristic for a 60-Hz input is given, for full-wave rectification, by

$$L_C \cong \frac{R_L}{1130}$$ (A–23)

The dc output voltage of a shunt-C filter circuit tends to approach the peak value of the input, while that of the L-section filter tends to approximate the average value of the input. Equation (A–23) shows that the critical value of inductance depends upon the load. An inductance value which is large enough at high load currents may be below the critical value at low load currents. Consequently, the output voltage may change from that which is characteristic of an L-section filter to that which is characteristic of a shunt-C filter as the load current varies. If good regulation is desired, the inductance must be large enough to meet the requirement of Equation (A–23) at the lowest anticipated load current. If it does not meet this requirement, the output voltage will change greatly as the load current changes from minimum to maximum. Figure A–19 illustrates this.

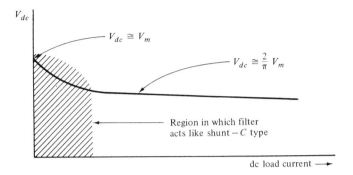

FIGURE A–19
Rise of dc output voltage at low load current in L-*section filter*

The Bleeder Resistor

A fixed resistance connected across the output of the power supply, so that it is effectively in parallel with the load, is often used to improve the regulation. In those cases where the load current goes to zero at some time during operation, the inductance required to prevent the poor regulation illustrated in Figure A–19 would have to be infinite. With a bleeder resistor connected, the power supply current would never fall to zero.

A large bleeder current is not necessary. A 200-v supply with a load current range of zero to 100 ma would require a choke of about 200 h to meet the requirement of Equation (A–23) at 1 ma. Adding a bleeder current equal to only 10 percent of the full-load current would reduce the requirement to 20 h.

Swinging Chokes

The inductance of coils using iron cores tends to be greater at low current. The increased flux density in the iron at high current causes operation in the portion of the iron's magnetization curve known as the saturation region, where the iron's permeability is decreased.

Chokes built with great enough inductance to satisfy Equation (A–23) at low currents would have to use excessively large and expensive iron cores to maintain high inductance at high load current. Consequently, chokes whose inductance decreases considerably due to saturation as the load current rises are often employed. Such inductors are known as *swinging chokes*.

Design Method for L-Section Filters

1. Choose the inductance value on the basis of the critical inductance requirement of Equation (A–23),

$$L \cong \frac{R_L}{1130} \tag{A–23}$$

in which R_L must represent the load resistance at minimum expected load current.

2. Then find the required capacitance on the basis of the desired ripple factor, from Equation (A–21):

$$r \cong \frac{0.83}{LC} \tag{A–21}$$

Multiple-Section Filters

Figure A–20 illustrates a two-section filter of the L-type. The design of such multiple-section filters may be based on the fact that each section attenuates the ripple by the ratio X_C/X_L. This simple voltage-divider ratio may be used

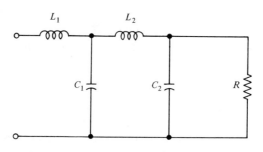

FIGURE A–20
A two-section L-type filter

because normally $X_L \gg X_C$ and $X_C \ll R$. It should be noted again that the reactances X_C and X_L must be computed for the ripple frequency, which in the full-wave rectifier is the second harmonic of the input frequency, or 120 Hz in the case of a 60 Hz input.

A.11 π-Section Filters

The π-section filter, or capacitor-input LC filter, is shown in Figure A–21. Because of the shunt capacitance at its input, this type of filter has much of the characteristics of the shunt-capacitance filter described earlier. The rectifier current flows in short-duration pulses (during the short charging time of the capacitance), and these current pulses must therefore be of quite large ampli-

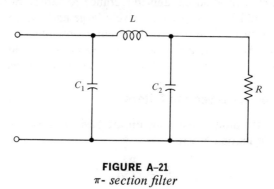

FIGURE A–21
π- section filter

tude for a given average load current. The voltage regulation is poor unless the capacitance is made very large.

Perhaps the simplest way to analyze the action of the π-section filter is to view it as a shunt-capacitor filter followed by an L-section filter. The ripple output is then simply the shunt-C ripple output multiplied by $X_{C2}X_L$.

The shunt-C peak-to-peak ripple output is given for the half-wave case by Equation (A–16).

$$V_r = \frac{I_{dc}}{fC} \tag{A-16}$$

and for the full-wave case it is one-half this. Again, as before, useful practical analysis can be done on the basis of the first harmonic. In the case of the triangular wave assumed in the earlier discussion, the rms value of this harmonic is

$$V_{r(rms)} = \frac{V_r}{\pi\sqrt{2}} = \frac{I_{dc}}{\pi fC\sqrt{2}} \tag{A-24}$$

and the ripple output of the π-filter is then

$$V_r = \frac{I_{dc}}{\pi fC_1\sqrt{2}}\left(\frac{X_{C2}}{X_L}\right) \tag{A-25}$$

It should be apparent that when more L-sections follow the basic π-section, the ripple is reduced in each section by the ratio X_C/X_L for that section.

It should be noted also that because of the higher ripple frequency in the output of the full-wave rectifier, the ratio X_C/X_L for the full-wave case, using the same values of L and C, will be one-fourth the half-wave values. Thus, in the single π-section filter, taking into account the 2:1 difference in ripple at the first capacitor [Equations (A–16) and (A–17)] and the difference in the X_{C2}/X_L ratio, it is apparent that full-wave operation permits achieving eight times better ripple reduction with the same components — or the same ripple with all L and C values reduced by half.

RC Filters

It is often advantageous to use a resistor in place of the inductor in a π-filter, as shown in Figure A–22. The ripple attenuation in the L-section is then X_{C2}/R_1. This frequently permits considerable saving in cost, weight, and size.

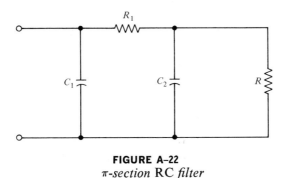

FIGURE A–22
π-section RC *filter*

However, for equal ripple reduction (i.e., for $R_1 = X_L$) the loss in dc output voltage due to the voltage drop in this resistor will be much greater in the case of the RC filter. Consequently, it sometimes is limited to use in low-current supplies. It is also possible in many cases to use large enough values for C_1 and C_2 so that the resistance R_1 and the resulting voltage drop will be acceptable.

Output Voltage of the π-Section Filter

The dc output voltage of the π-section filter approaches the peak value of the input, minus the voltage drop in the series element (the inductor or the resistor).

Ripple

In contrast with the L-section filter, whose ripple output is relatively unaffected by load current, the π-section ripple output increases with increasing load current due to the input capacitance.

Regulation

Regulation tends to be poor, as in the simple shunt-capacitance filter. Good regulation requires a very large input capacitance.

Design of the π-Section Filter

Since the π-section filter does not involve any critical values such as the critical inductance of the L-section type, it is possible to satisfy a given set of requirements with an infinite combination of values for C_1, C_2, and L. In such a situation it is customary to start with convenient values for two of the components and calculate the value of the remaining component which will satisfy the requirements.

For example, values which are readily available may be chosen for C_1 and L. These values along with the expected value of dc load current, the ripple frequency, and the maximum allowable ripple voltage V_r, are used in Equation (A–25) to calculate the required value for C_2. If this value for C_2 is too large, L or C_1, or both, may have to be increased. If the value of C_2 comes out very small, L or C_1 may be made smaller if desired.

A.12   Power Supply Component Ratings

The components in power supply circuits are subjected to unique operating conditions which depend upon the type of rectifier and type of filter circuit used as well as the voltage, current, and power output of the supply. These operating conditions must be taken into account when choosing the components.

Rectifier Peak Inverse Voltages

During the conducting portion of the cycle, the rectifier voltage drop in low to medium power circuits employing semiconductor diodes is generally a few volts or less. But during the nonconducting time, a large *inverse* voltage is impressed upon the diode. The peak value of this voltage approaches twice the peak value of the ac voltage applied to the rectifier input in some cases, while in others it approaches the peak value of the rectifier input.

Reference to Figure A–4 will show how the peak inverse voltage may be evaluated. When diode A is conducting, point (1) is at a potential which differs from the peak of the input voltage, V_m, by only a small amount. This point is, of course, connected to one side of diode B. The other side of diode B is connected to the other end of the transformer, and must therefore be at the potential $-V_m$. The total voltage impressed across diode B, when it is nonconducting, thus is approximately $2V_m$, or twice the peak value of the rectifier input.

Table A–1 lists the approximate peak inverse voltages existing in the principal power supply circuits. Rectifiers must be selected with inverse voltage ratings meeting these requirements, with sufficient safety margin to account for expected variations in transformer ratios, line voltage amplitude and the like.

TABLE A–1

Circuit Type	Peak Inverse Voltage (in terms of the peak rectifier input V_m as defined in Figures A–2, A–4, and A–5)
Half-wave, unfiltered or choke-input filter	V_m
Half-wave; capacitor-input filter	$2V_m$
Full-wave using CT transformer; any filter	$2V_m$
Full-wave bridge	V_m

Rectifier Current Ratings

Rectifiers must be rated for both their average current carrying ability and their ability to handle current peaks. This becomes particularly important in the case of capacitor-input filter circuits, where peak currents are large relative to the average current.

Two types of current peaks are encountered in power supply service. When a capacitor-input supply is first turned on, an initial current pulse or *surge current* occurs as the capacitor charges up from an uncharged condition. This surge is much greater than the current pulse which occurs each cycle in replenishing the small amount of charge the capacitor loses between peaks. Thus, diodes intended for rectifier service are rated for peak surge current and repetitive peak current as well as dc current.

Transformers

The transformers intended for use with rectifier-filter power supplies are called *power transformers*. They are usually rated in terms of the secondary voltage (for a 117 or 120 v primary) and the dc current in the secondary. When center-tapped for use with a full-wave rectifier, the secondary voltage may be given, for example, as either "400v CT" or "200-0-200." Because of the difference in the rectifier input current with the two kinds of filters, the transformer may be specified as "For capacitor input systems" or "For reactor input systems."

Capacitors

Electrolytic capacitors intended for power supply use are usually rated for their ability to withstand a continuous dc voltage, or *dc working voltage*. For example: "50 VDCW" or "50 DCWV." A surge voltage is specified in some cases, since some circuits are subject to brief intervals during which the voltage exceeds the normal working voltage.

Electrolytic capacitors, especially the aluminum foil type, are not usually made to close tolerance on capacitance values. For their intended use it is usually important only that they have enough capacitance; too much is not considered a disadvantage. Consequently, capacitance tolerances such as $-10 + 50\%$, or $-20 + 150\%$ are encountered.

Chokes

Filter reactor specifications usually list dc current carrying ability, dc resistance, and inductance value at a specified dc voltage across the coil. As in the case of capacitors for power supplies, too much inductance is not considered a disadvantage, so that tolerances such as $-15 + 50\%$ are not unusual. Swinging chokes may specify an inductance value at a given low value of current and an inductance value at a given high value of current.

APPENDIX B
Device Characteristics

Passivated

WITH FIXED-BED MOUNTING

SILICON TYPES
2N332A
2N333A
2N334A
2N335A
2N336A

The General Electric Types 2N332A, 2N333A, 2N334A, 2N335A, 2N336A, are surface passivated silicon NPN transistors intended for amplifier applications in the audio and radio frequency range and for general purpose switching circuits. They are grown diffused devices with a diffused base and are manufactured in the Fixed-Bed Mounting design for extremely high mechanical reliability under severe conditions of shock, vibration, centrifugal force, and temperature. These transistors are hermetically sealed in welded cases. The case dimensions and lead configuration conform to JEDEC standards and are suitable for insertion in printed boards by automatic assembly equipment. Surface passivation is making the surface insensitive to water, ions, and other contamination which historically have been the largest cause of semiconductor failures and/or drift of parameters. In these devices, passivation is achieved by protecting the junction area with a specially designed surface compound which is *chemically bonded* to the semiconductor crystal. Since this bonding is accomplished through the surface atoms of the silicon crystal, these formerly active surface sites are no longer available for absorbtion or reaction with moisture or other contamination. Since the surface is now completely stable, the leakage currents are lower; and greater power and higher temperature can be applied without degradation. The devices are superior to non passivated products in these characteristics. They are also superior in parameter stability and most significantly of all in reliability.

Voltages				
Collector to Base	V_{CB}	45	volts	
Collector to Emitter	V_{CE}	45	volts	
Emitter to Base	V_{EB}	4	volts	
Current				
Collector	I_C	25	ma	
Power				
Collector Dissipation RMS	P_c	500	mw @ 25°C (Free Air)	
	P_c	83	mw @ 150°C (Free Air)	
Temperature				
Storage	T_{STG}	—65 to 200	°C	
Operating Junction	T_J	—65 to 175	°C	

		Min.*	Typ.	Max.*	Min.*	Typ.	Max.*	Min.*	Typ.	Max.*
Collector to Base Voltage ($I_C = 50$ μa, $I_E = 0$)	V_{CBO}	45			45			45		
Collector to Emitter Voltage ($I_B = 0$, $I_C = 1$ ma)	V_{CEO}	45			45			45		
Emitter to Base Voltage ($I_E = 100$ μa, $I_C = 0$)	V_{EBO}	4			4			4		
Forward Current Transfer Ratio (low current) ($I_C = 1$ ma, $V_{CE} = 5$V)	h_{FE}		16			27			36	
Saturation Voltage ($I_B = 1$ ma, $I_C = 5$ ma)	$V_{CE\ (SAT)}$		.5	1.0		.45	1.0		.42	1.0
Collector Current ($V_{CB} = 30$ V; $I_E = 0$; $T_A = 25$°C)	I_{CBO}		1	500		1	500		1	500
Collector Current (high temperature) ($V_{CB} = 30$ V; $I_E = 0$; $T_A = 150$°C)	I_{CBO}		1	20		1	20		1	20
Collector Emitter Current ($V_{CE} = 30$ V; $I_B = 0$; $T_A = 150$°C)	I_{CEO}		60			60			60	
($V_{CB} = 5$ V; $I_E = -1$ ma; $f = 1000$ cps)										
Forward Current Transfer Ratio	h_{fe}	9	16	22	18	30	44	18	38	90
Input Impedance	h_{ie}	270	750	1760	540	1300	3520	540	1700	7200
Output Admittance	h_{oe}	0.0	3.5	20	0.0	5.0	25	0.0	6.0	30
Voltage Feedback Ratio	h_{re}		.7			1.0			1.3	
Input Impedance	h_{ib}	30	40	80	30	40	80	30	40	80
Output Admittance	h_{ob}	0.0	.25	1.2	0.0	.2	1.2	0.0	.18	1.2
Reverse Voltage Transfer Ratio	h_{rb}	.25	1.2	5	.25	1.2	10	.50	1.2	10
Noise Figure ($B_w = 1$ cycle)	NF		16	30		13	30		12	30
(Common Base) ($V_{CB} = 5$ V; $I_E = -1$ ma)										
Output Capacity ($f = 1$ mc)	C_{ob}		7	15		7	15		7	15
Cutoff Frequency	f_{ab}	2.5	10		2.5	11		8.0	12	
Power Gain (Common Emitter) ($V_{CE} = 20$ V; $I_E = -2$ ma; $f = 5$ mc)	G_e		11			11			12	

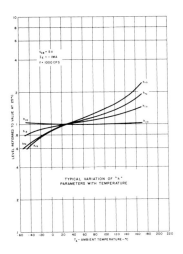

TYPICAL VARIATION OF "h"
PARAMETERS WITH TEMPERATURE

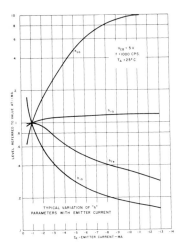

TYPICAL VARIATION OF "h"
PARAMETERS WITH EMITTER CURRENT

		Min.*	Typ.	Max.*	Min.*	Typ.	Max.*	
Collector to Base Voltage ($I_C = 50 \mu a$, $I_E = 0$)	V_{CBO}	45			45			volts
Collector to Emitter Voltage ($I_B = 0$, $I_C = 1$ ma)	V_{CEO}	45			45			volts
Emitter to Base Voltage ($I_E = 100 \mu a$, $I_C = 0$)	V_{EBO}	4			4			volts
Forward Current Transfer Ratio (low current) ($I_C = 1$ ma, $V_{CE} = 5$V)	h_{FE}		45			75		
Saturation Voltage ($I_B = 1$ ma, $I_C = 5$ ma)	$V_{CE\ (SAT)}$		.4	1.0		.4	1.0	volts
Collector Current ($V_{CB} = 30$ V; $I_E = 0$; $T_A = 25°C$)	I_{CBO}		1	500		1	500	mμa
Collector Current (high temperature) ($V_{CB} = 30$ V; $I_E = 0$; $T_A = 150°C$)	I_{CBO}		1	20		1	20	μa
Collector Emitter Current ($V_{CE} = 30$ V; $I_B = 0$; $T_A = 150°C$)	I_{CEO}		60			60		μa
($V_{CB} = 5$ V; $I_E = -1$ ma; f = 1000 cps)								
Forward Current Transfer Ratio	h_{fe}	37	52	90	76	95	333	
Input Impedance	h_{ie}	1110	2000	7200	2280	3700	15,000	ohms
Output Admittance	h_{oe}	0.0	7.0	30	0.0	8.0	35	μmhos
Voltage Feedback Ratio	h_{re}		1.5			2.3		$\times 10^{-4}$
Input Impedance	h_{ib}	30	40	80	30	40	80	ohms
Output Admittance	h_{ob}	0.0	.15	1.2	0.0	.13	1.2	μmhos
Reverse Voltage Transfer Ratio	h_{rb}	.50	1.2	10	.50	1.2	10×10^{-4}	
Noise Figure ($B_w = 1$ cycle)	NF		11	30		11	30	db
(Common Base) ($V_{CB} = 5$ V; $I_E = -1$ ma)								
Output Capacity (f = 1 mc)	C_{ob}		7	15		7	15	$\mu\mu$f
Cutoff Frequency	$f_{\alpha b}$	2.5	13		2.5	15		mc
Power Gain (Common Emitter) ($V_{CE} = 20$ V; $I_E = -2$ ma; f = 5 mc)	G_e		12			12		db

*All Absolute Maximum Ratings and all minimum and maximum Electrical Characteristics are per JEDEC registration of these types.

Courtesy of General Electric Company

6CB6-A

Average Plate Characteristics

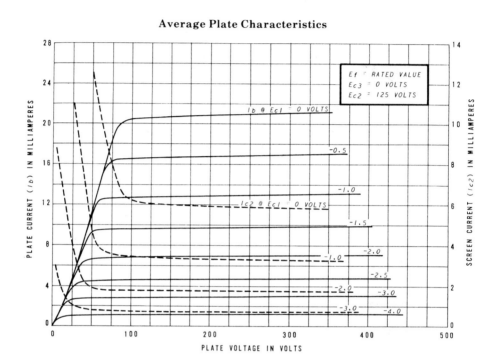

Average Plate Characteristics

6J6-A

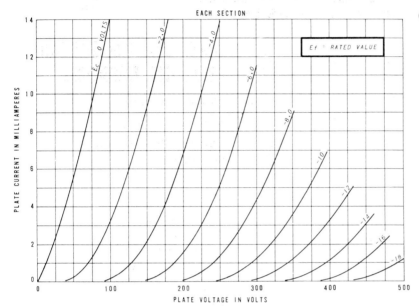

EACH SECTION

Ef = RATED VALUE

PLATE CURRENT IN MILLIAMPERES

PLATE VOLTAGE IN VOLTS

Courtesy of General Electric Company

MOS FIELD-EFFECT TRANSISTORS
Dual Insulated-Gate Types for RF Amplifier & Mixer Service

3N140
3N141

RCA-3N140 and 3N141* are n-channel silicon, depletion type, dual insulated-gate, field-effect transistors utilizing the MOS** construction. They have exceptional characteristics for rf-amplifier and mixer applications at frequencies up to 300 MHz. These transistors feature a series arrangement of two separate channels, each channel having an independent control gate.

The 3N140, used in a common-source configuration in which gate No.2 is ac grounded, reduces oscillator feedthrough to the antenna thereby minimizing oscillator radiation. The 3N141 provides excellent isolation between the oscillator and rf signals because each of the two signal frequencies being mixed has its own control element.

The mixing function performed by the 3N141 is unique in that the signal applied to gate No.2 is used to modulate the input-gate (gate No.1) transfer characteristic. This technique is superior to conventional "square law" mixing, which can only be accomplished in the non-linear region of the device transfer characteristic.

The use of the 3N141 as described provides high useful conversion gains at all vhf frequencies, and the reduction in spurious responses is substantial and easily obtainable in simple circuits.

The 3N140 and 3N141 are hermetically sealed in metal JEDEC TO-72 packages.

* Formerly Dev. Nos. TA2644 and TA7274, respectively.
** Metal-Oxide-Semiconductor.

Maximum Ratings, *Absolute-Maximum Values, at* $T_A = 25^oC$

DRAIN-TO-SOURCE VOLTAGE, V_{DS} · ·	0 to +20	V
GATE No.1-TO-SOURCE VOLTAGE, V_{G1S}:		
Continuous (dc)	-8 to +1	V
Peak ac	-8 to +20	V
GATE No.2-TO-SOURCE VOLTAGE, V_{G2S}:		
Continuous (dc)	-8 to 40% of V_{DS}	V
Peak ac	-8 to +20	V
DRAIN-TO-GATE VOLTAGE, V_{DG1} OR V_{DG2}	+20	V
DRAIN CURRENT, I_D		
(Pulsed): Pulse duration $\leq$ 20 ms, duty factor $\leq$ 0.15	50	mA
TRANSISTOR DISSIPATION, P_T:		
At ambient ⎰ up to 25°C	400	mW
temperatures ⎱ above 25°C	derate linearly at 2.67 mW/°C	
AMBIENT TEMPERATURE RANGE:		
Storage and Operating	-65 to +175	°C
LEAD TEMPERATURE (During soldering):		
At distances $\geq$ 1/32 inch from seating surface for 10 seconds max. . .	265	°C

SILICON DUAL INSULATED-GATE FIELD-EFFECT TRANSISTORS

N-Channel Depletion Types

For Military and Industrial Amplifier and Mixer Applications Up to 300 MHz

H-1299

JEDEC TO-72

APPLICATIONS

- RF amplifier and mixer in military and industrial communications equipment
- aircraft and marine vehicular receivers
- CATV and MATV equipment
- telemetry and multiplex equipment

PERFORMANCE FEATURES

- wide dynamic range permits large-signal handling before overload
- dual-gate permits simplified agc circuitry
- virtually no agc power required
- greatly reduces spurious responses in fm receivers
- permits use of vacuum-tube biasing techniques
- excellent thermal stability
- superior cross-modulation performance and greater dynamic range than bipolar or single-gate FET's

DEVICE FEATURES

- low gate leakage currents – – I_{G1SS} & I_{G2SS} = 1 nA max. at $T_A = 25°C$
- high forward transconductance – – g_{fs} = 6000 μmho min.
- high unneutralized RF power gain – – G_{ps} = 16 dB min. at 200 MHz
- low VHF noise figure – – 4.5 dB max. at 200 MHz

Courtesy of Radio Corporation of America

ELECTRICAL CHARACTERISTICS, at T_A = 25°C Unless Otherwise Specified. Common-Source Circuit.

CHARACTERISTICS	SYMBOLS	TEST CONDITIONS	TYPE 3N140 RF AMPLIFIER			TYPE 3N141 MIXER			UNITS
			MIN.	TYP.	MAX.	MIN.	TYP.	MAX.	
Gate No.1-to-Source Cutoff Voltage	$V_{G1S}(off)$	V_{DS} = +16V, I_D = 200 μA V_{G2S} = +4V	-	-2	-4	-	-2	-4	V
Gate No.2-to-Source Cutoff Voltage	$V_{G2S}(off)$	V_{DS} = +16V, I_D = 200 μA V_{G1S} = 0	-	-2	-4	-	-2	-4	V
Gate No.1 Leakage Current	I_{G1SS}	V_{G1S} = -20V, V_{G2S} = 0 V_{DS} = 0, T_A = 25°C	-	-	1	-	-	1	nA
		V_{G1S} = +1V, V_{G2S} = 0 V_{DS} = 0, T_A = 25°C	-	-	1	-	-	1	nA
		V_{G1S} = -20V, V_{G2S} = 0 V_{DS} = 0, T_A = 125°C	-	-	0.2	-	-	0.2	μA
Gate No.2 Leakage Current	I_{G2SS}	V_{G2S} = -20V, V_{G1S} = 0 V_{DS} = 0, T_A = 25°C	-	-	1	-	-	1	nA
		V_{G2S} = +1V V_{DS} = 0, V_{G1S} = 0, T_A = 25°C	-	-	1	-	-	1	nA
		V_{G2S} = -20V, V_{G1S} = 0 V_{DS} = 0, T_A = 125°C	-	-	0.2	-	-	0.2	μA
Zero-Bias Drain Current	I_{DSS}	V_{DD} = +14V, V_{G1S} = 0, V_{G2S} = +4	5	18	30	5	18	30	mA
Forward Transconductance (Gate No.1 to Drain)	g_{fs}	V_{DD} = +14V, I_D = 10 mA V_{G2S} = +4V, f = 1 kHz	6000	10000	18000	6000	10000	18000	μmho
Cutoff Forward Transconductance (Gate No.1 to Drain)	$g_{fs}(off)$	V_{DD} = +14V, V_{G1S} = -0.5V V_{G2S} = -2V, f = 1 kHz	-	-	100	-	-	-	μmho
Small-Signal, Short-Circuit Input Capacitance*	C_{iss}	V_{DS} = +13V, I_D = 10 mA V_{G2S} = +4V, f = 1 MHz	3	5.5	7	3	5.5	7	pF
Small-Signal, Short-Circuit Reverse Transfer Capacitance (Drain to Gate No.1)*	C_{rss}	V_{DS} = +13V, I_D = 10 mA V_{G2S} = +4V, f = 1 MHz	0.01	0.02	0.03	0.01	0.02	0.03	pF
Small-Signal Short-Circuit Output Capacitance	C_{oss}	V_{DS} = +13V, I_D = 10 mA V_{G2S} = +4V, f = 1 MHz	-	2.2	-	-	2.2	-	pF
Power Gain (See Fig.1 for Measurement Circuit)	G_{ps}	V_{DD} = +15V, R_S = 270Ω f = 200 MHz, R_G = 50Ω	16	18	-	-	-	-	dB
Conversion Power Gain (See Fig.2 for Measurement Circuit)	G_{psc}	V_{DD} = +15V, R_S = 120Ω, f_{IN} = 200 MHz, f_{OUT} = 30 MHz Oscillator injection voltage• = 2.5 V (rms)	-	-	-	13	17	-	dB
Measured Noise Figure (See Fig.1 for Measurement Circuit)	NF	V_{DD} = +15V, R_S = 270Ω f = 200 MHz, R_G = 50Ω	-	3.5	4.5	-	-	-	dB

* Pusle test: Pulse duration ≤ 20 ms, duty factor ≤ 0.15.
♣ Capacitance between Gate No.1 and all other terminals.

♠ Three-Terminal Measurement with Gate No.2 and Source Returned to Guard Terminal.
• Measured from gate No.2 to source.

MOS FIELD-EFFECT TRANSISTOR
For Audio, Video, and RF Amplifier Applications

3N139

RCA 3N139[+] is a silicon, insulated-gate field-effect transistor of the N-channel depletion type, utilizing the MOS* construction. It is a general purpose transistor especially suited for audio, video, and rf applications, and for wide-band amplifier designs. The insulated gate provides a very high input resistance (10^{14} Ω typ.) which is relatively insensitive to temperature and is independent of gate-bias conditions (positive, negative, or zero bias). The 3N139 also has a high transconductance, a low value of input capacitance (3 pF typ.), and a very low feedback capacitance (0.19 pF typ.).

This transistor features a New Terminal Arrangement in which the gate and source connections are interchanged to provide maximum isolation between the output (drain) and the input (gate) terminals. Although this new basing configuration does not appreciably change the measured device feedback capacitance, it permits the use of external inter-terminal shields to reduce the feedback due to external capacitances, particularly on printed circuit boards. This feature makes it possible to achieve greater circuit stability or higher useable gain per stage.

The 3N139 is hermetically sealed in the standard 4-lead JEDEC TO-72 package.

[+] Formerly Dev. No. TA7244

* Metal-Oxide-Semiconductor

Maximum Ratings, *Absolute-Maximum Values:*

DRAIN-TO-SOURCE VOLTAGE, V_{DS} . . .	+35 max.	V
DRAIN-TO-SUBSTRATE VOLTAGE, V_{DB}	+35, -0.3 max.	V
SOURCE-TO-SUBSTRATE VOLTAGE, V_{SB}	+35, -0.3 max.	V
DC GATE-TO-SOURCE VOLTAGE, V_{GS} .	±10 max.	V
PEAK GATE-TO-SOURCE VOLTAGE, V_{GS}	±14 max.	V
PEAK VOLTAGE, GATE-TO-ALL OTHER TERMINALS; V_{GS}, V_{GD}, V_{GB}, non-repetitive	±42 max.	V
DRAIN CURRENT, I_D (Pulse duration 20 ms, duty factor ≤ 0.10).	50 max.	mA
TRANSISTOR DISSIPATION, P_T: At ambient temperatures from -65 to +125ºC.	150 max.	mW
AMBIENT TEMPERATURE RANGE:		
Storage.	-65 to +150	ºC
Operating	-65 to +125	ºC
LEAD TEMPERATURE (During Soldering): At distance not closer than 1/32 inch to seating surface for 10 seconds max. . .	265 max.	ºC

SILICON MOS TRANSISTOR
For Audio, Video, and RF Amplifier Applications

JEDEC
TO-72

in **Military Communications, Instrumentation, & Navigation Equipment**

in **Mobile and Fixed Communication Equipment**

in **Industrial Instrumentation and Control Circuits**

FEATURES

● new terminal arrangement

1 - Drain
2 - Source
3 - Insulated Gate
4 - Bulk (Substrate) and Case

● high input resistance
   R_{GS} = 10^{14} Ω typ.

● high forward transconductance
   g_{fs} (V_{DS} = 15 V, R_S = 0, f = 1 kHz) = 6000 μmho typ.

● low input capacitance
   C_{iss} = 3 pF typ.

● high power gain
   G_{ps} = 17 dB typ. at 200 MHz

● low noise figure
   NF = 4 dB typ. at 200 MHz

● low gate leakage current
   I_{GSS} = 0.1 nA typ.

● high drain-to-source voltage: +35 max. V

ELECTRICAL CHARACTERISTICS: *At $T_A = 25^oC$, Unless Otherwise Indicated. Substrate Connected to Ground.*

CHARACTERISTICS	SYMBOLS	TEST CONDITIONS	LIMITS Min.	LIMITS Typ.	LIMITS Max.	UNITS
Gate Leakage Current	I_{GSS}	$V_{GS} = \pm 10$ V, $V_{DS} = 0$	-	0.1	1	nA
		$V_{GS} = \pm 10$ V, $V_{DS} = 0$, $T_A = 125^oC$	-	-	4	nA
Forward Transconductance *(See Fig.1)*	g_{fs}	$V_{DS} = 15$ V, $R_S = 0$, f = 1 kHz	3000	6000	-	μmho
		$V_{DD} = 15$ V, $R_S = 360$ Ω, f = 1 kHz	3000	4500	7500	μmho
		$V_{DD} = 15$ V, $R_S = 360$ Ω, f = 1 kHz, $T_A = 125^oC$	-	3300	-	μmho
Zero-Bias Drain Current*	I_{DSS}	$V_{DS} = 15$ V, $R_S = 0$	5	15	25	mA
Drain Current *(See Fig.1)*	I_D	$V_{DD} = 15$ V, $R_S = 360$ Ω	3	4.5	7	mA
		$V_{DD} = 15$ V, $R_S = 360$ Ω, $T_A = 125^oC$	-	3.3	-	mA
Output Resistance *(See Fig.1)*	r_d	$V_{DS} = 15$ V, $R_S = 0$, f = 1 kHz	-	5	-	KΩ
		$V_{DD} = 15$ V, $R_S = 360$ Ω, f = 1 kHz	-	20	-	KΩ
		$V_{DD} = 15$ V, $R_S = 360$ Ω, f = 1 kHz, $T_A = 125^oC$	-	23	-	KΩ
Drain-to-Source Cutoff Current	$I_{DS(off)}$	$V_{DS} = 15$ V, $V_{GS} = -6$ V	-	1	50	μA
		$V_{DS} = 15$ V, $V_{GS} = -6$ V, $T_A = 125^oC$	-	2	-	μA
		$V_{DS} = 35$ V, $V_{GS} = -6$ V	-	-	75	μA
Equivalent Input Noise Voltage	e_n	$V_{DS} = 15$ V, $R_S = 0$, $R_g = 0$, f = 1 kHz	-	0.06	-	μV/$\sqrt{Hz}$
		$V_{DD} = 15$ V, $R_S = 360$ Ω, $R_g = 0$, f = 1 kHz	-	0.06	-	μV/$\sqrt{Hz}$
Audio Spot Noise Figure**	NF	$V_{DD} = 15$ V, $R_S = 360$ Ω, $R_g = 1$ MΩ, f = 1 kHz	-	0.86	-	dB
Small-Signal, Short-Circuit, Input Capacitance	C_{iss}	$V_{DS} = 15$ V, $R_S = 0$, f = 1 MHz	-	3.3	-	pF
		$V_{DD} = 15$ V, $R_S = 360$ Ω, f = 1 MHz	-	3	7	pF
Small-Signal, Short-Circuit, Reverse Transfer Capacitance	C_{rss}	$V_{DS} = 15$ V, $R_S = 0$, f = 1 MHz	-	0.21	-	pF
		$V_{DD} = 15$ V, $R_S = 360$ Ω, f = 1 MHz	-	0.19	0.30	pF
Power Gain (Neutralized) *(See Fig.2)*	G_{ps}	$V_{DD} = 15$ V, $R_S = 360$ Ω, f = 200 MHz	15	17	-	dB
Noise Figure *(See Fig.2)*	NF	$V_{DD} = 15$ V, $R_S = 360$ Ω, f = 200 MHz	-	4	6	dB

* Pulse Test: Pulse Duration = 300 μS, Duty factor ≤ 0.10.

** Noise Figure = $10 \log_{10}\left[1 + \dfrac{e_n^2}{4 \text{ KT BW } R_g}\right]$ where K = 1.38×10^{-23}; T = Temperature in ^{o}Kelvin; BW = Bandwidth in Hz;
R_g = Generator resistance

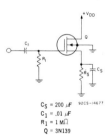

C_S = 200 μF 92CS-14677
C_1 = .01 μF
R_1 = 1 MΩ
Q = 3N139

Fig.1 - Basic test circuit.

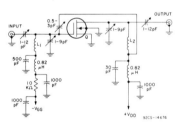

L_1 = 4 turns #20 AWG wire 3/16 "dia.,1/2 "long
L_2 = 3-1/2 turns #20 AWG wire 3/8 "dia.,approx. 1/2 "long
Q = 3N139

Fig.2 - 200-MHz noise figure & power gain test circuit.

TYPICAL CHARACTERISTICS

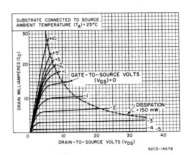

Fig.3 - Drain current vs. drain-to-source voltage.

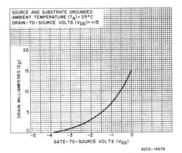

Fig.4 - Drain current vs. gate-to-source voltage.

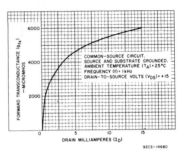

Fig.5 - 1-kHz forward transconductance vs. drain current.

Courtesy of Radio Corporation of America

MOS FIELD-EFFECT TRANSISTOR
For Critical Chopper Applications & Multiplex Service

3N138

RCA-3N138‡ is a silicon, insulated-gate field-effect transistor of the N-channel depletion type, utilizing the MOS* construction. It is intended primarily for critical chopper and multiplex applications up to 60MHz.

This transistor features a New Terminal Arrangement in which the gate and source connections are interchanged to provide maximum isolation between the output (drain) and the input (gate) terminals. Although this new basing configuration does not appreciably change the measured device feedback capacitance, it permits the use of external interterminal shields to reduce the feedback due to external capacitances, particularly on printed circuit boards. This feature makes it possible to minimize feedthrough capacitance.

The insulated gate provides a very high value of input resistance (10^{14} ohms typ.) which is relatively insensitive to temperature and is independent of gate-bias conditions (positive, negative, or zero bias). The 3N138 also features extremely low feedthrough capacitance (0.18pF typ.) and zero inherent offset voltage.

The 3N138 is hermetically sealed in the JEDEC TO-72 package and features a gate metallization that covers the entire source-to-drain channel.

‡ Formerly Dev. No. TA7032.
* Metal-Oxide-Semiconductor.

Maximum Ratings, Absolute-Maximum Values:

(Substrate connected to source unless otherwise specified)

DRAIN-TO-SOURCE VOLTAGE, V_{DS}	+35 max.	V
DRAIN-TO-SUBSTRATE VOLTAGE, V_{DB}	+35, −0.3 max.	V
SOURCE-TO-SUBSTRATE VOLTAGE, V_{SB}	+35, −0.3 max.	V
DC GATE-TO-SOURCE VOLTAGE, V_{GS}	±10 max.	V
PEAK GATE-TO-SOURCE VOLTAGE, V_{GS}	±14 max.	V
PEAK VOLTAGE, GATE-TO-ALL OTHER TERMINALS: V_{GS}, V_{GD}, V_{GB}, non-repetitive	±45 max.	V
DRAIN CURRENT, I_D (Pulse duration 20 ms, duty factor ≤ 0.10)	50 max.	mA
TRANSISTOR DISSIPATION, P_T: At ambient temperatures from −65 to +125°C	150 max.	mW
AMBIENT TEMPERATURE RANGE:		
Storage	−65 to +150	°C
Operating	−65 to +125	°C
LEAD TEMPERATURE (During Soldering): At distances ≥ 1/32″ to seating surface for 10 seconds max.	265 max.	°C

SILICON INSULATED-GATE FIELD-EFFECT TRANSISTOR
N-Channel Depletion Type
For Critical Chopper Applications and Multiplex Service up to 60 MHz:

in Military Communications, Navigation, and Instrumentation Equipment

in Industrial Instrumentation and Control Circuits

JEDEC TO-72

Applications
* Servo Amplifiers
* Telemetry Amplifiers
* Computer Operational Amplifiers
* Sampling Circuits
* Electrometer Amplifiers

Features
* new terminal arrangement

1 - Drain
2 - Source
3 - Insulated Gate
4 - Bulk (Substrate) and Case

* excellent thermal stability
* zero inherent offset voltage
* low leakage current: 10 pA max.
* low "on" resistance —
  r_{DS}(on) = 240Ω typ. (V_{GS} = 0V)
* high "off" resistance —
  R_{DS}(off) = 10^{10}Ω typ.
* low feedback capacitance —
  C_{rss} = 0.18pF typ.
* low input capacitance —
  C_{iss} = 3pF typ.
* symmetrical configuration —
  permits interchangeability of drain and source

ELECTRICAL CHARACTERISTICS, at T$_A$ = 25° C, Unless Otherwise Specified. Substrate Connected to Source.

CHARACTERISTICS	SYMBOLS	TEST CONDITIONS	LIMITS Type 3N138			UNITS
			Min.	Typ.	Max.	
Gate-Leakage Current	I$_{GSS}$	V$_{GS}$ = ± 10, V$_{DS}$ = 0, T$_A$ = 25°C V$_{GS}$ = ± 10, V$_{DS}$ = 0, T$_A$ = 125°C	— —	0.1 20	10 200	pA pA
Drain-to-Source "ON" Resistance	r$_{DS}$(on)	V$_{GS}$ = 0, V$_{DS}$ = 0, f = 1 KHz, T$_A$ = 25°C V$_{GS}$ = +10, V$_{DS}$ = 0, f = 1 KHz, T$_A$ = 25°C V$_{GS}$ = 0, V$_{DS}$ = 0, f = 1 KHz, T$_A$ = 125°C	— — —	240 135 350	300 — —	Ω Ω Ω
Drain-to-Source "OFF" Resistance	R$_{DS}$(off)	V$_{GS}$ = −10, V$_{DS}$ = +1	2 × 10^8	10^{10}	—	Ω
Drain-to-Source Cutoff Current	I$_D$(off)	V$_{GS}$ = −10, V$_{DS}$ = +1, T$_A$ = 25°C V$_{GS}$ = −10, V$_{DS}$ = +1, T$_A$ = 125°C	— —	0.01 0.01	0.5 0.5	nA μA
Small-Signal, Short-Circuit, Reverse Transfer Capacitance	C$_{rss}$	V$_{GS}$ = −10, V$_{DS}$ = 0, f = 1 MHz	—	0.18	0.25	pF
Small-Signal, Short-Circuit, Input Capacitance	C$_{iss}$	V$_{GS}$ = −10, V$_{DS}$ = 0, f = 1 MHz	—	3	5	pF
Zero-Gate-Bias Forward Transconductance	g$_{fs}$	V$_{GS}$ = 0, V$_{DS}$ = 12	—	6000	—	μmho
Offset Voltage	V$_O$	V$_{GS}$ = ± 10, V$_{DS}$ = 0	—	0*	—	V

* In measurements of Offset Voltage, thermocouple effects and contact potentials in the measurement setup may cause erroneous readings of 1 microvolt or more. These errors may be minimized by the use of solder having a low thermal e.m.f., such as Leeds & Northrup No. 107-1.0.1, or equivalent.

OPERATING CONSIDERATIONS

The flexible leads of the 3N138 are usually soldered to the circuit elements. As in the case of any high-frequency semiconductor device, the tips of soldering irons should be grounded, and appropriate precautions should be taken to protect the device against high electric fields.

This device should not be connected into or disconnected from circuits with the power on because high transient voltages may cause permanent damage to the device.

TYPICAL CHARACTERISTICS

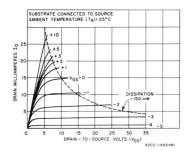

Fig. 1 – Drain Current vs Drain-to-Source Voltage

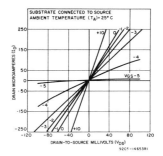

Fig. 2 – Low-Level Drain Current vs
Drain-to-Source Voltage

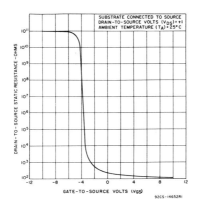

Fig. 3 – Drain-to-Source Static Resistance vs
Gate-to-Source Voltage

Courtesy of Radio Corporation of America

RCA MOS Insulated-Gate Field-Effect Transistors

Types for RF Applications in Industrial and Military Equipment

RCA Type	Features	Drain-to-Source Volts V_{DS} Neg.	Drain-to-Source Volts V_{DS} Pos.	Gate 1-to-Source Volts V_{G1S} DC	Gate 1-to-Source Volts V_{G1S} PeakAC	Gate 2-to-Source Volts V_{G2S} DC	Gate 2-to-Source Volts V_{G2S} PeakAC	Max. Drain Current I_D# mA	Device Dissipation at T_A=25°C P_T‡ mW	Ambient Temperature T_A °C Operating and Storage

Absolute Maximum Ratings

Single-Gate Devices■

RCA Type	Features	V_{DS} Neg.	V_{DS} Pos.	V_{G1S} DC	PeakAC	V_{G2S} DC	PeakAC	I_D mA	P_T mW	T_A
3N128	**200-MHz High-Gain, Low-Noise, RF Amplifier** • Low Feedback Capacitance – C_{rs} = 0.2 pF max. • High Forward Transconductance – 7500 μmho typ. • Superior Cross-Modulation Characteristics • High VHF Power Gain – 18dB typ. at 200 MHz • Low VHF Noise Figure – 3.5 dB typ. at 200 MHz • Bulk (Substrate) Terminal Available	0	+20	+1 to −8	±15	—	—	50	400	−65 to +175
3N139	**Video, AF and RF Amplifier** • Low Input Capacitance – C_{is} = 3 pF typ. • High Gate Voltage – V_{GS} = ± 10V DC • High Forward Transconductance – 6000 μmho typ. • High Power Gain – 17 dB typ. at 200 MHz • Low Noise Figure – 4 dB typ. at 200 MHz • High Drain-to-Source Voltage V_{DS} = + 35V max. • Bulk (Substrate) Terminal Available	0	+35	±10	±14	—	—	50	400	−65 to +175
3N142	**100-MHz High-Gain, Low-Noise, RF Amplifier and Oscillator** • Power Gain (unneutralized) – 17 dB typ. at 100 MHz • High Forward Transconductance – 7500 μmho typ. • Low Noise Figure – 2.5 dB typ. at 100 MHz • Bulk (Substrate) Terminal Available	0	+20	+1 to −8	±15	—	—	50	400	−65 to +175
3N143	**200-MHz Mixer and Oscillator** • Conversion Power Gain – 13.5 dB typ at 200/30 MHz • Bulk (Substrate) Terminal Available	0	+20	+1 to −8	±15	—	—	50	400	−65 to +175
3N152	**200-MHz Premium-Performance RF Amplifier** • Low RF Noise • High Forward Transconductance – 7500 μmho typ. • Bulk (Substrate) Terminal Available	0	+20	+1 to −8	±15	—	—	50	400	−65 to +175
40467	**200-MHz General-Purpose RF Amplifier and Oscillator** • High Forward Transconductance – 7500 μmho typ. • Low Noise Figure – 4.5 dB typ. at 200 MHz • Power Gain – 16 dB typ. at 200 MHz • Low Feedback Capacitance C_{rs} = 0.2 pF max. • Bulk (Substrate) Terminal Available	0	+20	±15	±15	—	—	50	400	−65 to +175

Dual-Gate Devices

RCA Type	Features	V_{DS} Neg.	V_{DS} Pos.	V_{G1S} DC	PeakAC	V_{G2S} DC	PeakAC	I_D mA	P_T mW	T_A
3N140	**200-MHz High-Gain, Low-Noise, Gain-Controlled RF Amplifier** • Power Gain (unneutralized) – 19 dB typ. at 200 MHz • Low Noise Figure – 3.5 dB typ. at 200 MHz • High Forward Transconductance – 8000 μmho typ. • Useful up to 300 MHz • Excellent AGC Capability from High-Impedance Source	0	+20	+1 to −8	+20 to −8	−8 to 40% of V_{DS}	−8 to +20	50	400	−65 to +175
3N141	**200-MHz Mixer** • 200-MHz Conversion Gain – 18 dB typ. • High Forward Conversion Transconductance – 10,000 μmho typ. • Useful up to 300 MHz • Product Detector • Current Source	0	+20	+1 to −8	+20 to −8	−8 to 40% of V_{DS}	−8 to +20	50	400	−65 to +175
TA7153▲	**400-MHz High-Gain, Low-Noise, Gain-Controlled RF Amplifier** • Power Gain (unneutralized) – 14 dB typ. at 400 MHz • Low Noise Figure – 4.5 dB typ. at 400 MHz • High Forward Transconductance – 10,000 μmho typ. • Useful up to 500 MHz	0	+20	+1 to −8	+20 to −8	−8 to 40% of V_{DS}	−8 to +20	50	400	−65 to +175
TA7035▲†	**200-MHz RF Amplifier and Mixer** • Power gain – 20 dB typ. at 200 MHz • Noise Figure – 4 dB typ. at 200 MHz • Forward Transconductance – 10,000 μmho typ. • Operation to 250 MHz • Bulk (Substrate) Terminal Available	0	+20	+1 to −8	+20 to −8	−8 to 40% of V_{DS}	−8 to +20	50	400	−65 to +175

▲ Developmental Type
Pulsed: pulse duration ≦ 20 ms; duty factor ≦ 0.15
†Plastic-Case Double-Ended Type

■ Bulk (Substrate) brought out as a separate terminal lead (connected to case internally).
‡ For derating information, see Technical Bulletins

Typical Electrical Characteristics at $T_A = 25\,°C$ (With Substrate Connected to Source)

Package	Power Gain (G_{ps}) dB			NF & Power Gain Test Freq. MHz	Noise Figure (NF) dB		Forward Trans-conductance g_{fs} μmho		Gate Leakage Current I_{GSS} nA	Input Cap. C_{iss} pF	Gate-to-Source Cutoff Volts		Reverse Transfer Capacitance C_{rss} pF		RCA Type
	Min.	Typ.	Max.		Typ.	Max.	Min.	Typ.	Max.		Gate 1 V_{G1S} (off)	Gate 2 V_{G2S} (off)	Typ.	Max.	
TO-72	15	18	—	200	3.5	5	5000	7500	50 pA	5.5	−3.5 typ. −8 max.	—	0.12	0.2	3N128
TO-72	14	17	—	200	4	6	3000	6000	1	3	−6 max.	—	0.18	0.25	3N139
TO-72	15	17	—	100	2.5	5	4000	7500	1	5.5	—	—	0.12	0.2	3N142
TO-72	10φ	13.5φ	—	f_{in} 200 f_{out} 30	—	—	5000◊	7500◊	1	5.5	−3.5 typ. −8 max.	—	0.12	0.2	3N143
TO-72	16	20	—	200	2.5	3.5	5000	7500	1	5.5	—	—	0.12	0.2	3N152
TO-72	12	16	—	200	4.5	6	—	7500	1	5.5	—	—	0.12	0.2	40467
TO-72	16	18	22	200	3.5	4.5	6000	10,000	1	5.5	−2 typ. −4 max.	−2 typ. −4 max.	0.02	0.03	3N140
TO-72	—	18φ	—	f_{in} 200 f_{out} 30	—	—	6000◊	10,000◊	1	5.5	−2 typ. −4 max.	−2 typ. −4 max.	0.02	0.03	3N141
TO-72	12	14	—	400	4.5	6	6000	10,000	1	4.5	−2 typ. −4 max.	−2 typ. −4 max.	0.02	0.03	TA7153▲
Double Ended Plastic	—	18	—	200	3.5	—	—	10,000	1	—	−4 max.	−4 max.	0.03	0.04	TA7035▲

μ Conversion gain ◊ Conversion transconductance

Courtesy of Radio Corporation of America

DIMENSIONAL OUTLINE
JEDEC TO-72

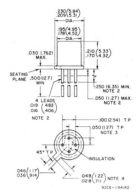

92CS-1194IR2

Dimensions in inches and millimeters

Note 1: *Dimensions in parentheses are in millimeters and are derived from the basic inch dimensions as indicated.*

Note 2: The specified lead diameter applies in the zone between 0.050" (1.27 mm) and 0.250" (6.35 mm) from the seating plane. From 0 250" (6.35 mm) to the end of the lead a maximum diameter of 0.021" (0.533 mm) is held. Outside of these zones, the lead diameter is not controlled.

Note 3: Leads having a maximum diameter of 0.019" (0.482 mm) at a gauging plane of 0.054" (1.372 mm) + 0.001" (0.025 mm) - 0.000" (0.000 mm) below seating plane shall be within 0.007" (0.177 mm) of their true position (location) relative to a maximum width of tab.

Note 4: Measured from actual maximum diameter.

TERMINAL DIAGRAM

1 - Drain
2 - Source
3 - Insulated Gate
4 - Bulk (Substrate)
    and Case

Courtesy of Radio Corporation of America

TYPES 2N4874 THRU 2N4876
N-P-N EPITAXIAL PLANAR SILICON TRANSISTORS

DESIGNED FOR VHF THRU MICROWAVE APPLICATIONS

- Ideal Broad-Band Amplifiers for CATV
  Line Amplifiers (50 MHz to 250 MHz)
- Linear Amplifiers for Single-Sideband Applications

Calculated f_{max}† ...1.9 GHz Min (2N4874)

*mechanical data

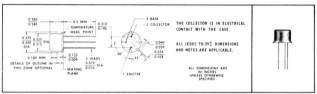

‡TO-39 is similar to TO-5 except for minimum lead length.

*absolute maximum ratings at 25°C free-air temperature (unless otherwise noted)

	2N4874	2N4875	2N4876
Collector-Base Voltage	30 V	40 V	40 V
Collector-Emitter Voltage (See Note 1)	20 V	25 V	30 V
Emitter-Base Voltage	2 V	2 V	2 V
Continuous Collector Current	←—— 200 mA ——→		
Continuous Device Dissipation at (or below) 25°C Free-Air Temperature (See Note 2)	←—— 720 mW ——→		
Continuous Device Dissipation at (or below) 25°C Case Temperature (See Note 3)	←—— 6 W ——→		
Storage Temperature Range	←— −65°C to 200°C —→		
Lead Temperature ¹⁄₁₆ Inch from Case for 10 Seconds	←—— 300°C ——→		

NOTES: 1. This value applies between 0 and 100 mA collector current when the base-emitter diode is open-circuited.
2. Derate linearly to 175°C free-air temperature at the rate of 4.8 mW/deg.
3. Derate linearly to 175°C case temperature at the rate of 40 mW/deg.

*Indicates JEDEC registered data.

†Maximum Frequency of Oscillation may be calculated from the equation: f_{max} (MHz) $= 200 \sqrt{\dfrac{|h_{fe}| \times f_{meas} \text{ (MHz)}}{r_{b'} C_c \text{ (ps)}}}$

Courtesy of Texas Instruments Incorporated

TYPES 2N4874 THRU 2N4876
N-P-N EPITAXIAL PLANAR SILICON TRANSISTORS

*electrical characteristics at 25°C free-air temperature (unless otherwise noted)

	PARAMETER	TEST CONDITIONS	2N4874		2N4875		2N4876		UNIT
			MIN	MAX	MIN	MAX	MIN	MAX	
$V_{(BR)CBO}$	Collector-Base Breakdown Voltage	$I_C = 100\ \mu A,\ I_E = 0$	30		40		40		V
$V_{(BR)CEO}$	Collector-Emitter Breakdown Voltage	$I_C = 10\ mA,\quad I_B = 0,\qquad$ See Note 4	20		25		30		V
I_{CBO}	Collector Cutoff Current	$V_{CB} = 15\ V,\quad I_E = 0$		0.5		0.5		0.5	μA
		$V_{CB} = 15\ V,\quad I_E = 0,\qquad T_A = 150°C$		0.5		0.5		0.5	mA
I_{EBO}	Emitter Cutoff Current	$V_{EB} = 2\ V,\quad I_C = 0$		10		10		10	μA
h_{fe}	Small-Signal Common-Emitter Forward Current Transfer Ratio	$V_{CE} = 10\ V,\quad I_C = 50\ mA,\ f = 1\ kHz$	20	200	20	200	20	200	
$|h_{fe}|$	Small-Signal Common-Emitter Forward Current Transfer Ratio	$V_{CE} = 10\ V,\quad I_C = 20\ mA,\ f = 100\ MHz$	7	24	6	24			
		$V_{CE} = 10\ V,\quad I_C = 50\ mA,\ f = 100\ MHz$	9	25	8	25	6.5		
C_{cb}	Collector-Base Capacitance	$V_{CB} = 10\ V,\quad I_E = 0,\qquad f = 1\ MHz,$ See Note 5		3.5		3.5		3.5	pF
$r_b'C_c$	Collector-Base Time Constant	$V_{CB} = 10\ V,\quad I_E = -50\ mA, f = 79.8\ MHz$		10		10		10	ps

NOTES: 4. These parameters must be measured using pulse techniques. $t_p = 300\ \mu s$, duty cycle $\leq 2\%$.
 5. Collector-Base Capacitance is measured using three-terminal measurement techniques with the emitter guarded.

*operating characteristics at 25°C free-air temperature

	PARAMETER	TEST CONDITIONS	2N4874	2N4875	2N4876	UNIT
			MIN	MIN	MIN	
G_{PE}	Large-Signal Common-Emitter Insertion Power Gain	$V_{BB} = 20\ V,\ I_E = -100\ mA,$ $P_{IE} = 0.1\ W,\ f = 400\ MHz,$ See Figure 1	10	9.5	8.5	dB

*PARAMETER MEASUREMENT INFORMATION

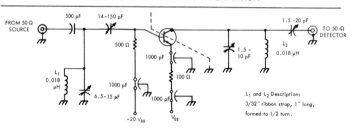

*Indicates JEDEC registered data   FIGURE 1 — 400-MHz INSERTION-POWER-GAIN TEST CIRCUIT

Courtesy of Texas Instruments Incorporated

TYPES 2N4874 THRU 2N4876
N-P-N EPITAXIAL PLANAR SILICON TRANSISTORS

TYPICAL CHARACTERISTICS

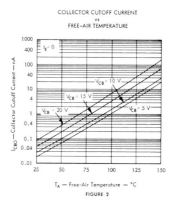

COLLECTOR CUTOFF CURRENT
vs
FREE–AIR TEMPERATURE

FIGURE 2

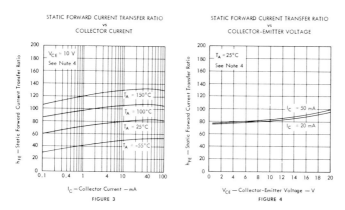

FIGURE 3

FIGURE 4

NOTE 4: These parameters must be measured using pulse techniques. $t_p = 300 \ \mu s$, duty cycle $\leq 2\%$.

TYPES 2N4874 THRU 2N4876
N-P-N EPITAXIAL PLANAR SILICON TRANSISTORS

TYPICAL CHARACTERISTICS

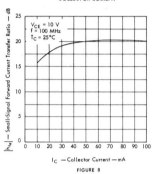

MAGNITUDE OF SMALL-SIGNAL COMMON-EMITTER
FORWARD CURRENT TRANSFER RATIO
vs
COLLECTOR CURRENT

FIGURE 8

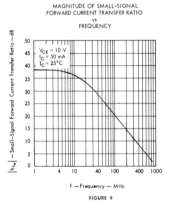

MAGNITUDE OF SMALL-SIGNAL
FORWARD CURRENT TRANSFER RATIO
vs
FREQUENCY

FIGURE 9

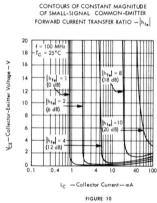

CONTOURS OF CONSTANT MAGNITUDE
OF SMALL-SIGNAL COMMON-EMITTER
FORWARD CURRENT TRANSFER RATIO $-|h_{fe}|$

FIGURE 10

TYPES 2N4874 THRU 2N4876
N-P-N EPITAXIAL PLANAR SILICON TRANSISTORS

TYPICAL CHARACTERISTICS

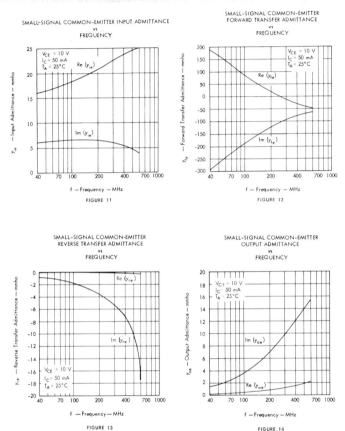

SMALL-SIGNAL COMMON-EMITTER INPUT ADMITTANCE
vs
FREQUENCY

FIGURE 11

SMALL-SIGNAL COMMON-EMITTER
FORWARD TRANSFER ADMITTANCE
vs
FREQUENCY

FIGURE 12

SMALL-SIGNAL COMMON-EMITTER
REVERSE TRANSFER ADMITTANCE
vs
FREQUENCY

FIGURE 13

SMALL-SIGNAL COMMON-EMITTER
OUTPUT ADMITTANCE
vs
FREQUENCY

FIGURE 14

Courtesy of Texas Instruments Incorporated

TYPES 2N4416, 2N4416A
N-CHANNEL EPITAXIAL PLANAR SILICON FIELD-EFFECT TRANSISTORS

FOR VHF AMPLIFIER AND MIXER APPLICATIONS

- High Power Gain...10 dB Min at 400 MHz
- Low Noise Figure...4 dB Max at 400 MHz
- High Transconductance...4000 μmho Min at 400 MHz
- Low C_{rss} ...0.8 pF Max
- High y_{fs}/C_{iss} Ratio (High-Frequency Figure-of-Merit)
- Cross-Modulation Minimized by Square-Law Transfer Characteristic
- Recommended for Use in VHF-UHF Bandpass Amplifiers
- Excellent for General-Purpose Amplifier and Chopper Applications

*mechanical data

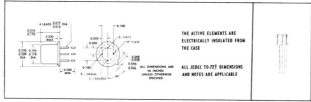

THE ACTIVE ELEMENTS ARE ELECTRICALLY INSULATED FROM THE CASE

ALL DIMENSIONS ARE IN INCHES UNLESS OTHERWISE SPECIFIED

ALL JEDEC TO-72† DIMENSIONS AND NOTES ARE APPLICABLE

†TO-72 outline is same as TO-18 outline with the addition of a fourth lead.

absolute maximum ratings at 25°C free-air temperature (unless otherwise noted)

	2N4416	2N4416A
*Drain-Gate Voltage	30 V	35 V
*Drain-Source Voltage	30 V	35 V
*Reverse Gate-Source Voltage	−30 V	−35 V
*Continuous Forward Gate Current	⟵ 10 mA ⟶	
*Continuous Device Dissipation at (or below) 25°C Free-Air Temperature (See Note 1)	⟵ 300 mW ⟶	
Continuous Device Dissipation at (or below) 125°C Case Temperature (See Note 2)	⟵ 450 mW ⟶	
*Storage Temperature Range	−65°C to 200°C	
*Lead Temperature 1/16 Inch from Case for 60 Seconds	⟵ 300°C ⟶	

NOTES: 1. Derate linearly to 200°C free-air temperature at the rate of 1.7 mW/deg.

2. Derate linearly to 200°C case temperature at the rate of 6 mW/deg.

*Indicates JEDEC registered data

Courtesy of Texas Instruments Incorporated

TYPES 2N4416, 2N4416A
N-CHANNEL EPITAXIAL PLANAR SILICON FIELD-EFFECT TRANSISTORS

electrical characteristics at 25°C free-air temperature (unless otherwise noted)

PARAMETER		TEST CONDITIONS	2N4416 MIN	2N4416 MAX	2N4416A MIN	2N4416A MAX	UNIT
$V_{(BR)GSS}$	Gate-Source Breakdown Voltage	$I_G = -1\ \mu A,\quad V_{DS} = 0$	-30^*		-35^*		V
$V_{GS(f)}$	Gate-Source Forward Voltage	$I_G = 1\ mA,\quad V_{DS} = 0$		1^*		1^*	V
I_{GSS}	Gate Reverse Current	$V_{GS} = -20\ V,\quad V_{DS} = 0$		-0.1^*		-0.1^*	nA
		$V_{GS} = -20\ V,\quad V_{DS} = 0,\quad T_A = 150°C$		-0.2^* $-0.1†$		-0.2^* $-0.1†$	μA
$V_{GS(off)}$	Gate-Source Cutoff Voltage	$V_{DS} = 15\ V,\quad I_D = 1\ nA$		-6^*	-2.5^*	-6^*	V
V_{GS}	Gate-Source Voltage	$V_{DS} = 15\ V,\quad I_D = 0.5\ mA$	-1^*	-5.5^*	-1^*	-5.5^*	V
I_{DSS}	Zero-Gate-Voltage Drain Current	$V_{DS} = 15\ V,\quad V_{GS} = 0,$ See Note 3	5^*	15^*	5^*	15^*	mA
$|y_{fs}|$	Small-Signal Common-Source Forward Transfer Admittance	$V_{DS} = 15\ V,$	4.5^*	7.5^*	4.5^*	7.5^*	mmho
$|y_{os}|$	Small-Signal Common-Source Output Admittance	$V_{GS} = 0,$ $f = 1\ kHz$		0.05^*		0.05^*	mmho
C_{iss}	Common-Source Short-Circuit Input Capacitance	$V_{DS} = 15\ V,$		4^*		4^*	
C_{rss}	Common-Source Short-Circuit Reverse Transfer Capacitance	$V_{GS} = 0,$		0.8^*		0.8^*	pF
C_{oss}	Common-Source Short-Circuit Output Capacitance	$f = 1\ MHz$		2^*		2^*	
$Re(y_{is})$	Small-Signal Common-Source Input Conductance	$V_{DS} = 15\ V,$		0.1^*		0.1^*	
$Im(y_{is})$	Small-Signal Common-Source Input Susceptance	$V_{GS} = 0,$		2.5^*		2.5^*	mmho
$Re(y_{os})$	Small-Signal Common-Source Output Conductance	$f = 100\ MHz$		0.075^*		0.075^*	
$Im(y_{os})$	Small-Signal Common-Source Output Susceptance			1^*		1^*	
$Re(y_{is})$	Small-Signal Common-Source Input Conductance			1^*		1^*	
$Im(y_{is})$	Small-Signal Common-Source Input Susceptance	$V_{DS} = 15\ V,$		10^*		10^*	
$Re(y_{fs})$	Small-Signal Common-Source Forward Transfer Conductance	$V_{GS} = 0,$	4^*		4^*		mmho
$Re(y_{os})$	Small-Signal Common-Source Output Conductance	$f = 400\ MHz$		0.1^*		0.1^*	
$Im(y_{os})$	Small-Signal Common-Source Output Susceptance			4^*		4^*	

NOTE 3: This parameter must be measured using pulse techniques. $t_p = 300\ \mu s$, duty cycle $\leq 1\%$.
†Texas Instruments guarantees this value in addition to the JEDEC registered value, which is also shown.

*operating characteristics at 25°C free-air temperature

PARAMETER		TEST CONDITIONS	MIN	MAX	UNIT
G_{ps}	Small-Signal Common-Source Neutralized Insertion Power Gain	$V_{DS} = 15\ V,\quad I_D = 5\ mA,\quad f = 100\ MHz,$ $R_G' = 1\ k\Omega,$ See Figure 1	18		dB
		$V_{DS} = 15\ V,\quad I_D = 5\ mA,\quad f = 400\ MHz,$ $R_G' = 1\ k\Omega,$ See Figure 1	10		
NF	Spot Noise Figure	$V_{DS} = 15\ V,\quad I_D = 5\ mA,\quad f = 100\ MHz,$ $R_G' = 1\ k\Omega,$ See Figure 1		2	dB
		$V_{DS} = 15\ V,\quad I_D = 5\ mA,\quad f = 400\ MHz,$ $R_G' = 1\ k\Omega,$ See Figure 1		4	

*Indicates JEDEC registered data

Courtesy of Texas Instruments Incorporated

TYPES 2N4416, 2N4416A
N-CHANNEL EPITAXIAL PLANAR SILICON FIELD-EFFECT TRANSISTORS

TYPICAL CHARACTERISTICS

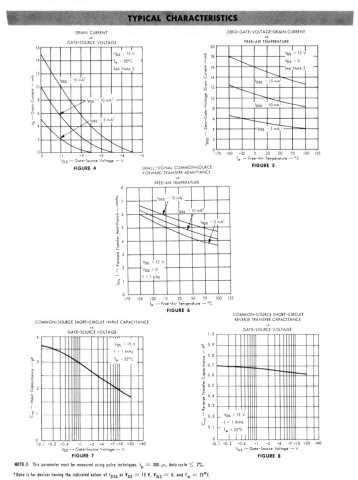

FIGURE 4

FIGURE 5

FIGURE 6

FIGURE 7

FIGURE 8

NOTE 3: This parameter must be measured using pulse techniques. $t_p = 300 \ \mu s$, duty cycle $\leq 2\%$.

†Data is for devices having the indicated values of I_{DSS} at $V_{DS} = 15 \ V$, $V_{GS} = 0$, and $T_A = 25°C$.

TYPES 2N4416, 2N4416A
N-CHANNEL EPITAXIAL PLANAR SILICON FIELD-EFFECT TRANSISTORS

TYPICAL CHARACTERISTICS

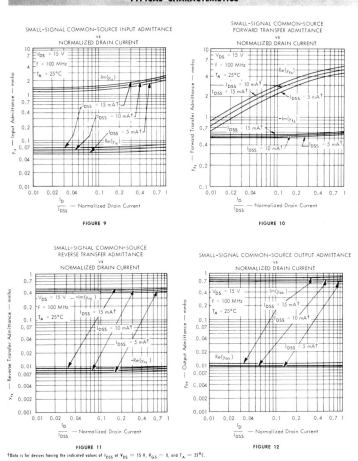

SMALL-SIGNAL COMMON-SOURCE INPUT ADMITTANCE
vs
NORMALIZED DRAIN CURRENT

FIGURE 9

SMALL-SIGNAL COMMON-SOURCE
FORWARD TRANSFER ADMITTANCE
vs
NORMALIZED DRAIN CURRENT

FIGURE 10

SMALL-SIGNAL COMMON-SOURCE
REVERSE TRANSFER ADMITTANCE
vs
NORMALIZED DRAIN CURRENT

FIGURE 11

SMALL-SIGNAL COMMON-SOURCE OUTPUT ADMITTANCE
vs
NORMALIZED DRAIN CURRENT

FIGURE 12

†Data is for devices having the indicated values of I_{DSS} at V_{DS} = 15 V, V_{GS} = 0, and T_A = 25°C.

Courtesy of Texas Instruments Incorporated

TYPES 2N4416, 2N4416A
N-CHANNEL EPITAXIAL PLANAR SILICON FIELD-EFFECT TRANSISTORS

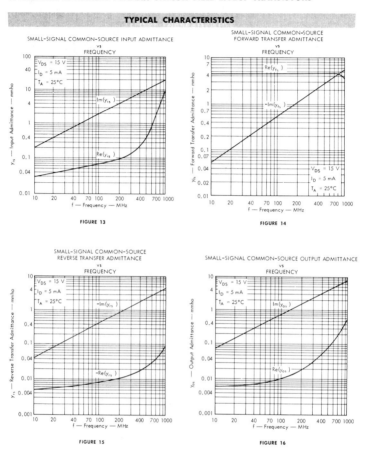

FIGURE 13

FIGURE 14

FIGURE 15

FIGURE 16

Courtesy of Texas Instruments Incorporated

——— *Germanium Milliwatt Transistors* ———

2N**464** thru 2N**467**
2N465 USA/JAN
2N466 JAN
2N467 USA/JAN

$V_{CB} = 45\ V$
h_{fe} – **to 112 (min)**
f_{α_b} – **to 1.2 MHz (typ)**

CASE 31
(TO-5)
All leads isolated

PNP germanium transistor for general purpose applications in the audio-frequency range.

MAXIMUM RATINGS

Rating	Symbol	2N464	2N465	2N466	2N467	Unit
Collector-Base Voltage	V_{CB}	45	45	35	35	Volts
Collector-Emitter Voltage	V_{CE}	40	30	20	15	Volts
Emitter-Base Voltage	V_{EB}	←——— 12 ———→				Volts
DC Collector Current	I_C	←——— 500 ———→				mA
Max. Junction & Storage Temperature	T_J and T_{stg}	←——— 100 ———→				°C
Collector Dissipation in Free Air	P_D	←——— 200 ———→				mW
Derate above 25°C		←——— 2.67 ———→				mW/°C
Thermal Resistance, Junction to Air	θ_{JA}	←——— 0.375 ———→				°C/mW

ELECTRICAL CHARACTERISTICS (T$_A$ = 25°C unless otherwise noted)

Characteristic		Symbol	Min	Typ	Max	Unit
Collector-Emitter Breakdown Voltage (I_C = 0.6 mAdc, R_{BE} = 10 K ohms)		BV_{CER}				Vdc
	2N464		40	–	–	
	2N465		30	–	–	
	2N466		20	–	–	
	2N467		15	–	–	
Collector-Base Cutoff Current (V_{CB} = 20 Vdc)		I_{CBO}	–	6	15	µAdc
Small Signal Current Gain Cutoff Frequency (V_{CB} = 6 Vdc, I_E = 1 mAdc)		$f_{\alpha b}$				MHz
	2N464		–	0.7	–	
	2N465		–	0.8	–	
	2N466		–	1.0	–	
	2N467		–	1.2	–	
Small Signal Current Gain (V_{CE} = 6 Vdc, I_E = 1.0 mAdc, f = 1 kHz)		h_{fe}				–
	2N464		14	26	–	
	2N465		27	45	–	
	2N466		56	90	–	
	2N467		112	180	–	

Courtesy of Motorola Semiconductor Products Inc.

——— *Germanium Milliwatt Transistors* ———

2N464 thru 2N467 (continued)

ELECTRICAL CHARACTERISTICS (continued)

Characteristic		Symbol	Min	Typ	Max	Unit
Small Signal Input Impedance (V_{CE} = 6 Vdc, I_E = 1.0 mAdc, f = 1 kHz)	2N464	h_{ie}	–	900	–	Ohms
	2N465		–	1400	–	
	2N466		–	3000	–	
	2N467		.–	5500	–	
Small Signal Power Gain (V_{CE} = 6 Vdc, I_E = 1.0 mAdc, f = 1 kHz, matched)	2N464	G_e	–	40	–	dB
	2N465		–	42	–	
	2N466		–	44	–	
	2N467		–	45	–	
Noise Figure (V_{CE} = 2.5 Vdc, I_E = 0.5 mAdc, f = 1 kHz, R_S = 10 Kohms, Δf = 1 Hz		NF	•–	–	22	dB

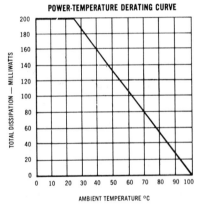

POWER-TEMPERATURE DERATING CURVE

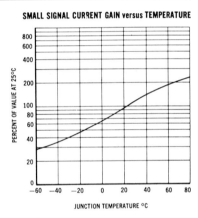

SMALL SIGNAL CURRENT GAIN versus TEMPERATURE

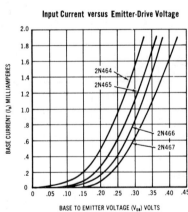

Input Current versus Emitter-Drive Voltage

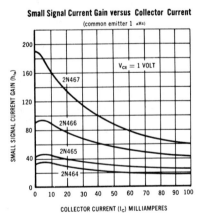

Small Signal Current Gain versus Collector Current
(common emitter 1 kHz)

Courtesy of Motorola Semiconductor Products Inc.

—— Power Transistors ——

2N4234 (SILICON)

2N4235

2N4236

$V_{CEO} = 40\text{-}80$ V
$I_C = 3$ A
$P_D = 1.0$ W

PNP silicon power transistors ideal for use as drivers, switches, and direct replacement of germanium medium-power devices. Complement to NPN 2N4237 thru 2N4239.

CASE 31
(TO-5)

Collector connected to case

MAXIMUM RATINGS

Rating	Symbol	2N4234	2N4235	2N4236	Unit
Collector-Emitter Voltage	V_{CEO}	40	60	80	Vdc
Collector-Base Voltage	V_{CB}	40	60	80	Vdc
Emitter-Base Voltage	V_{EB}	← 7 →			Vdc
Collector Current — Continuous	I_C	← 3.0 →			Adc
Base Current	I_B	← 0.2 →			Adc
Total Device Dissipation @ T_A = 25°C Derate above 25°C	P_D	← 1.0 → ← 5.7 →			Watt mW/°C
Total Device Dissipation @ T_C = 25°C Derate above 25°C	P_D	← 6 → ← 34 →			Watts mW/°C
Operating and Storage Junction Temperature Range	T_J, T_{stg}	← -65 to +200 →			°C

THERMAL CHARACTERISTICS

Characteristic	Symbol	Max	Unit
Thermal Resistance, Junction to Case	θJC	29	°C/W

FIGURE 1 — POWER-TEMPERATURE DERATING CURVE

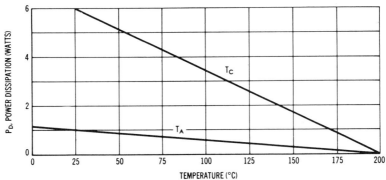

Safe Area Curves are indicated by Figure 2.

All limits are applicable and must be observed.

Courtesy of Motorola Semiconductor Products Inc.

——— *Power Transistors* ———

2N4234, 2N4235, 2N4236 (continued)

ELECTRICAL CHARACTERISTICS ($T_C = 25°C$ unless otherwise noted)

Characteristic		Symbol	Min	Max	Unit
OFF CHARACTERISTICS					
Collector-Emitter Sustaining Voltage * ($I_C = 100$ mAdc, $I_B = 0$)	2N4234 2N4235 2N4236	$BV_{CEO(sus)}$*	40 60 80	— — —	Vdc
Collector Cutoff Current ($V_{CE} = 30$ Vdc, $I_B = 0$) ($V_{CE} = 40$ Vdc, $I_B = 0$) ($V_{CE} = 60$ Vdc, $I_B = 0$)	2N4234 2N4235 2N4236	I_{CEO}	— — —	1.0 1.0 1.0	mAdc
Collector Cutoff Current ($V_{CE} = 40$ Vdc, $V_{BE(off)} = 1.5$ Vdc) ($V_{CE} = 60$ Vdc, $V_{BE(off)} = 1.5$ Vdc) ($V_{CE} = 80$ Vdc, $V_{BE(off)} = 1.5$ Vdc) ($V_{CE} = 30$ Vdc, $V_{BE(off)} = 1.5$ Vdc, $T_C = 150°C$) ($V_{CE} = 40$ Vdc, $V_{BE(off)} = 1.5$ Vdc, $T_C = 150°C$) ($V_{CE} = 60$ Vdc, $V_{BE(off)} = 1.5$ Vdc, $T_C = 150°C$)	2N4234 2N4235 2N4236 2N4234 2N4235 2N4236	I_{CEX}	— — — — — —	0.1 0.1 0.1 1.0 1.0 1.0	mAdc
Collector Cutoff Current ($V_{CB} = 40$ Vdc, $I_E = 0$) ($V_{CB} = 60$ Vdc, $I_E = 0$) ($V_{CB} = 80$ Vdc, $I_E = 0$)	2N4234 2N4235 2N4236	I_{CBO}	— — —	0.1 0.1 0.1	mAdc
Emitter Cutoff Current ($V_{BE} = 7$ Vdc, $I_C = 0$)		I_{EBO}	—	0.5	mAdc
ON CHARACTERISTICS					
DC Current Gain * ($I_C = 100$ mAdc, $V_{CE} = 1$ Vdc) ($I_C = 250$ mAdc, $V_{CE} = 1$ Vdc) ($I_C = 500$ mAdc, $V_{CE} = 1$ Vdc) ($I_C = 1.0$ Adc, $V_{CE} = 1$ Vdc)		h_{FE}*	40 30 20 10	— 150 — —	—
Collector-Emitter Saturation Voltage * ($I_C = 1.0$ Adc, $I_B = 125$ mAdc)		$V_{CE(sat)}$*	—	0.6	Vdc
Base-Emitter Saturation Voltage * ($I_C = 1.0$ Adc, $I_B = 100$ mAdc)		$V_{BE(sat)}$*	—	1.5	Vdc
Base-Emitter On Voltage ($I_C = 250$ mAdc, $V_{CE} = 1.0$ Vdc)		$V_{BE(on)}$	—	1.0	Vdc
SMALL-SIGNAL CHARACTERISTICS					
Current-Gain — Bandwidth Product ($I_C = 100$ mAdc, $V_{CE} = 10$ Vdc, $f = 1.0$ MHz)		f_T	3.0	—	MHz
Output Capacitance ($V_{CB} = 10$ Vdc, $I_E = 0$, $f = 100$ kHz)		C_{ob}	—	100	pF
Small-Signal Current Gain ($I_C = 50$ mAdc, $V_{CE} = 10$ Vdc, $f = 1.0$ kHz)		h_{fe}	25	—	—

*Pulse Test: PW $\leq 300 \mu s$, Duty Cycle $\leq 2\%$

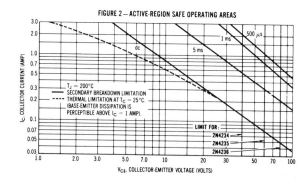

FIGURE 2 — ACTIVE-REGION SAFE OPERATING AREAS

The Safe Operating Area Curves indicate $I_C - V_{CE}$ limits below which the device will not enter secondary breakdown. Collector load lines for specific circuits must fall within the applicable Safe Area to avoid causing a catastrophic failure. To insure operation below the maximum T_J, power-temperature derating must be observed for both steady state and pulse power conditions.

Courtesy of Motorola Semiconductor Products Inc.

———— *Power Transistors* ————

2N4234, 2N4235, 2N4236 (continued)

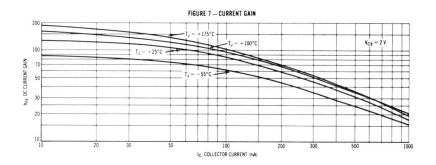

FIGURE 7 — CURRENT GAIN

SATURATION REGION CHARACTERISTICS

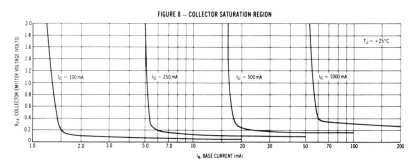

FIGURE 8 — COLLECTOR SATURATION REGION

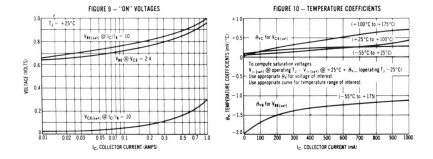

FIGURE 9 — "ON" VOLTAGES

FIGURE 10 — TEMPERATURE COEFFICIENTS

Courtesy of Motorola Semiconductor Products Inc.

—— *Switching and General Purpose Transistors* ——

2N**3250, A** (SILICON)
2N**3251, A**

2N3250A, 2N3251A JAN
2N3250,A, 2N3251,A HI-REL

$V_{CEO} = 40\text{-}60\,V$
$I_C = 200\,mA$
$f_T = 250\text{-}300\,MHz$

PNP silicon annular transistors for high-speed switching and amplifier applications.

Collector connected to case

CASE 22
(TO-18)

MAXIMUM RATINGS

Rating	Symbol	2N3250 2N3251	2N3250A 2N3251A	Unit
Collector-Base Voltage	V_{CB}	50	60	Vdc
Collector-Emitter Voltage	V_{CEO}	40	60	Vdc
Emitter-Base Voltage	V_{EB}	5		Vdc
Collector Current	I_C	200		mAdc
Total Device Dissipation @ 25°C Case Temperature Derating Factor Above 25°C	P_D	1.2 6.9		Watts mW/°C
Total Device Dissipation @ 25°C Ambient Temperature Derating Factor Above 25°C	P_D	0.36 2.06		Watts mW/°C
Junction Operating Temperature	T_J	200		°C
Storage Temperature Range	T_{stg}	−65 to +200		°C
Thermal Resistance	θ_{JA} θ_{JC}	0.49 0.15		°C/mW °C/mW

Courtesy of Motorola Semiconductor Products Inc.

—— *Switching and General Purpose Transistors* ——

2N3250, A, 2N3251, A (Continued)

ELECTRICAL CHARACTERISTICS (At 25°C unless otherwise noted)

Characteristic		Symbol	Min	Max	Unit
Collector Cutoff Current (V_{CE} = 40 Vdc, $V_{BE(off)}$ = 3 Vdc)		I_{CEX}	--	20	nAdc
Base Cutoff Current (V_{CE} = 40 Vdc, $V_{BE(off)}$ = 3 Vdc)		I_{BL}	--	50	nAdc
Collector-Base Breakdown Voltage (I_C = 10 μAdc)	2N3250, 2N3251 2N3250A, 2N3251A	BV_{CBO}	50 60	--	Vdc
Collector-Emitter Breakdown Voltage * (I_C = 10 mAdc)	2N3250, 2N3251 2N3250A, 2N3251A	BV_{CEO} *	40 60	--	Vdc
Emitter-Base Breakdown Voltage (I_E = 10 μAdc)		BV_{EBO}	5	--	Vdc
Collector Saturation Voltage * (I_C = 10 mAdc, I_B = 1 mAdc)		$V_{CE(sat)}$ *	--	0.25	Vdc
(I_C = 50 mAdc, I_B = 5 mAdc)			--	0.5	
Base-Emitter Saturation Voltage * (I_C = 10 mAdc, I_B = 1 mAdc)		$V_{BE(sat)}$ *	0.6	0.9	Vdc
(I_C = 50 mAdc, I_B = 5 mAdc)			--	1.2	
DC Forward Current Transfer Ratio * (I_C = 0.1 mAdc, V_{CE} = 1 Vdc)	2N3250, 2N3250A 2N3251, 2N3251A	h_{FE} *	40 80	-- --	--
(I_C = 1 mAdc, V_{CE} = 1 Vdc)	2N3250, 2N3250A 2N3251, 2N3251A		45 90	-- --	
(I_C = 10 mAdc, V_{CE} = 1 Vdc)	2N3250, 2N3250A 2N3251, 2N3251A		50 100	150 300	
(I_C = 50 mAdc, V_{CE} = 1 Vdc)	2N3250, 2N3250A 2N3251, 2N3251A		15 30	-- --	
Output Capacitance (V_{CB} = 10 Vdc, I_E = 0, f = 100 kHz)		C_{ob}	--	6	pF
Input Capacitance (V_{CB} = 1 Vdc, I_C = 0, f = 100 kHz)		C_{ib}	--	8	pF
Current-Gain - Bandwidth Product (I_C = 10 mAdc, V_{CE} = 20 Vdc, f = 100 MHz)	2N3250, 2N3250A 2N3251, 2N3251A	f_T	250 300	-- --	MHz

SMALL SIGNAL CHARACTERISTICS

Characteristic		Symbol	Min	Max	Unit
Small Signal Current Gain (I_C = 1.0 mA, V_{CE} = 10 V, f = 1 kHz)	2N3250, 2N3250A 2N3251, 2N3251A	h_{fe}	50 100	200 400	--
Voltage Feedback Ratio (I_C = 1.0 mA, V_{CE} = 10 V, f = 1 kHz)	2N3250, 2N3250A 2N3251, 2N3251A	h_{re}	-- --	10 20	$\times 10^{-4}$
Input Impedance (I_C = 1.0 mA, V_{CE} = 10 V, f = 1 kHz)	2N3250, 2N3250A 2N3251, 2N3251A	h_{ie}	1 2	6 12	kohms
Output Admittance (I_C = 1.0 mA, V_{CE} = 10 V, f = 1 kHz)	2N3250, 2N3250A 2N3251, 2N3251A	h_{oe}	4 10	40 60	μ mhos
Collector-Base Time Constant (I_C = 10 mA, V_{CE} = 20 V)		$r'_b C_C$	--	250	ps
Noise Figure (I_C = 100 μA, V_{CE} = 5 V, R_s = 1 kΩ, f = 100 Hz)		NF	--	6	dB

*Pulse Test: PW = 300 μs, Duty Cycle = 2%

Courtesy of Motorola Semiconductor Products Inc.

—— *Switching and General Purpose Transistors* ——

2N3250, A, 2N3251, A (Continued)

AUDIO SMALL SIGNAL CHARACTERISTICS
NOISE FIGURE VARIATIONS
($V_{CE} = 6$ V, $T_A = 25°C$)

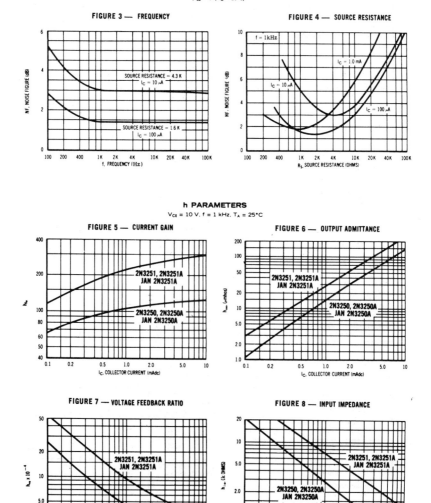

FIGURE 3 — FREQUENCY

FIGURE 4 — SOURCE RESISTANCE

h PARAMETERS
$V_{CE} = 10$ V, $f = 1$ kHz, $T_A = 25°C$

FIGURE 5 — CURRENT GAIN

FIGURE 6 — OUTPUT ADMITTANCE

FIGURE 7 — VOLTAGE FEEDBACK RATIO

FIGURE 8 — INPUT IMPEDANCE

Courtesy of Motorola Semiconductor Products Inc.

—— Switching and General Purpose Transistors ——

2N3250, A, 2N3251, A (Continued)

FIGURE 9 — NORMALIZED CURRENT GAIN CHARACTERISTICS

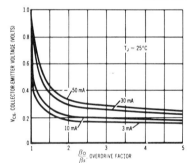

FIGURE 10 — COLLECTOR SATURATION REGION

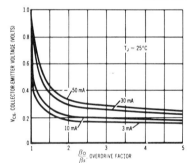

This graph shows the effect of base current on collector current. β_O is the current gain of the transistor at 1 volt, and β_F (forced gain) is the ratio of I_C/I_{BF} in a circuit. EXAMPLE: For type 2N3251, estimate a base current (I_{BF}) to insure saturation at a temperature of 25°C and a collector current of 10 mA.

Observe that at $I_C - 10$ mA an overdrive factor of at least 2.5 is required to drive the transistor well into the saturation region. From Figure 9, it is seen that h_{FE} @ 1 volts is typically 167 (guaranteed limits from the Table of Characteristics can be used for "worst case" design) . . .

$$\frac{\beta_O}{\beta_F} = \frac{h_{FE} @ 1 \text{ Volt}}{I_C/I_{BF}} \qquad 2.5 = \frac{167}{10 \text{ mA}/I_{BF}} \qquad I_{BF} \approx 6.68 \text{ mA typ}$$

FIGURE 11 — SATURATION VOLTAGES

FIGURE 12 — TEMPERATURE COEFFICIENTS

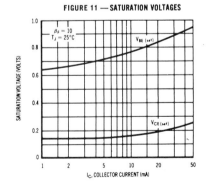

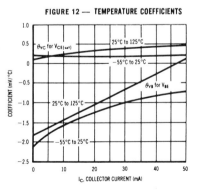

Courtesy of Motorola Semiconductor Products Inc.

Industrial

RELIABILITY-INDEX

2N1924
2N1925
2N1926

The General Electric types 2N1924, 2N1925, and 2N1926 are PNP germanium alloy transistors for high voltage general purpose low frequency applications.

Excellent reliability in use is assured by inclusion of a 100% hermeticity test* and military environmental testing.

Reliable circuit design is assured by a unique Reliability-Index, and high temperature I_{CBO} and low temperature forward current gain 1000 hour life end points.

The high value of Reliability-Index is achieved by exacting control of parts and processes, and getter encapsulation, to prevent junction contamination.

Voltages

Collector to Base	V_{CBO}	— 60 volts
Collector to Emitter ($R_{BE} \leqq 10K$)	V_{CER}	— 40 volts
Collector to Emitter ($R_{BE} \leqq 10K$) ($V_{BE} = +1.5v$)	V_{CEX}	— 50 volts
Emitter to Base	V_{EBO}	— 25 volts
Collector Current (RMS)	I_{CM}	— 500 ma

Temperatures

Storage	T_{STG}	— 65 to + 100°C
Operating	T_j	— 65 to + 85°C
Lead Temperature, 1/16″ ±1/32″ from case for 10 seconds maximum		260°C
Total Transistor Dissipation	P_T	225 mw

(Derate 3.7 mw/°C increase in ambient temperature above 25°C)

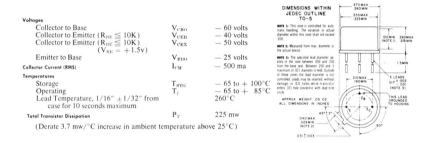

The Reliability-Index (RI_1) has been developed by General Electric to increase customer assurance of stable life performance. It is based on quality control information on each lot for normalized distribution and dispersion shift of the gain characteristic. A factor of 3.0 or greater for RI_1 indicates excellent extended life performance.

The Reliability-Index is obtained by:

1. Computing the percentage shift (+ or —) in the forward current gain of each unit during life test.
2. Determining the 10th, 50th and 90th percentiles in a distribution of the individual unit percent shifts.
3. Adding the magnitude of the 50th percentile to the magnitude of the algebraic difference between the 90th and 10th percentiles, and
4. Multiplying the reciprocal by 100.

$$RI_1 = \frac{100}{\left| \alpha 50 \right| + \left| \alpha 90 - \alpha 10 \right|}$$

Where α_{50}, α_{90}, and α_{10} are the particular percentile values of a distribution of αi, and

$$\alpha i = \frac{h_{FE} F_i - h_{FE} I_i}{h_{FE} I_i}$$

Where $h_{FE} F_i$ is the final and $h_{FE} I_i$ the initial value of forward current gain of the ith transistor.

*All transistors are stabilized for at least 100 hours at 100°C minimum and are subjected to a 100% hermetic seal test insuring a maximum leak rate of 10⁻⁸ cc/sec.

Courtesy of General Electric Company

ELECTRICAL CHARACTERISTICS ($T_A = 25°C$)

DC Characteristics

Subgroup I

Collector to Base Voltage	$I_C = -200 \mu a$	V_{CBO}	volts
Collector to Emitter Voltage	$R_{BE} = 10K$ ohms, $I_C = -600 \mu a$	V_{CER}	volts
Collector to Emitter Voltage	$V_{BE} = +1.5v$, $R_{BE} = 10K$ ohms, $I_C = -50 \mu a$	V_{CEX}	volts
Reach-through Voltage		V_{RT}	volts
Emitter Cutoff Current	$V_{EB} = -25v$	I_{EBO}	μa

Subgroup II

Collector Cutoff Current	$V_{CB} = -45v$	I_{CBO}	μa
Forward Current Transfer Ratio	$I_C = -20ma$, $V_{CE} = -1v$ (Note 1)	h_{FE}	
Forward Current Transfer Ratio	$I_C = -100$ ma, $V_{CE} = -1v$	h_{FE}	

Subgroup III

Base Input Voltage, Common Emitter	$I_C = -20$ ma, $V_{CE} = -1v$	V_{BE}	volts
Collector Saturation Voltage	$I_C = -20$ ma, I_B as shown	V_{CE} (SAT)	volts
		$@I_B$	ma

Small Signal Characertistics

Subgroup I

AC Forward Current Transfer Ratio	$I_E = 1$ ma, $V_{CE} = -5v$, $f = 1kc$	h_{fe}	
Input Impedance	$I_E = 1$ ma, $V_{CE} = -5v$, $f = 1kc$	h_{ie}	ohms
Output Admittance	$I_E = 1$ ma, $V_{CE} = -5v$, $f = 1kc$	h_{oe}	μmhos
Reverse Voltage Transfer Ratio	$I_E = 1$ ma, $V_{CE} = -5v$, $f = 1kc$	h_{re}	$x10^{-4}$

Subgroup II

Cutoff Frequency	$I_E = 1ma, V_{CB} = -5v$	f_{hfb}	mc
Output Capacity	$I_E = 1$ ma, $V_{CB} = -5v$, $f = 1mc$	C_{ob}	pf

Note 1: A minimum of 95% of the h_{FE} distribution is normally contained between values in parenthesis.

2N1924 TYP.			2N1925 TYP.			2N1926 TYP.				
						— 60				
— 60			— 60			— 40				
— 40			— 40			— 50			1%	II
— 50			— 50			— 50				
— 50			— 50							
	— 3	— 10		— 3	— 10		— 3	— 10		
	— 4	— 10		— 4	— 10		— 4	— 10		
34(38)	50	(59)65	53(59)	70	(80)90	72(80)	95	(110)121	0.65%	II
30	45		47	60		65	80			
—.200	—.235	—.300	—.190	—.230	—.290	—.180	—.225	—.280		
—.050	—.080	—.110	—.055	—.085	—.110	—.060	—.090	—.110	1%	L6
	—1.33			—1.00			—0.67			
30	44	64	44	64	88	60	80	120		
700	1400	2200	1200	2000	3200	1500	2500	4200	2.5%	L6
15	30	60	20	35	65	25	40	70		
2.0	4.5	8.0	3.0	6.0	9.0	4.0	7.0	10.0		
1.0	3.0		1.3	3.5		1.5	4.0			
	18	30		18	30		18	30		

Courtesy of General Electric Company

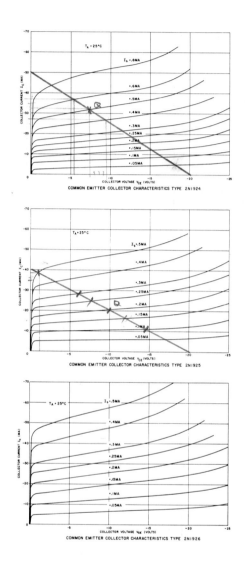

COMMON EMITTER COLLECTOR CHARACTERISTICS TYPE 2N1924

COMMON EMITTER COLLECTOR CHARACTERISTICS TYPE 2N1925

COMMON EMITTER COLLECTOR CHARACTERISTICS TYPE 2N1926

Courtesy of General Electric Company

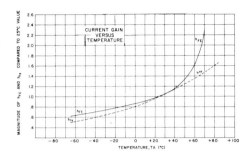

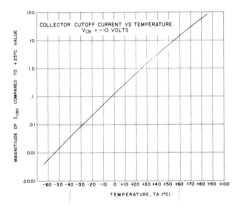

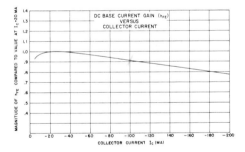

Courtesy of General Electric Company

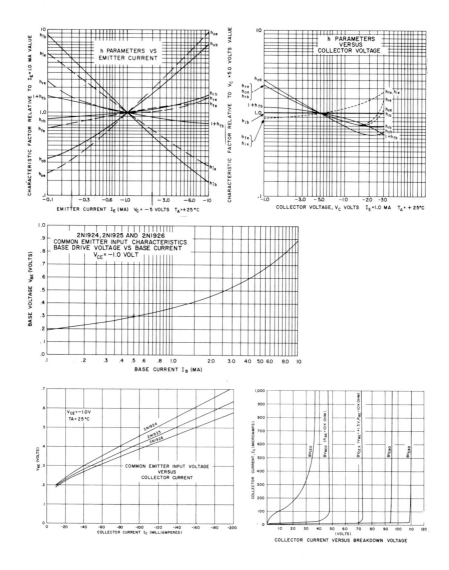

INDEX